"Mary Dalgleish has created an eminently
book. Whilst containing detailed inforr
anatomy and physiology appropriate for the medical level, it remains
a delightful and pleasing read. A deep and expansive addition to any
library; it is an edition no serious student of human health should be
without!"

Michael S. Fenster, MD FACC, FSCA&I, PEMBA
Adjunct Professor of Medicine (Culinary Medicine), The Kansas
Health Science Center, Wichita, Kansas
Executive Faculty, West Virginia University School of Medicine
Faculty, University of Montana College of Health
Faculty, University of Montana, Missoula College Culinary Arts
Program
https://chefdrmike.com

"This is a wonderful book, crammed full of information, a truly
valuable resource for complementary therapists and bodyworkers.
Together with the KNOW YOUR BODY Workbook, it is excellent
for studying anatomy and physiology, and great for revising and
refreshing knowledge."

Sally Kay: Multi-award winning reflexology practitioner, researcher,
educator, author and innovator of Reflexology Lymph Drainage
https://www.reflexologylymphdrainage.co.uk/sally-kay.html

"This is what you have been waiting for, it's the best book on this
subject I have read! I highly recommend it and so do our tutors too.
You will not be disappointed."

Sue Bailey: Director Gateway Workshops Ltd.
https://www.gatewayworkshops.co.uk

"I'd just like to tell you that since purchasing and reading your book a couple of months ago, I love it – Congratulations! You must feel very proud. Anatomy & Physiology is not an easy topic for many students to understand. However, with regards to 'Know your Body' it encompasses comprehensive knowledge and appealing content, with great visuals – I will definitely recommend it to College students – et al."

Judith Hadley: Experienced complementary therapy practitioner and educator; Feng Shui consultant
http://naturalharmonytherapies.co.uk

"As a complementary therapies teacher of over 18 years and an examiner, it is always paramount to me to find the perfect textbook for my students. Know Your Body is just that. It is perfectly pitched at the level needed for students who are studying to become professional practitioners in aromatherapy, massage or reflexology. Containing all the necessary elements of the syllabus for those disciplines, Mary has elegantly woven the key information into a readable and enjoyable text. Written in a style that will make it easy to understand and memorable come exam time and for years afterwards. I highly recommend this text to all therapists, student and qualified practitioners alike as a great source of information and reference."

Julia Oyeleye: Complementary therapist, teacher, examiner, author
https://www.juliaoyeleye.com/

KNOW YOUR BODY

The Essential Guide to
Human Anatomy and Physiology

MARY DALGLEISH

First printing 2020

ISBN (Print): 978-1-8380641-1-2
ISBN (E-book): 978-1-8380641-2-9

www.anatomyandphysiology.co.uk

Disclaimer

This book contains general information about the structure and functions of the body and about medical conditions, for educational purposes only. It is not meant as medical advice, diagnosis or treatment and you must not rely on the information in this book as an alternative or substitute to medical advice from your doctor or other professional healthcare provider.

If you have specific questions about any medical matter, you should consult your doctor or other professional healthcare provider.

If you think you may be suffering from any medical condition, you should seek immediate attention from your doctor or other professional healthcare provider.

You should never delay in seeking medical advice, disregard medical advice or discontinue medical treatment based on information in this book.

To the extent that you rely on any information contained in this book, you assume all risks involved in such reliance.

NOTE: All website links in the reference section were active in October 2020. However, due to the dynamic nature of the Internet, any web addresses or links contained in this book may have changed since publication and may no longer be valid. UK spelling has been used throughout this text and every effort has been made to ensure accuracy.

Links to other sites and resources provided by third parties are provided for your information only. I have no control over the contents of those sites or resources, and accept no responsibility for them, or for any loss or damage that may arise from your use of them. Please exercise due diligence in regard to any website content.

Contents

Foreword...1

1. Introduction 3

2. A Message from the Body.................................11

3. Body Compounds 25

4. Histology..35

5. Skin 59

6. Hair 90

7. Nails...100

8. The Skeletal System.......................................107

9. The Muscular System.....................................142

10. The Cardiovascular System...........................179

11. The Lymphatic System and Immunity...........210

12. The Respiratory System.................................236

13. The Digestive System 254

14. The Nervous System......................................280

15. The Senses 314

16. The Endocrine System 331

17. The Urinary System 362

18. The Reproductive System 377

19. Ageing and the body 415

References...433

Picture Credits 453

Acknowledgements 455

About the Author 457

Index..459

Foreword

"The noblest pleasure is the joy of understanding." So wrote Leonardo da Vinci, famous not only as a Renaissance painter and artist of the *Mona Lisa,* but for his anatomical drawings, which, together with their extensive notations, were far ahead of their time. Leonardo's simple words convey the satisfaction we derive as thinking beings, of comprehending our world and all that we rely upon, often unthinkingly. This same sense of delight – of feeding a fascination – was part of Mary Dalgleish's early immersion into the detailed study of anatomy and physiology, writing in her introduction to this book that she "found it intriguing to think of the massive and complicated orchestration going on inside my body every second of my life without me having to give it a second thought."

It is this very sense of feeling intrigued, of the learning process as a pleasure and a joy that Mary invariably infused into her approach to teaching anatomy and physiology, and now into this - her 'Essential Guide to Human Anatomy and Physiology - *Know Your Body'.* Approaching the study of the human body with curiosity and wonderment, and combining it with clarity, Mary ensures that we remain stimulated and engaged. This not only makes the study of anatomy and physiology pleasurable, but also means that we absorb and digest important facts and concepts for optimum effect.

For healthcare professionals in every sector, having a solid scientific understanding of the body in health and disease is of course vital. It is the foundation stone of every type of therapeutic practice, whether conventional or complementary. Thus, by making such essential information both accessible and enjoyable, Mary performs a valuable service to those whose professional lives are dedicated to the wellbeing of others. In particular, for those working in the field of complementary and holistic therapies, *Know Your Body* is a pivotal resource and encouraging companion – just as Mary herself, in the classroom, is engaging and passionate about understanding the functioning of the human body.

Indeed, I am especially grateful to her for, over a number of years, instilling within the students of our professional diploma course at the Institute of Traditional Herbal Medicine and Aromatherapy, the conspicuous enthusiasm for a subject that is often initially viewed upon as a "required" part of the programme. Mary consistently transformed this expectation to make anatomy and physiology as enjoyable and rewarding as studying essential oils and therapeutic massage. It is therefore with gratitude and considerable confidence that I can recommend this book to the reader – as an essential guide that not only makes the human body eminently comprehensible, but also puts its healthy functioning in an admirably holistic context.

All in all, *Know Your Body* delivers three principal benefits: it is a joy to read; its contents meet an important requirement for the practitioner dedicated to improving the health of their patients; and it provides those who invest time in reading it with a deeper grasp of how the innumerable complex processes of the body function together holistically as an orchestra performs a symphony.

Leonardo had his own holistic appreciation of the body's profound significance not only to our physical self, but to our totality of being, writing: "The spirit desires to remain with its body, because, without the organic instruments of that body, it can neither act, nor feel anything."

Gabriel Mojay *http://aromatherapy-studies.com/gabrielmojay.html*
Institute of Traditional Herbal Medicine & Aromatherapy (Principal);
Founding Co-Chair of the International Federation of Professional
Aromatherapists (IFPA) and author of "Aromatherapy for Healing the Spirit

1. Introduction

When I began my studies in complementary therapies in 1997 anatomy and physiology quickly became my favourite subject, and I read every book on the topic that I could lay my hands on. I had studied human biology at school, but it was at a time when my interests lay more with what was going on outside my body than inside it! Later in life I experienced some health issues that prompted me to explore fitness, nutrition and complementary therapies. I sought the advice of various experts who inspired me to make small and gradual lifestyle changes. My health and sense of wellbeing greatly improved, and it felt empowering to start taking responsibility for my own health and to see how much of a positive difference it made. This led to me enrolling in several complementary therapy courses, all of which included an anatomy and physiology component that fascinated me, and opened my eyes to the wonders of the human 'machine' and how it works. I found it intriguing to think of the massive and complicated orchestration going on inside my body every second of my life, without me having to give it a second thought.

After I qualified in a range of complementary therapies, including aromatherapy, reflexology and massage, I had an opportunity to use the teaching skills from my previous career to teach anatomy and physiology to complementary therapy students in several adult education centres and private colleges in London. Students would often arrive at their first class filled with trepidation about this subject, and I made it my mission to prepare classes that were interesting and engaging. Some body processes are extremely sophisticated and complicated e.g. the workings of the immune system, and many aspects of human biology are still being investigated. Scientific understanding of the human body is now much better than it used to be, but there are still mysteries to solve and new things being discovered. We are still learning more about immunity, the endocrine system, and about how the brain and nervous system function.

This book is a condensation of all the anatomy and physiology books I have read and the many lecture notes that I spent countless hours researching and preparing over my twenty years of teaching this subject. My students often complained about the size and weight of their textbooks, so I wanted to create a book that is easy to carry around and also not too expensive! I didn't want it to look or read too much like a textbook, but at the same time I wanted it to be very comprehensive and include up-to-date information on topics such as fascia, current diseases like metabolic syndrome and novel viral infections, as well as topics that interest me personally such as telomeres, genetics, psychoneuroimmunology and the gut-brain axis.

Many people know more about how their car works than about how their body functions, so I wanted the information to be presented in a very accessible way that can be understood and enjoyed not just by students, but by anyone interested in knowing more about the workings of their own body. People rarely skip their vehicle's maintenance requirements as they know this can have an adverse effect on its performance and longevity on the road, and the exact same can be said about the human body. The more we know about its inner workings, the better placed we are to look after its needs and optimise its function. I was particularly inspired by J.D. Ratcliff's articles using the "I am Joe's Body" format in the Reader's Digest which my parents used to get when I was a child. I found these articles very readable and easy to understand and they sparked my initial interest in human anatomy and physiology. I managed to get a copy of a paperback containing a collection of these articles with some black and white illustrations, and decided to use a similar angle when writing this book.

In writing the chapters, I imagined I was standing in front of my students and explaining the workings of the body in a way that was understandable and accessible, but still detailed enough to address what they needed to know for their exams. I recalled some of the many questions I was asked and addressed these as clearly as I could. I referred to the anatomy and physiology syllabi of major UK exam boards as these are mapped to current national occupational standards, and I made sure to address all the topics listed on those syllabi. I hope you enjoy reading my guide to human anatomy and physiology and that you will find it engaging, entertaining and educational without being overwhelming.

Although I wrote this book primarily for holistic therapy students who need to study anatomy and physiology as part of their training, I hope that it will appeal to others such as yoga students and teachers, fitness instructors, therapists of all modalities wishing to refresh their knowledge, or anyone wanting to know more about the workings of their body. The terms 'complementary', 'alternative' and 'holistic' are often used interchangeably and I am sometimes asked what these terms mean, so I hope this explanation of complementary, alternative and holistic healthcare and how it sits alongside conventional medicine will be helpful.

According to a 2017 report by the UK's College of Medicine, around 9 million people in the UK use some kind of complementary or alternative medicine - often referred to as CAM. The growing awareness and use of complementary and alternative therapies has not gone unnoticed, and as far back as November 2000, a House of Lords Select Committee in the UK reported "the use of complementary and alternative medicine is widespread and increasing across the developed world." Even though they are frequently grouped together in one category, a distinction should be made between complementary and alternative medicine. Complementary therapies do not focus on diagnosing or curing disease, but can be used simultaneously with conventional medicine to reduce side effects and stress and to increase wellbeing. Alternative therapies such as osteopathy, chiropractic, acupuncture, herbal medicine and homeopathy have an individual diagnostic approach, and can in some instances be used in place of conventional medicine, although they are used more frequently in a complementary capacity.

The Select Committee proposed three groups of CAM therapies with the above five disciplines regarded as the "most organised" professions. Osteopathy and chiropractic have statutory regulation in the UK, while the others are at various stages of regulation. The second group contains bodywork therapies that do not embrace diagnostic skills, and are most often used to complement conventional medicine. Examples of these are massage, reflexology, aromatherapy and other touch therapies. The third group includes other disciplines that offer diagnostic information as well as treatment and which, in general, "favour a philosophical approach and are indifferent to the scientific principles of conventional medicine" according to the report. These therapies are split into two sub- groups: group 3a includes long-established and traditional systems of healthcare such as Ayurvedic medicine and traditional Chinese medicine, and group 3b covers energy based disciplines e.g. energy therapies such as crystal therapy, iridology, radionics, dowsing and other therapies. The report also stressed the issues of public health policy raised by the growth of interest in CAM, and recommended research, adequate information and sound practitioner training to ensure safety of treatments available to the public.

With these aims in mind, The Prince of Wales Foundation for Integrated Health published 'Complementary Healthcare, a Guide for Patients' in February 2005. The aim of this guide was to help members of the public make informed choices about complementary therapies and to find properly trained and qualified practitioners. The Prince of Wales Foundation for Integrated Health (originally named the Foundation for Integrated Medicine) was formed in 1993 at the personal initiative of His Royal Highness, The Prince of Wales. Its aim was to facilitate the development of safe, effective and efficient forms of healthcare to patients and their families by supporting the development and delivery of integrated healthcare. This means encouraging conventional and complementary practitioners to work together to integrate their approaches.

Following on from this, the Complementary and Natural Healthcare Council (CNHC) was founded in 2008 and became fully operational in early 2009. The aim of the CNHC is to protect the public by providing an independent UK register of complementary healthcare practitioners, accredited by the Professional Standards Authority for Health and Social Care - an independent body accountable to the UK Parliament. The aim of the register is to support the use of CAM therapies as a uniquely positive, safe and effective experience.

UK professional associations for CAM therapists generally have their own Code of Conduct and Professional Practice that clearly defines the high standards expected of its members, and offers guidance on how these standards are to be met. For example, the Code of the Federation of Holistic Therapists (FHT) – the UK's largest professional association for therapists - was first published in 1962, when the association was founded. It was the first Code produced for professional therapists and has been updated regularly over the years, to reflect changes in legislation, therapy standards and best practice. In applying for membership, members of the FHT voluntarily agree to abide by the content of the FHT Code and any future amendments or additions.

CAM therapies are sometimes referred to as holistic therapies due to the fact that the CAM approach considers the whole person - body, mind, spirit and emotions - in the quest for optimal health and wellness. According to holistic philosophy, the best way to achieve optimal health is by having a proper balance in life. Holistic practitioners believe that the whole person is made up of interdependent parts, and if one part is not working properly all the other parts will be affected. In this way, if people have imbalances (physical, emotional or spiritual) in their lives, it can negatively affect their overall health.

A 2015 Commission in the UK estimated that about 20% of patient consultations with medical professionals were for social problems rather than medical problems, and so the idea of a new initiative called 'social prescribing' was born. Social prescribing is when health professionals refer patients to support in the community in order to improve their health and wellbeing. This holistic concept has gained support in the UK's National Health Service (NHS) as well as in other countries e.g. Ireland and the Netherlands. The goals of social prescribing are to reduce the rise of healthcare costs and ease pressure on general practice (GP) clinics by referring patients to a range of local, non-clinical services. It recognises that health can be determined by a range of social, economic and environmental factors, and seeks to address people's needs in a holistic way, supporting individuals to take greater control of their own health. Social prescribing schemes involve a variety of activities that are typically provided by voluntary and community sector organisations. Examples include volunteering, arts activities, group learning, gardening, befriending, cookery, healthy eating advice, and a range of sports and other activities.

There are many different models for social prescribing, but most involve a link worker or navigator who works with people to access local sources of support. The Social Prescribing Network, which oversees this initiative, consists of health professionals, researchers, academics, social prescribing practitioners, representatives from the community and voluntary sector, commissioners and funders, patients and citizens, all working together to share knowledge and best practices to support social prescribing at a local and national level, and to inform good quality research and evaluation. It is an innovative and growing movement in the UK with the potential to reduce the financial burden on the National Health Service and particularly on primary care.

In a document published by the UK's Department of Health & Social Care in November 2018 entitled 'Prevention is better than Cure – our vision to help you live well for longer' the Rt. Hon. Matt Hancock MP, Secretary of State for Health and Social Care, stated "Securing our nation's health requires a significant and sustained effort to prevent illness and support good physical and mental health. We need to see a greater investment in prevention - to support people to live longer, healthier and more independent lives, and help to guarantee our health and social care services for the long term."

In the UK, we have several organisations helping to promote a holistic and integrated healthcare agenda. One example is The College of Medicine headed up by Dr. Michael Dixon LVO, OBE, FRCGP, FRCC who says: "We advocate for a new attitude to healthcare: one which forges partnerships across society, emphasises prevention and a multi-faceted approach, and empowers a healthier, happier population. We think everyone should be part of the conversation about health, not just a select professional elite." Another is the King's Fund, an independent charitable organisation working to improve healthcare in England, with a vision that the best possible health and care is available to all. Another group doing important work is the UK All Party Group on Beauty, Aesthetics and Wellbeing. It highlights and celebrates the British Beauty Industry, and provides a forum that explores challenges and facilitates discussion, debate and action.

A report in December 2018 by the All-Party Parliamentary Group for Integrated Healthcare (PGIH) states: "The future of healthcare lies in our health system recognising that physical, emotional and mental health are intrinsically linked, and that only by treating a patient as a whole person can we tackle the root cause of illness and deal with the problem of patients presenting with multiple and complex conditions." Building on the work of the PGIH, the Integrated Healthcare Collaborative (IHC) is a collection of leading professional associations and stakeholders within complementary, traditional and natural healthcare, working together on common areas of interest to increase access to these therapies, promote greater integration with conventional Western medicine, and improve patient outcomes.

I was honoured to be a guest speaker at the second Integrative Health Convention in London in 2019. The audience at this 2-day convention on Complementary Health & Integrative Medicine included conventional medical practitioners, i.e. doctors, nurses, as well as complementary and alternative therapists and members of the public. It is hoped that this will be an annual event, with the aim of integrating the knowledge and skills from complementary and conventional healthcare and using them to the advantage of all.

I hope that my little book will help educate people about the wonders of the human body, and inspire them to get the best out of this valuable machine. As Benjamin Franklin once said: "An ounce of prevention is worth a pound of cure." (Although he was apparently referring to fire safety at the time!)

At the back of this book you will find a list of all the textbooks I referred to in my research. Nowadays we are lucky to have such a wealth of information online at our fingertips, and I have also included a list of all the websites I found useful in my research. There is a list of general references as well as references pertaining to each chapter, so that you can check out any studies or articles I have referred to in a specific chapter.

I have also created an accompanying "Know your Body" Workbook, full of tests and quizzes for use alongside this book, and do keep in touch for my "Know your Body" online course and audiobook, which are in development!

2. A Message from the Body

Some say I am the most fantastic machine in existence, because unlike most machines that can only do one or two jobs at a time, I can perform many tasks simultaneously - and I'm going to let you in on my secrets! Unlike other machines, I don't come with spare parts, so I hope this book will inspire you to do everything you can to keep me running in tip-top condition. My basic needs are quite simple - good quality fuel in the form of nutritious food, pure water, rest, exercise (and some fun!), will keep me operating smoothly and prevent me from getting gunged up and breaking down unnecessarily.

The study of the structure and relationship between my body parts is termed 'anatomy' while 'physiology' is the study of how all these parts function together. 'Pathology' looks at the causes, mechanisms and consequence of dis-ease that impairs my normal functioning and typically manifests with various 'abnormal' signs and symptoms. 'Homeostasis' - homeo (unchanging) + stasis (standing) - refers to my ability to seek and maintain a condition of internal equilibrium or stability when dealing with external changes. For example, I sweat to cool off during the hot summer days and I shiver to produce heat when I'm cold.

At a chemical level, I'm made up of tiny building blocks called atoms – apparently around 7,000,000,000,000,000,000,000,000,000 (7 octillion) as an adult! Atoms such as carbon, hydrogen, oxygen and nitrogen are essential for keeping me alive, and combine to form molecules such as fats, proteins and carbohydrates. These molecules then combine to form cells, which are my basic structural and functional units. I am made up of many different types of cells, each with specific functions, but more about that later!

My cells combine to form four tissue types – epithelial, muscular, connective and nervous - and my various organs are composed of at least two types of tissue - for example, my heart is made up of all four tissue types. Organs with a common function make up my systems that perform particular activities - for example, my digestive system is composed of organs such as the stomach, liver, pancreas, small intestine and large intestine, and it functions to break down and digest my fuel (food). All of my systems combine to form me - the human organism.

My body systems include the integumentary, skeletal, muscular, cardiovascular, lymphatic, respiratory, digestive, nervous, endocrine, urinary and reproductive systems. Each of my systems depends on the others - either directly or indirectly - and they all interrelate to ensure that I function normally. My integumentary system, composed of my skin, hair and nails, protects my internal structures from damage, stores fat, prevents dehydration and produces vitamins and hormones. The bones, joints, ligaments, tendons and cartilage of my skeletal system support and protect, giving me shape and form. My skeletal, muscular and nervous systems work together enabling me to move, while internal muscles enable my heart to beat and my organs and vessels to contract and relax for internal movement. My respiratory system ensures that I receive a steady supply of oxygen, which is delivered to all my cells and tissues by my cardiovascular system. My digestive system breaks food down into smaller particles that I can absorb, and these are delivered to all my cells and tissues by my cardiovascular system. My lymphatic and urinary systems both work to keep my body fluids healthy and balanced, as well as removing waste. My endocrine organs secrete hormones that regulate many internal processes including growth, homeostasis, metabolism, sexual development and reproduction. My brain receives information from all body systems to ensure my proper functioning, and my amazing nerves extend to all parts, including my muscles and internal organs. And just like the white pith inside a citrus fruit that holds all its cells and segments together, layers of connective tissue hold all my internal bits and pieces in place, running through my entire body from my head to my toes.

As you study my anatomy and physiology, I want to make sure you are viewing me from the correct perspective, so I'd like you to do a little exercise. Stand up, looking straight ahead with your feet together, and let your arms hang by your sides with your palms facing forward. You are now in the 'anatomical position', and whenever you see an anatomical drawing the body is assumed to be in that position. The 'midline' is an imaginary line that runs right through the centre of the body, dividing it into right and left sides. Health care practitioners and body workers use anatomical terms of location when they discuss patients or make notes that they or other practitioners may need to refer to, and their descriptions involving anatomical features are usually framed with this position in mind. In the medical field, it's important for everyone to have the same frame of reference - especially during a medical procedure - otherwise it could be disastrous if the people involved didn't understand directions given to them by their colleagues. My anatomical position puts everyone on the same page.

In your studies, you will come across many anatomical descriptive terms and an understanding of these can make things easier. Many of the words used to describe human anatomy and physiology derive from Latin. If you take each word apart, you can often work out the meaning. Here are examples of some common word parts that you will come across when studying the structure and function of the human body in health and disease:

a- lack of   mal- abnormal

adren- towards the kidney   mamm- of breast

angi- vessel

angin- choked feeling

anti- opposed to

ante- before, preceding

arth- of joints

auto – self generated

basal- base

bi- having two

bili- of bile

brachi- of the arm

brady- slow

brev- brief or short

broncho- of the bronchi

carcin- cancer

cephal- of the head

cerebro- of the brain

mast- of breast

medull- middle

melan- black

micro- small

myle- of spinal cord or bone marrow

myo- muscle

neo- new

nephro- kidney

neuro- nerve

olfact- smell

osteo- of bone

oxy- oxygen

pect- breast area

peri- around

phleb- vein

poly- many

chrondo- of cartilage

cili- small hair

contra- against

cort- outer layer

cyan- blue

cyst- bladder or sac

de- removal or reversal

dia- between

dialys- break apart or separate

diastol- stand apart

dors- the back

ec/ex- outside

entero- of the intestine

eryth- red

fasci- bundle

gastr- of the stomach

glosso- of the tongue

pulmo- of the lungs

ren- of kidney

sclero- hard

seb- grease

sphin- squeeze

sub- beneath

super/supra- above

systol- contraction

tachy- rapid

tetan-rigid

thromb- clot

trans- across

tri- three

tuber- swelling

tunic- covering

-able capable of

-algia pain in

glute- of the buttock	-cide destroy/kill
haem- of the blood	-cyte cell
hepat- of the liver	-ectomy cut out
hiat- gap	-itis inflammation
hist- of tissue	-malacia softening of
hyper- excess	-oma tumour
hypo- below	-phil to love
jugul- of the throat	-phragm partition
lact- of milk	-rrhagia excessive discharge
leuco- white	-rrhea flow or discharge
leva- to raise	-stalsis compression
macro- large	-stasis to fix

The following orientation and directional terms help explain where one body part is when compared to another:

Superior (cranial): above - towards the head or upper part of the body.

Inferior (caudal): below - away from the head or towards the lower part of the body.

Ventral (anterior): towards or at the front of the body.

Dorsal (posterior): towards or at the back of the body.

Supine: lying face up.

Prone: lying face down.

Medial: towards or at the midline of the body.

Lateral: away from the midline of the body.

Intermediate: between a medial and lateral position.

Proximal: closer to the body trunk/torso e.g. the shoulder is proximal in relation to the elbow.

Distal: further away from the body trunk/torso e.g. the wrist is distal in relation to the elbow.

Superficial (external): towards or at the body surface.

Deep (internal): away from the body surface.

Bilateral: involving both sides of the body e.g. eyes, ears, legs, arms are bilateral.

Unilateral: involving or affecting only one side of an organ or of the body.

Ipsilateral: on the same side of the body e.g. the right eye and right ear are ipsilateral.

Contralateral: on opposite sides of the body e.g. the right eye is contralateral to the left eye.

Parietal: relating to a body cavity wall (the parietal pleura is the outer part of a 2-layered membrane covering the lungs, and is attached to the inside of the ribcage).

Visceral: relating to organs within body cavities (the visceral pleura is the inner part of a 2-layered membrane covering the lungs, and it covers the lungs themselves).

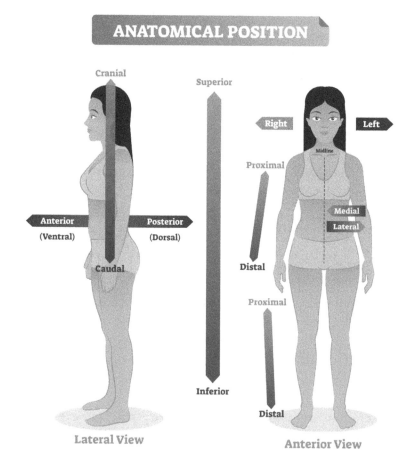

2.1 Anatomical positions

To understand my 'anatomical planes', imagine me standing in an upright position, and now imagine dissecting me with vertical and horizontal lines. The lateral or sagittal plane is an imaginary vertical line that runs from front to back or back to front, dividing me, or one of my organs, into right and left regions. If the vertical plane runs exactly down the middle, it's referred to as the median or mid-sagittal plane, while the parasagittal plane divides me, or one of my organs, into unequal right and left regions.

The frontal or coronal plane is a vertical plane that runs through my centre from top to bottom, dividing me, or one of my organs, into front (anterior) and back (posterior) regions.

The transverse plane is a horizontal plane dividing me, or one of my organs, into upper (superior) and lower (inferior) regions. Dividing horizontally does not mean two equal divisions but can go anywhere to create cross sections.

My skeleton has two major components – my axial skeleton consisting of 80 bones located along the axis of my body, and my appendicular skeleton consisting of the 126 bones of my appendages (limbs) and girdles (shoulder and pelvic girdles).

Just like on a map, my 'regions' refers to certain body areas. In my axial area, the head and neck regions include: cephalic (head), cervical (neck), cranial (skull), frontal (forehead), occipital (back of head), ophthalmic or orbital (eyes), oral (mouth) and nasal (nose). My thoracic regions are axillary (armpit), costal (ribs), mammary (breast), pectoral (chest) and vertebral (backbone), while my abdominal regions are celiac (abdomen), gluteal (buttocks), groin/inguinal (area of abdomen near inner thigh), lumbar (lower back), pelvic (lower part of abdomen), perineal (between anus and external genitalia) and sacral (end of spine). In my appendicular area, my arm regions are termed brachial (arm), carpal (wrist), cubital (elbow), forearm (lower arm) and palmar (palm), while my leg regions are femoral (thigh), lower leg (below knee), pedal (foot) and popliteal (back of knee).

My 'cavities' are the spaces that hold my internal organs, my two main cavities being my dorsal and my ventral cavities. My dorsal cavity is subdivided into the cranial cavity housing my brain, and the spinal cavity housing my spinal cord. My ventral cavity houses the rest of my organs and is subdivided into the thoracic cavity containing my heart and lungs, and the abdomino-pelvic cavity containing the organs of my abdomen and pelvis.

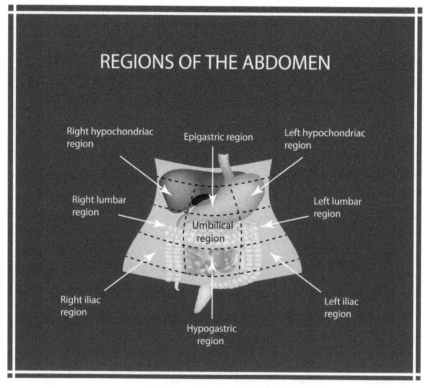

2.2 Regions of the abdomen

My abdomen is also divided into nine 'regions' and four 'quadrants' (quarters). The epigastric region is in the centre, just above my navel, on or over my stomach. The hypochondriac region (hypo = below;

chondral = cartilage) lies to the right and left of my epigastric region, just below the cartilage of my ribcage. The hypogastric region is in the centre, below my stomach and navel, while the iliac region lies to the right and left of this, close to my hipbones. My umbilical region is the area around my navel, and my lumbar region forms the area of my lower back to the right and left of my umbilical region. An imaginary cross on my abdomen passing through my navel divides my abdomen into four quadrants – the right and left upper quadrants and right and left lower quadrants. Whenever I suffer from abdominal pain, the medical practitioner checks these areas to determine what organ might be affected.

The term disease refers to any condition that causes pain, dysfunction, distress or death to the afflicted person. Diseases can affect people not only physically but also mentally, as contracting and living with a disease can alter a person's perspective on life. Diseases are generally classified as infectious diseases that can be transmitted to others, deficiency diseases due to lack of nutrients in the diet, hereditary diseases (both genetic and non-genetic), physiological diseases in which a particular abnormal condition affects the functioning of the body, and neuropsychiatric disorders encompassing a broad range of medical conditions that involve both neurology and psychiatry e.g. seizures, eating disorders, depression, anxiety. A disease that is of uncertain or unknown origin is termed 'idiopathic'. Death due to ageing in the absence of a specific disease is generally termed 'death by natural causes'.

Diseases can also be classified in other ways, such as communicable versus non-communicable diseases. Communicable diseases - also known as infectious or transmissible diseases - are illnesses that result from infection by pathogenic (disease causing) organisms e.g. bacteria, viruses etc. and can be transmitted to others. Non-communicable diseases - also known as chronic diseases - tend to be of long duration and can result from a combination of genetic, physiological, environmental and behavioural factors. They include cardiovascular diseases (e.g. heart attack and stroke), cancers, chronic respiratory diseases and diabetes. Pathology - the study of disease - also includes the study of its aetiology, or cause. The terms 'contagious' and 'infectious' sometimes cause confusion. Contagious diseases are spread by contact, while germs such as bacteria or viruses that get into the body leading to problems, cause infectious diseases. Infectious diseases that spread from person to person are said to be contagious, but something infectious isn't always contagious e.g. you can be infected with food poisoning, which in itself is not contagious. A zoonotic disease is a disease that is spread from animals to humans e.g. bird flu, brucellosis, anthrax.

The terms disease, disorder, syndrome and condition are often used interchangeably but there are some subtle differences, and describing these is sometimes difficult. The word 'disease' is normally used in the sense of a sickness or illness due to external or internal factors e.g. cardiovascular disease can cause both physical and emotional signs and symptoms, as well as pain, dysfunction, distress or death. A 'disorder' is regarded as a disruption to the normal or regular functions in the body - or a part of the body - due to disease e.g. a disorder resulting from cardiovascular disease is an arrhythmia or irregular heartbeat, which is not a disease in itself, but a problem that occurs as a result of having cardiovascular disease.

A 'syndrome' is a collection of signs and symptoms that characterise a particular medical condition or disease e.g. Down syndrome is a well-known genetic syndrome that is characterised by having an extra copy of chromosome 21, in combination with a number of distinctive physical features at birth. Sometimes a syndrome can be caused by a number of diseases, or it can be a medical 'condition' itself. A 'condition' is sometimes described as an abnormal state of health that interferes with usual activities or affects wellbeing e.g. chronic fatigue syndrome is a neurological condition diagnosed from a collection of symptoms, as well as the main symptom of exhaustion following physical activity.

Health and wellbeing can be affected by many factors - often referred to as risk factors. A risk factor is something that may increase a person's susceptibility to disease, and includes things such as behaviour, genetics, lifestyle, age, gender, social factors, disability and environmental factors. For example, physical inactivity can, over time, be a risk factor for weight gain, high blood pressure and high cholesterol levels.

The terms 'sign' and 'symptom' are often used interchangeably when discussing disease, but there are differences. Visible evidence of a disease such as a skin rash or a cough is a sign, while back pain, headache and fatigue are symptoms and can only be recognised by the person experiencing them. Some things can be signs as well as symptoms e.g. a person in pain who is writhing in agony. 'Red flag' signs and symptoms refer to those that may indicate a more serious underlying pathology and should always be medically investigated e.g. abnormal discharges, blood in the urine or sputum, breast lumps, changing moles or lumps on the skin, breathlessness, bone pain, persistent cough, etc. 'Prognosis' refers to the likely outcome of a disease or ailment, including whether the signs and symptoms will improve, worsen or remain stable over time. For example, the prognosis for melanoma (skin cancer) is good if it is detected and treated before it spreads.

According to Professor Daniel Lieberman of Harvard University, many modern-day diseases, which he calls 'mismatch diseases', are caused by a discrepancy between contemporary lifestyles and the original hunter-gatherer purposes for which the human body evolved. Examples include the rise of type 2 diabetes and cardiovascular disease, and he states that some of the main culprits are lack of movement, excess sugar in the diet, poor sleep and stress. Dr.

Lieberman says that we could avoid most of these diseases by making different lifestyle choices. In an article published by the "European Scientist" regarding the COVID-19 pandemic, UK cardiologist, Dr. Aseem Malhotra echoes this. Dr. Malhotra states that "obesity and chronic metabolic disease is killing COVID-19 patients: now is the time to eat real food, protect the NHS (National Health Service) and save lives... the elephant in the room is that the baseline general health in many western populations was already in a horrendous state to begin with."

Each of us has our own unique constitution or physical makeup with respect to the health, strength and appearance of our bodies. The term 'constitutional rhythm' is sometimes used to describe the particular patterns of a person's body or mind that are unique to that person. We each have our own 'rhythm' that feels 'normal' to us and we can sense there is something wrong if this rhythm suddenly changes e.g. sudden changes in bowel movements, weight, sleep, appetite etc. usually prompt us to seek medical advice and attention.

I hope that I haven't bored you with all this 'jargon' and that it will prove useful in your studies. As you continue your journey inside the body, I hope that you will realise what a wonderful, complex and clever creation the human body is, and become inspired to make wise choices that can improve your own health and wellbeing. Knowledge is empowerment and the more we know about the workings of our own bodies, the more capable we become at making better lifestyle choices to improve the quality of our lives. 'Health is wealth' and the body really is our most valuable possession in life!

3. Body Compounds

The word 'organic' means something very different in chemistry than it does when we talk about produce and food. Organic compounds and inorganic compounds form the basis of chemistry. Organic compounds contain carbon atoms, while inorganic compounds do not. Inorganic compounds are small, simple compounds such as water, salt, simple acids like hydrochloric acid, and simple bases like ammonia. These substances are required for fluid balance and for many cellular activities such as transporting materials through cell membranes. Organic compounds are large, complex compounds containing carbon. These are the chemical building blocks of the body, and they also serve as fuel molecules that provide energy for body activities. Organic compounds regulate and participate in thousands of chemical reactions necessary for life.

Four important groups of organic compounds needed by the body are carbohydrates, lipids (fats), proteins and nucleic acid. Carbohydrates are sugars and starches, and are used as fuel by the body as well as an energy store. Lipids include fats that store energy, phospholipids, which are components of cell membranes, and steroids that make several hormones. Proteins are large, complex compounds composed of smaller units called amino acids. Some proteins serve as enzymes that regulate chemical reactions and other proteins are the structural components of cells and tissues e.g. muscle cells have large amounts of the proteins myosin and actin that are responsible for their appearance and their ability to work. Nucleic acids are also large, complex compounds and include DNA (deoxyribonucleic acid), which makes up our hereditary material (genes) and RNA (ribonucleic acid), which is important in the process of manufacturing proteins.

Four major elements make up 96% of human body mass. Oxygen (65%) is needed for cellular respiration - the set of metabolic reactions and processes that takes place inside cells to convert biochemical energy from nutrients in the food we eat into adenosine triphosphate (ATP or stored energy), and then release waste products. Carbon (18%) is the basic building block required to form proteins, carbohydrates and fats, and it plays a crucial role in regulating the physiology of the body. For example, it is used to regulate the pH (acidity/alkalinity) of blood and is exhaled in the form of CO_2. Carbon atoms form the thousands of molecules in virtually every cell of the body. Hydrogen (10%) is an element found in all body fluids, allowing toxins and waste to be transported and eliminated as well as keeping joints lubricated and the immune system healthy. It is a component of water, all foods and most organic molecules, and it influences the pH of body fluids. Nitrogen (3%) is needed to make amino acids in the body, which in turn make proteins. It is also needed to make nucleic acids that form DNA and RNA - more about those in the next chapter.

Nine lesser elements make up 3.9% of human body mass. Calcium (1.5%) is needed for healthy bones and teeth, muscle contractions and nerve signal transmission. A tingly mouth, hands/feet or muscle spasms may indicate low calcium levels.

Phosphorus (1%) is needed for healthy bones and teeth as well as playing an important role in how the body uses carbohydrates and fats. It is also needed for the body to make protein for growth, maintenance and repair of cells and tissues. Weak bones and teeth, joint pain and stiffness, lack of appetite and energy may indicate low levels of phosphorous.

Potassium (0.35%) plays a major role in recharging nerve and muscle cells after they have been activated. Muscle weakness, constipation, shortness of breath and heart palpitations may indicate low potassium levels.

Sulphur (0.25%) is found in muscles, skin and bones and is needed for enzymes to function properly. Enzymes are complex proteins produced by cells to speed up chemical reactions in the body. Sulphur is also found in foods such as onions, eggs, garlic and protein-rich foods. A shortage of sulphur may contribute to age-related skin, muscle and bone problems.

Sodium (0.15%) plays a major role in activating nerve cells, muscle contractions and regulating water balance. Muscle weakness, spasms, cramp, stomach upset or sluggish thinking may indicate low sodium levels. Excess sodium can cause issues with blood pressure that can lead to health problems. It is easy to get enough sodium from a regular diet and it's quite likely that most of us get more sodium than we need.

Chlorine (0.15%) is usually associated with swimming pools but is also found in tiny amounts in the body as a negative ion, called chloride. This electrolyte is important for maintaining the normal balance of body fluids.

Magnesium (0.05%) plays an important role in the structure of the skeleton and muscles, and is involved in many cellular chemical reactions. Feeling miserable, muscle tremors, spasm and cramp may indicate low magnesium levels.

Iron (0.006%) is a critical ingredient in haemoglobin, the molecule that transports oxygen around the body in red blood cells. Looking pale, feeling weak and having a fast heart rate may indicate a possible iron deficiency.

Iodine (0.000016%) is found in highest concentrations in the thyroid gland, muscles and various endocrine tissues and is necessary for thyroid hormone production.

Thirteen other 'trace elements' make up 0.1% of body mass. These include aluminium, boron, chromium, cobalt, copper, flourine, manganese, molybdenum, selenium, silicon, tin, vanadium and zinc. Although the amounts of these elements are tiny, they are nonetheless important. For example, zinc is found in most cells throughout the body and is needed for the immune system to work properly. It plays a role in cell division, cell growth, wound healing and the breakdown of carbohydrates. The body also needs zinc to make proteins and DNA - the genetic material in all cells - and it is important for maintaining the senses of smell and taste.

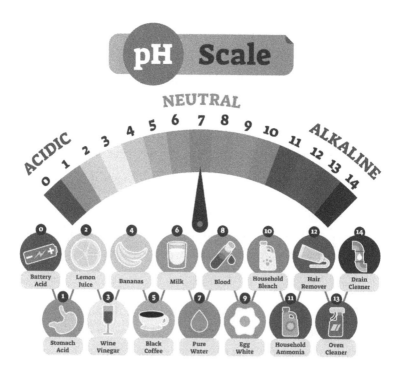

3.1 The pH Scale

The pH scale measures acidity and alkalinity. Substances with a pH of less than 7 are acids, while alkaline substances have a pH of more than 7. Neutral solutions e.g. pure water, have a pH of 7. The body is built to naturally maintain a healthy balance of acidity and alkalinity (the acid/base balance) and the lungs and kidneys play a key role in this process. The kidneys excrete excess hydrogen and the lungs get rid of carbonic acid in carbon dioxide, preventing acid build up in the blood. If the lungs or kidneys are malfunctioning, the blood's pH level can become imbalanced, leading to medical conditions known as acidosis (too much acid in body fluids) and alkalosis (blood too alkaline). Respiratory acidosis and alkalosis are due to a problem with the lungs. Metabolic acidosis and alkalosis are due to a problem with the kidneys. These conditions require treatment from a medical professional and usually some dietary changes.

3.2 Vitamins

The discovery of vitamins was a major scientific achievement in our understanding of health and disease. Kazimierz (Casimir) Funk (1884-1967), a Polish biochemist, is generally credited with being among the first to formulate the concept of vitamins, which he called 'vital amines' or 'vitamines'. Funk found that vitamins B1, B2, C and D were necessary to human health and that vitamins contributed to the normal functioning of the hormonal system. His work led to the prevention of beriberi, rickets, scurvy and other diseases caused by vitamin deficiency.

There are 2 major vitamin groups – fat-soluble (A, D, E, K) and water-soluble (B & C). The difference between the two groups determines how they act within the body. The fat-soluble vitamins are absorbed into lymphatic vessels called lacteals in the small intestine and then into the bloodstream, and any excess is stored in body tissues e.g. liver and adipose tissue. If a person takes in too much of a fat-soluble vitamin, over time they may have toxic levels of that vitamin present in their body. Water-soluble vitamins dissolve in water and are readily absorbed into body tissues for immediate use. Any excess of water-soluble vitamins is excreted in urine and will rarely accumulate to toxic levels. Because they are not stored in the body, they need to be replenished regularly in the diet.

Vitamin A (retinol, retinoic acid) is important for vision, healthy skin, wound healing, growth, cell division, reproduction and immunity. Vitamin A also has antioxidant properties. Antioxidants are compounds that inhibit oxidation - an internal chemical reaction that can produce harmful chemicals called free radicals that may damage cells. Vitamin A is found in many foods, such as dairy products and liver. Vegetable food sources of vitamin A are called carotenes or beta-carotenes, and include green leafy vegetables, carrots and cantaloupe. The body converts beta-carotene into the active form of vitamin A.

Vitamin D (D3 cholecalciferol and D2 ergocalciferol) is needed for healthy bones and teeth and is derived from sunlight, milk, fish, eggs and cereals. Two studies carried out in Ireland in early 2020 showed that vitamin D plays a critical role in preventing respiratory infections, reducing antibiotic use and boosting the immune system in response to infections, and the studies recommended vitamin D supplementation for those cocooning during the COVID-19 pandemic. They also reported there is good evidence that vitamin D helps the mood: "If you have low vitamin D you are more likely to have a low mood."

Vitamin E (alpha-tocopherol) is regarded as an important antioxidant. Vitamin E is also important for the functioning of the nervous system, and is found in whole grains, nuts, seeds, and egg yolks. Vitamin E is known for its benefits for skin health and appearance and is a component of many topical skin care products.

Vitamin K1 (phylloquinone) is important for the regulation of blood clotting – it does not trigger clotting, but activates both the clotting and anti-clotting systems so that they work effectively. Vitamin K2 (menaquinone) is important for the formation of strong bones and preventing heart disease. Vitamin K1 is found in dark green, leafy vegetables. Vitamin K2 is produced by beneficial microbes in the large intestine, and is also found in foods such as egg yolks, chicken breast, beef, fermented foods and dairy products e.g. hard cheese. A baby's vitamin K1 stores at birth are very low and most newborns are given a vitamin K1 shot shortly after delivery to prevent a type of bleeding called vitamin K1 deficiency bleeding (VKDB), also known as hemorrhagic disease of the newborn. VKDB can range from bruising of the skin to bleeding inside the baby's brain, and can occur from birth to months later.

It has been found that COVID-19 can cause blood clotting and lead to the degradation of elastic fibres in the lungs of some affected patients. Vitamin K is key to the production of proteins that regulate clotting and can protect against lung disease, according to a group of Dutch researchers who studied COVID-19 patients admitted to the Canisius Wilhelmina hospital in the Dutch city of Nijmegen. They extolled the benefits of vitamin K after discovering a link between deficiency and the worst coronavirus outcomes, and encourage a healthy intake of vitamin K, except for those on blood-thinning medications such as warfarin.

B vitamins are a class of water-soluble vitamins that play important roles in cell metabolism. They are chemically distinct vitamins that often coexist in the same foods. Foods rich in B vitamins include salmon, leafy greens, organ meats, eggs, milk, beef, oysters, clams, mussels, legumes, chicken, turkey and yoghurt. Vitamin B12 is challenging to obtain if a person doesn't eat animal products, so vegetarians - and vegans in particular - are usually advised to use supplements or eat foods that are fortified with B12 e.g. nutritional yeast. Dietary supplements containing all eight B vitamins are referred to as vitamin B complex. The B vitamins include B1 (thiamine), B2 (riboflavin), B3 (niacin or PP), B5 (pantothenic acid), B6 (pyridoxine), B7 (biotin), B9 (folic acid) and B12 (cobalamin).

The B vitamins are needed in the body for a healthy digestive and nervous system, and each one has its own specific benefits. For example, B3 is important for maintaining a healthy heart, brain function and skin health, and aiding in the balance of blood cholesterol levels. A deficiency of B6 and zinc is associated with a condition called pyrrole disorder - also known as pyroluria or mauve factor - a metabolic disorder that most commonly manifests as a mental health condition with depression, anxiety, poor ability to handle stress and a weakened immune system. Sufferers have an elevated level of an enzyme called hydroxyhempyrolin (HPL) - a molecule naturally excreted in urine - and this binds to B6 and zinc and prevents proper absorption. Environmental, emotional and physical stress may increase the body's production of HPL. Pyroluria is not a recognised medical condition by many physicians.

Vitamin B12 is needed to produce an adequate amount of healthy red blood cells in bone marrow. Some individuals - particularly elderly people - often cannot absorb enough B12 due to lack of a substance called intrinsic factor, normally found in stomach acid and needed for this purpose. In this case, vitamin B12 is typically given as an intramuscular injection at regular intervals. Symptoms of B12 deficiency include fatigue, shortness of breath, muscle weakness, dizziness, poor vision, pale or yellow skin, a smooth tongue and 'pins and needles' i.e. numbness, as well as episodes of brain fog and depression. However some of these symptoms may have other causes and anyone concerned about B vitamin or any other nutritional deficiency should seek professional advice and accurate testing for a correct diagnosis, rather than self-prescribing.

Vitamin C (ascorbic acid) is needed for growth and repair of body tissues, the formation of collagen, cartilage, bones and teeth, wound healing, immune function and iron absorption. 40mg is the minimum recommended daily amount (RDA) but in cases of wounds, burns, infection or post surgery, more is recommended. Alcohol impairs absorption of vitamin C and smoking depletes levels of this vitamin. Vitamin C occurs naturally in foods such as citrus fruits, potatoes, tomatoes (even more in cooked tomatoes!) and leafy vegetables.

'Vitamin P' is the name once used to describe a group of plant-based substances we now know as flavonoids or bioflavonoids. When you're eating a salad with colorful plant foods, you're getting a dose of vitamin P that can contribute to optimal health and chronic disease prevention. 'Vitamin U' is actually an enzyme, known as s-methylmethionine and is regarded as helpful for issues related to the digestive system. It is found in green vegetables such as cabbage, celery, spinach, kale and parsley. Alpha-lipoic acid (acidum lipocium) is a naturally occurring fatty acid that can be found in many foods such as yeast, spinach, broccoli, potatoes, as well as organ meats such as liver or kidney.

And let us not forget the most important and often overlooked compound needed by the human body – water! Water - which makes up about 60% of human body weight - is composed of hydrogen and oxygen, and its functions are vital for life. It transports nutrients and oxygen into body cells, moisturises air in the lungs, protects and cushions vital organs (e.g. cerebrospinal fluid around the brain), helps organs absorb nutrients, regulates body temperature, detoxifies, and acts as a lubricant for internal organs and joints. Because the body loses water through breathing, sweating and digestion, it's important to rehydrate by drinking fluids and eating foods containing water. The amount of water needed depends on a variety of factors, including climate, level of physical activity, body size and state of health. If you're not sure about your hydration level, check your urine. If it's clear, it's a healthy sign, and if it's dark, you may be dehydrated.

4. Histology

Histology is study of the structure and function of the microscopic anatomy of living organisms, including the cells and tissues of the human body. The body is composed of an estimated 10 trillion 'cells' – so named by scientist Robert Hooke in 1665 for the resemblance of plant cells to the cells (small rooms) inhabited by Christian monks as he looked at a sliver of cork through a microscope lens. There are over 200 cell types in the body and they come in all shapes and sizes, each doing unique jobs, and together, allowing the body to function as a whole. Cells contain molecules that are made up of even smaller components called atoms.

Cells are a bit like factories, with each cell surrounded by a membrane made up of a mixture of proteins and lipids (fats). The membrane acts like a security fence and gateway to the 'factory', only allowing approved substances to enter and leave the premises. Lipids provide flexibility while proteins transmit chemical messages, as well as monitor and maintain the cell's chemical climate. Cell membranes have special gates, channels and pumps to let in - or force out - selected molecules. This protects the internal environment, a thick 'cytoplasm' of salts, nutrients and proteins that accounts for about 50% of cell volume, along with various tiny structures called 'organelles' that make up the other 50%. The cytoplasm is a jelly-like substance - sometimes described as the cell matrix - and it holds the organelles in place within the cell.

Movement through cell membranes can be 'active' requiring energy - like a door being held open - or 'passive' - like going through an automatic door. In active transport, protein carrier molecules embedded in the membrane help with carrying substances across. This happens a lot in nerve cells (neurons), as the membrane proteins have to constantly pump sodium and potassium in and out to get the membrane of the neuron ready to transmit electrical impulses. The membrane proteins are very specific, and one protein that moves for example glucose, will not move calcium. There are hundreds of types of membrane protein in the many cells of the body. Another process requiring active transport is pinocytosis, whereby a cell absorbs small particles outside of itself and brings them inside. The word pinocytosis comes from the Greek for 'cell drinking'. During this process, the cell surrounds particles and 'pinches off' part of its membrane to enclose the particles within vesicles (little bubbles), which are small parts of the membrane. This process is used for taking in fluid containing various solutes like sugars and proteins that can dissolve in the fluid. Phagocytosis -'cell eating' - is used to absorb solid materials such as bacteria. During pinocytosis, the contents of the vesicles are emptied directly into the cell, but in phagocytosis, tiny structures called lysosomes (discussed later), combine with the vesicles to break down the contents.

Some substances are small enough to pass in and out of cells without help and this 'passive transport' happens in three ways. Molecules can simply 'diffuse' from areas of high concentration to areas of low concentration, and this is the process by which oxygen and carbon dioxide are exchanged in blood capillaries inside the lungs. 'Osmosis' is the movement of water across cell membranes, while 'filtration' is the passage of materials through membranes by a physical force like gravity - this is how the kidneys constantly filter the blood. A physical pump - the heart - influences the rate of filtration by affecting the pressure of blood through the blood vessels. The smallest blood vessels - called capillaries - are only one cell thick, so substances like carbon dioxide, water, glucose and oxygen can pass in and out between capillaries and tissue fluid and from there, these substances can enter (or exit) the cells of the body.

Structure of a Typical Animal Cell

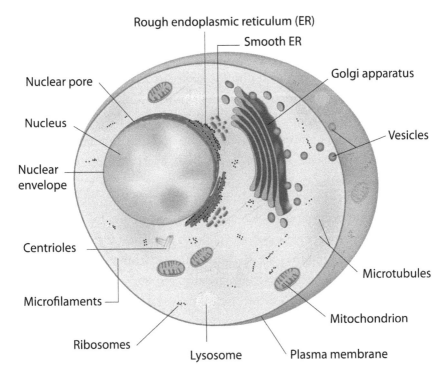

Rough endoplasmic reticulum (ER)

Smooth ER

Golgi apparatus

Nuclear pore

Nucleus

Vesicles

Nuclear envelope

Centrioles

Microtubules

Microfilaments

Mitochondrion

Ribosomes

Lysosome

Plasma membrane

4.1 A typical cell

Most body cells contain tiny structures called organelles. The energy generators are the mitochondria – sausage shaped power stations that burn fuel (glucose), produce electricity (energy) and leave 'ash' (water and carbon dioxide) behind. In this complex chemical process, they produce a substance called adenosine tri-phosphate (ATP), which is considered the universal energy currency for metabolism. Metabolism refers to the biochemical reactions that happen inside cells to produce energy and remove waste, and involves anabolism and catabolism. Anabolism is the creation or synthesis of complex molecules from simpler ones and requires energy, while catabolism is the breakdown of complex molecules into simpler ones and releases energy.

Whenever there is a need for energy e.g. to make the heart beat or lungs expand, ATP breaks down into simpler substances, releasing energy in the process. Even in deepest sleep, the breakdown (and building up) of ATP is constant to keep the body alive. The only cells that don't have mitochondria are red blood cells, as they do no manufacturing and are swept along in the bloodstream with no need for energy on their part. Mitochondrial diseases are long-term, genetic or inherited disorders that occur when mitochondria fail to produce enough energy for the body to function properly. Mitochondrial diseases can affect almost any part of the body, including cells of the brain, nerves, muscles, kidneys, heart, liver, eyes, ears or pancreas.

Another organelle is the endoplasmic reticulum (ER), which functions as a manufacturing and packaging system. Structurally, the ER is a network of membranes found throughout a cell and connected to the nucleus. The membranes are slightly different from cell to cell, and a cell's function determines the size and structure of the ER. For example, some cells such as red blood cells don't have any ER, while cells that synthesise and release a lot of proteins - like those found in the liver or pancreas - have a large amount of ER. There are two basic types of ER - smooth and rough - and they have different shapes. Smooth ER is important in the creation and storage of lipids (fats) and steroids. Steroids are a type of molecule used in the body for many purposes such as making hormones, and are not always about building the muscle mass of a weight lifter. Rough ER - so called because it has tiny bead shaped organelles called ribosomes attached to its surface - looks like sheets or discs of bumpy membranes while smooth ER looks more like tubes.

When cells need to make proteins they look for ribosomes, which are the protein builders. Just like construction workers, they connect one amino acid at a time and build long protein chains. When the body digests protein in food, it is broken down into amino acids, and the body needs twenty different amino acids to grow and function properly. Though all twenty of these are important for good health, only nine amino acids are classified as essential - which means they are necessary for human life and health. These essential amino acids cannot be produced in the body, so need to be obtained from food. There are several nonessential amino acids that are classified as conditionally essential - meaning they are only needed under specific circumstances such as illness or stress. One example is L-arginine, which improves blood flow and can be produced in the body from other amino acids and also obtained from foods. Foods high in L-arginine include meats, fish, cheese, wheat, nuts, seeds and beans. Five amino acids are classified as non-essential. These amino acids can be synthesised in the body from other amino acids, glucose and fatty acids, so we do not need to get them from foods.

Ribosomes are found in many places inside cells, and some float in the cytoplasm making proteins that will be used inside the cell. Other ribosomes are found on the rough ER, and these attached ribosomes make proteins that will be used inside the cell, as well as proteins made for export out of the cell. Protein makes up around 20% of the body and plays a crucial role in almost all biological processes. For example, enzymes are proteins that allow certain chemical reactions to take place much faster than they would on their own. They function as catalysts, which means that they speed up the rate at which metabolic processes and reactions occur in the body. Other proteins help support cell functions and are found embedded in cell membranes e.g. carrier proteins that help transport glucose and amino acids across the membrane.

Keratin and collagen are proteins found in the skin, and keratin also makes up a large portion of hair and nails. Collagen is a protein found in bones, tendons and ligaments, providing strength and flexibility. Protein is also found in muscle tissue and the haemoglobin of red blood cells. A mixture of fat and protein - called lipoprotein - carries cholesterol around the body in the bloodstream.

The Golgi apparatus or Golgi complex - named after Italian biologist Camillo Golgi - is found in most body cells. It is another packaging organelle like the endoplasmic reticulum, and is responsible for packaging proteins into little bubble-like sacs called vesicles and sending them to the correct destinations within the cell, where the proteins are used to carry out their functions. The Golgi is composed of a pile of sacs filled with liquid and stacked up like pancakes. All the time, small bits (vesicles) are cut off around the edge and travel to deliver proteins that may for example, make new parts for the cell membrane or exit the cell. It is also the organelle that builds lysosomes (cell digestion machines) from proteins created in the rough ER.

Lysosomes are full of liquid proteins and hungry enzymes that digest things. They are used to digest food or break down the cell when it dies. They also break down useless and potentially harmful materials, such as old worn-out parts of the cell or potential threats such as bacteria, and are sometimes referred to as the waste disposal units within cells.

Most body cells are busy and create waste during their activities. Peroxisomes are small sacs - similar to lysosomes - that digest fatty acids and break down toxic waste that might cause cell damage. They also play a part in the way alcohol is digested, and liver cells have more peroxisomes than most other cells in the body. Their enzymes attack complex molecules and break them down into smaller molecules, thereby producing hydrogen peroxide as a by-product. Hydrogen peroxide is toxic to the cell, but peroxisomes also contain an enzyme that is capable of converting hydrogen peroxide to water and oxygen. The water is harmless to the cell, and the oxygen can be used in the next digestive reaction.

Vacuoles are little parts of a cell that work like carrier bags or storage bubbles, storing a variety of nutrients that the cell needs to survive as well as waste products, so that the rest of the cell is protected from contamination. Eventually, those waste products are sent out of the cell.

The centrosome is a darker, more condensed area of the cytoplasm that appears when a cell is about to replicate. In the middle of the centrosome, two stacks looking like empty pipes lie across each other. These are the centrioles (imagine two piles of matches sitting inside a piece of chewing gum!) When the cell is about to divide, the centrioles move away from each other to opposite ends of the cell, and the dense centrosome (chewing gum!) forms threads attached to the centrioles. These threads are called 'mitotic spindles' and it is here that the pairs of chromosomes line up during cell division, and the moving centrioles pull them apart.

The nucleus is the brain inside the cell, controlling all its activities including reproduction. The nucleus - with its own special nuclear membrane - is a big dark spot somewhere in the cytoplasm, but not too close to the edge of a cell because it needs to be protected. Red blood cells do not have a nucleus as this helps them maximise storage space for haemoglobin, which is essential in the transport of oxygen. The nucleus stores most of the cell's DNA (deoxyribonucleic acid), which is responsible for carrying genetic information on chromosomes. The cytoplasm inside the nucleus is referred to as 'nucleoplasm'. Inside the nucleus is an organelle called the nucleolus - through a microscope it looks like a nucleus inside the nucleus. It is a round granular structure composed of RNA (ribonucleic acid) created from DNA - the DNA unwinds and copies itself into single-stranded molecules of RNA. If DNA is the building plan or blueprint, RNA is the translator of instructions written in the blueprint – like an architect who executes a building plan, it acts as a messenger, carrying vital genetic information from the DNA to ribosomes (the builders) to create the building materials - proteins - for many different body functions. As already mentioned, protein is essential for almost all biological activities that take place in the human body, so RNA is crucial for life. There are three main types of RNA - messenger RNA (mRNA) is the one that transcribes the genetic code from DNA into a form that can be read and used to make proteins, and it carries this genetic information from the nucleus to the cytoplasm of a cell. In the cytoplasm, ribosomal RNA (rRNA) forms the ribosomes that carry the enzymes necessary for building up proteins. Transfer RNA (tRNA) decodes the information from the mRNA and delivers the correct amino acids to the ribosomes – depending on what proteins need to be made.

When we think about DNA, we usually think about James Watson and Francis Crick who discovered the famous double helix structure of DNA at Cambridge University in 1953. However, many scientists before them laid the groundwork. In 1866, Austrian born Gregor Mendel - known as the 'Father of Genetics' - was the first to suggest that characteristics are passed down from generation to generation. Through his work in breeding and cultivating pea plants, he deduced that genes come in pairs and are inherited as distinct units - one from each parent - and he coined the terms we know today as 'recessive' and 'dominant' in relation to genes.

Swiss chemist, Johann Friedrich Miescher was the first to identify DNA in 1869. While extracting proteins from white blood cells, he found a phosphorus-containing substance much different from a protein, which he called a 'nuclein' - later known as nucleic acid. In 1919, Russian biochemist Phoebus Levene proposed that nucleic acids were molecules made of phosphate, sugar and four nitrogenous bases - adenine (A), guanine (G), cytosine (C) and thymine (T).

By 1944, scientists from the Rockefeller Institute in New York (Avery, MacLeod & McCarty) showed that DNA and not protein was the substance that passed along genetic information. 'Genetics' is the study of inherited characteristics or genes.

A relatively new field of scientific study is 'epigenetics' which shows that DNA blueprints passed down through genes are not set in stone at birth. Although each person inherits their own unique variation of the genetic code, scientists are now finding that 'epigenetic' factors such as lifestyle and diet can radically change what our genes do.

Genes are segments of DNA located on chromosomes that determine traits, or characteristics - such as eye, skin or hair colour. The information stored in a gene's DNA is transferred to RNA - this is called transcription. RNA then carries it out of the nucleus to make proteins – this is called translation. Variations in the proteins involved in growth and development can lead to differences in physical features. For example, enzymes - proteins that catalyse chemical reactions - produce the pigments that give skin and hair their colour. Variations in the structure and quantity of the proteins produced give rise to different hair and skin colours.

Since human cells carry two copies of each chromosome, they have two versions of each gene. Each gene in an individual consists of two 'alleles' - two variants of each gene that control specific traits - one inherited from each parent. Some alleles are 'dominant', meaning that they show their effect even if the individual has only one copy of the allele. For example, the allele for brown eyes is dominant, so a person only needs one copy of the 'brown eye' allele to have brown eyes - although, with two copies they will still have brown eyes. Other alleles are 'recessive' and only show their effect if the individual has two copies of the allele. For example, the allele for blue eyes is recessive, therefore to have blue eyes you need to have two copies of the 'blue eye' allele.

Aging process

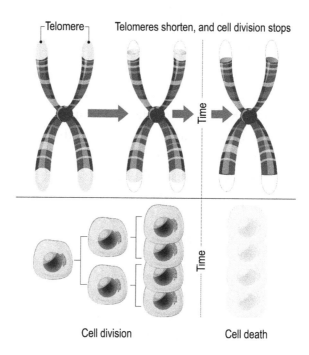

Telomere — Telomeres shorten, and cell division stops

Time

Time

Cell division   Cell death

4.2 Telomeres protect the ends of chromosomes

While almost all body cells have the same genes - apart from red blood cells which have no DNA as they have no nucleus - cells turn on different genes at different times in order to become specialised in their functions. The molecules of DNA in the nucleus of cells are found on a substance called chromatin, which is organised into special structures called chromosomes just before cells divide. Chromatids are each of the two threadlike strands into which a chromosome divides longitudinally during cell division. A functional chromosome consists of a centromere (the part of the chromosome in the middle that appears pinched together) and a pair of telomeres (stable chromosome ends that protect the DNA – often described as resembling the caps at the ends of shoelaces). We inherit telomeres from our parents, but no matter the length of our telomeres at birth, they get shorter with age and during different pathological processes. Shorter telomeres have a negative effect on health, and when telomeres get too short cells can no longer reproduce and this causes tissues to degenerate and eventually die. Some cells, like those found in skin, hair and the immune system, are most affected by telomere shortening because they reproduce more often. Although telomeres were first observed in the 1930's, it was not until the 1990's that researchers realised their importance. In 2009, scientist Elizabeth Blackburn and her colleagues won the Nobel Prize in Medicine for unlocking the mysteries of telomeres. In her book on the subject, she argues that to lengthen our telomeres, or at least stop them from shortening, we need to improve our lifestyle by managing chronic stress, exercising, eating better and getting adequate sleep.

Each cell has 46 chromosomes, including 2 sex chromosomes determining gender (if you're female, you have two X sex chromosomes, and if you're male, you have an X and a Y sex chromosome) and 44 autosomal (non-sex) chromosomes. In humans, chromosomes come in pairs. That means cells have 22 pairs of uniquely shaped autosomal chromosomes plus 1 pair of sex chromosomes - a total of 23 chromosome pairs. 'Homologous chromosomes' refer to each pair of chromosomes and they are identified by numbers - there are two chromosome 1s, two 2s, 3's, etc. Cells duplicate their DNA before division so that two new cells (daughter cells) have the same pieces and genetic code, giving two identical copies from one original. Some cells, like those found in the skin, are constantly dividing, as we need to continuously make new skin cells to replace the skin cells lost, while fully developed nerve cells do not divide anymore.

Mitosis is the simple duplication of a cell and all of its parts. Prior to duplication, a chromosome appears as a single-stranded chromatid.

After duplication, the chromosome has the familiar X-shape. Chromosomes must be duplicated and sister chromatids separated during cell division to ensure that each 'daughter cell' receives the appropriate number of chromosomes. There are five basic phases in the process of cell division.

Interphase is regarded as a resting stage in cell division, but actually many activities or processes happen at this phase, including duplication of the genetic material that makes chromosomes.

In the first stage of mitosis – prophase - the centrioles become well defined in a dense area of cytoplasm called the centrosome (as mentioned already - think of two matchsticks inside some chewing gum!). The nucleolus disappears and the nuclear membrane starts to break down. The replicated chromatin (the chromatids) forms into 46 X-shaped chromosomes, each composed of two identical sister chromatids. There are 92 chromatids present at this stage because two identical chromatids form each chromosome. The chromatids are connected at a bead-like point called the centromere (at the centre of the X) and this is the point of attachment for the long protein strands called spindle fibres that pull them apart during cell division.

In phase two – metaphase - the membrane surrounding the nucleus disappears, the 46 chromosome pairs line up at the middle of the cell, each attached by the bead-like centromere to the spindle fibres formed from the thick centrosome. Then the chromosome pairs begin to separate, pulled apart by the centrioles.

The next phase is anaphase, and here the centromeres split and chromosomes are pulled apart towards opposite ends of the cell. Now that the sister chromatids have separated, each chromatid is considered a 'daughter' chromosome, so during anaphase, there are 92 chromosomes (46 at each end of the cell). Chromosomes and chromatids can often be confused but the terms are used to refer to the same thing at different stages of a cell's reproduction. A chromosome is a single form of DNA and protein that lives within a cell. A chromatid is the sister and exact replica of a chromosome that is created when the cell divides.

Telophase is the final stage in cell division. During telophase, nuclear membranes re-form around the new nuclei in each half of the dividing cell. The nucleolus, which is the ribosome-producing portion of the nucleus, returns. As the cell has finished moving the chromosomes, the main parts of the spindle fibres fall apart. As telophase moves towards completion, the chromosomes release from their tightly bound structure back into loose chromatin. A process known as cytokinesis - which cleaves the cell into two new cells - marks the end of telophase. Both cells are identical and contain the same number of chromosomes.

When a cell divides during mitosis, some organelles are divided between the two daughter cells. For example, mitochondria are capable of growing and dividing during interphase, so the daughter cells each have enough mitochondria. The Golgi apparatus, however, breaks down before mitosis and reassembles in each of the new daughter cells. Many of the specifics about what happens to organelles before, during and after cell division are still unknown and being researched.

Interphase comes around again and the cell gets a rest, but as mentioned already, it is still busy going about the business of surviving, and also preparing for another division that will happen one day. Some cells divide more often than others, and the average cell will divide 50-70 times before cell death.

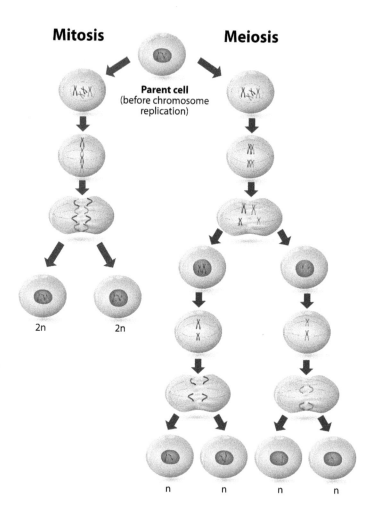

4.3 Mitosis & meiosis cell division

Meiosis is the two-part cell division process of the female egg cells (ova) and male sperm cells. It is similar to mitosis consisting of prophase, metaphase, anaphase and telophase, but in meiosis, cells go through these stages twice. In meiosis, sister chromatids do not separate until anaphase II. After cytokinesis, four daughter cells are produced and these are called 'haploid' cells as they contain half the number of chromosomes in their nuclei – a total of 23. All other cells are called 'diploid' cells as they contain 2 sets of chromosomes in their nuclei – a total of 46. When human fertilisation takes place, the 23 paternal chromosomes from the father's sperm and the 23 maternal chromosomes from the mother's ovum combine to form the diploid (46) number of chromosomes in the fertilised ovum. During meiosis, a small portion of each chromosome breaks off and reattaches to another chromosome. This process is called 'crossing over' or 'genetic recombination'. Genetic recombination is the reason full siblings made from egg and sperm cells from the same two parents can look very different from one another.

Patau syndrome

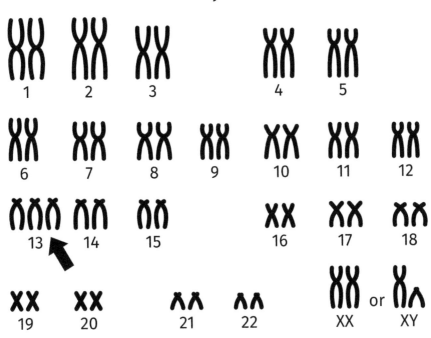

4.4 Patau syndrome karyotype

Sometimes problems can occur during meiosis. Nondisjunction is when chromosomes do not divide properly. As we have already seen, chromosomes contain the cell's DNA, which is needed for it to function and reproduce. Normally when a cell divides, the chromosomes line up in an orderly way and then separate from each other before cell division. When these chromosomes fail to separate properly nondisjunction occurs, and the resulting daughter cells have an incorrect number of chromosomes i.e. one may have too many, while another may have too few. This causes problems in cell function, because a cell cannot function normally without the right number of chromosomes. Some disorders caused by non-disjunction include: Down Syndrome - the result of an extra copy of chromosome 21; Patau Syndrome - the result of an extra copy of chromosome 13 and Edward's Syndrome - the result of an extra copy of chromosome 18. The consequences of having either too many or not enough chromosomes are sometimes serious or even fatal and are a major cause of many miscarriages.

DNA mutations are alterations that happen when there are changes in the nitrogenous bases that make up a strand of DNA. The four bases in DNA are thymine (T), adenine (A), guanine (G) and cytosine (C), and a mutation is a change somewhere in the long strings of T's, A's, G's and C's that make up the DNA of a living organism. These can be big changes that affect a large amount of DNA, or tiny changes that only alter the DNA at a single position. They can be caused by random mistakes in DNA replication or by environmental influences e.g. chemicals or UV rays. Unprotected exposure to UVA and UVB can damage the DNA in skin cells, producing mutations that can lead to skin cancers and premature ageing. These rays can also cause eye damage, including cataracts and eyelid cancers.

DNA mutations can be completely harmless, potentially fatal, or fall somewhere in between. Types of mutations include inversions, duplications, deletions and translocations. An inversion is a chromosome rearrangement in which a segment of a chromosome is reversed end to end. Inversions may or may not cause symptoms, depending on the chromosome involved and the degree of inversion. Duplication occurs when a segment of DNA is repeated, and deletion occurs when a segment of DNA is removed. The segment that is removed can become attached to another chromosome or the sister chromatid, causing a duplication or a translocation.

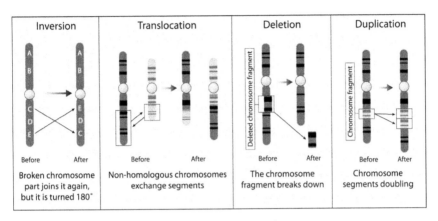

4.5 Chromosome mutations

A translocation means that there is an unusual arrangement of the chromosomes. This can happen because a change occurred during meiosis of the ovum or the sperm or around the time of conception, or an altered chromosome arrangement has been inherited from either the mother or the father. A reciprocal translocation occurs when two fragments break off from two different chromosomes and swap places, while a Robertsonian translocation occurs when one chromosome becomes attached to another. Although about 1 person in 500 has a translocation, we still don't really understand why they happen. We know that chromosomes seem to break and rejoin quite often during the making of sperm and ova or around the time of conception, and it is only sometimes that this leads to problems.

If the chromosomes have been rearranged so that no chromosome material has been lost or gained, this is called a balanced translocation and a person who carries this arrangement is not usually affected by it, and may be totally unaware of having it. In a balanced translocation, a person usually has all the genetic material necessary for normal growth - part of a chromosome has simply broken off and attached to another one. However, when that person's cells divide to create an egg or sperm cells for reproduction, the egg or sperm cells can end up with extra genetic material or missing genetic material that could lead to miscarriage, depending on which chromosomes and genes are affected. If either parent carries a balanced translocation, it is possible that their child may inherit an unbalanced translocation in which there is an extra piece of one chromosome and/or a missing piece of another chromosome, and may be born with some degree of developmental delay, learning disability or health problems - if the pregnancy does not end in miscarriage. The seriousness of the problem depends on exactly which parts of which chromosomes are involved, and how much missing or extra chromosome material there is. This is because some parts of the chromosome are more important than other parts. It is quite possible for a person who carries a balanced translocation to have healthy children. A child can be born with a translocation although both parents' chromosomes are normal. This is called a 'de novo' (Latin) or 'new' rearrangement. In this case the parents are unlikely to have another child with a translocation.

Genetic testing is available to find out whether a person carries a translocation. A blood sample is taken and the cells are examined to look at the arrangement of the chromosomes - this is called a karyotype test. It is also possible to do a test during pregnancy to find out whether a baby has a chromosome translocation. If a translocation is found, other family members are usually advised to have a blood test to see if they also carry the translocation. If they do not carry it, then they cannot pass it on to their children, but if they do carry a translocation, they too could be offered a test during pregnancy to check the baby's chromosomes.

Cancer results from cells that divide at an abnormally high rate resulting in tumours that may be either benign or malignant. The term 'cancer' originates from the Latin, 'crab' or 'creeping ulcer', because the swollen veins around them resembled the limbs of a crab. Benign tumours are not life threatening, as they do not invade other areas of the body and most can be removed. Malignant tumours can invade other parts of the body through the blood and lymphatic system, and this is called metastasis. Cancer-causing substances are referred to as carcinogens - these include environmental chemicals or toxins, physical agents such as nuclear radiation, X-rays or UV light, and biological agents such as viruses. Certain types of cancer can run in families, but only a small portion of all cancers are inherited. Lifestyle factors including cigarette smoking, diet (e.g. fried foods, red meat), excess alcohol consumption, sun exposure, environmental pollutants, infections, stress, obesity and physical inactivity are also attributed to the development of some cancers.

There are six main types of cancer. Carcinomas are cancers that begin in the skin or tissues that line or cover internal organs. Subtypes include adenocarcinomas (form in mucus-secreting glands), basal cell carcinomas (skin), squamous cell carcinomas (skin) and transitional cell carcinomas (urinary system). Sarcomas arise in connective or supportive tissues such as bone, muscle, fat, cartilage and blood vessels, and are relatively uncommon. Melanomas are cancers that arise in cells called melanocytes that make the pigment, melanin, in the skin. Lymphomas are cancers of lymphocytes in the lymphatic system, while myelomas affect the white blood cells (plasma cells) in bone marrow. Leukemia is a cancer of white blood cells causing large numbers of abnormal cells to be produced. It can occur in cells of the lymphatic system (lymphoid) or white blood cells in bone marrow (myeloid) and can be acute or chronic. Brain and spinal cord cancers are known as central nervous system cancers. These days, cancer can be treated - often successfully - with surgery to remove the tumour, radiation to burn out the tumour and chemotherapy drugs to poison the tumour – and often a combination of all three methods are used.

Cells come together to form tissues, which can be defined as groups of cells that have a similar shape and function. Different types of tissues can be found in different organs of the body. In humans, there are four basic types of tissue: epithelial, muscular, nervous and connective tissue.

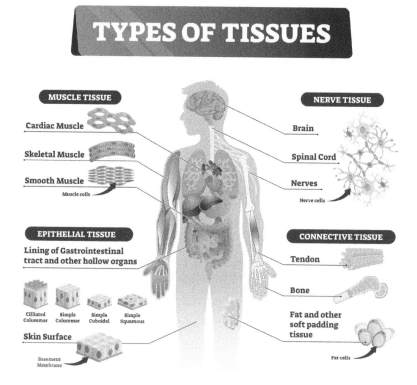

4.6 Body tissues

Epithelial tissue covers body surfaces and forms the lining for most internal body cavities. Its function includes protection, secretion, absorption and filtration. The skin - the largest body organ - is made up of epithelial tissue that protects the body from dirt, dust, bacteria and other microbes that could cause harm. Epithelial tissue cells have different shapes, from thin and flat to cuboidal and elongated or columnar. Some epithelial tissue cells in the lining of the respiratory system and other areas of the body have tiny hairs called cilia. The rhythmic movement of the cilia helps in the movement of material in one direction e.g. pushing mucus to the throat to be swallowed.

There are three types of muscle tissue: skeletal, smooth and cardiac. Skeletal muscle is a type of voluntary muscle tissue that is attached to bones, and contracts for body movement. Smooth muscle is found in the walls of internal organs and blood vessels, and contracts involuntarily to move substances through the body. Cardiac muscle is found only in the walls of the heart and is involuntary in nature, providing the synchronised contractions of the heartbeat.

Nerve tissue is composed of specialised cells that not only receive stimuli, but also conduct impulses to and from all parts of the body. The nervous system contains two types of cells: neurons and neuroglial (nerve glue) cells. Neurons are the cells that receive and transmit signals. The neuroglial cells are the support systems for the neurons as they protect and nourish them. Neurons are long and string-like, with dendrites that act like tiny antennae picking up signals from other cells, and long thin fibres called axons at the ends, sending signals out.

Connective tissue is said to be the most abundant and most widely distributed body tissue, providing support and protection. It is composed of three elements - cells, fibres providing strength, elasticity and support, and 'ground substance' - a gel-like substance around the cells and fibres. The loose connective tissue - sometimes referred to as areolar tissue - provides a cushion around organs. It binds skin to the muscles beneath, forms a link between organs, and enables a high degree of movement between adjacent body parts. Blood and lymph are regarded as liquid or fluid connective tissues. Other categories of connective tissue include adipose or fatty tissue, bone, and the dense fibrous tissue found in tendons, ligaments and cartilage.

When an embryo is developing, cartilage is the precursor to bone. Cartilage cells - called chondrocytes – do not have blood vessels or nerves, and are located in a gel-like matrix that provides nourishment to the cells. Cartilage is a strong but flexible tissue, and three different types exist in the body. Elastic cartilage is found in the ear and epiglottis (in the throat) as well as parts of the nose and trachea. This cartilage provides strength and elasticity to organs and body structures. Fibrocartilage is found in 'cushions' around joints, known as 'menisci', and in the discs between the spinal vertebrae. It helps to reduce friction in joints such as the knee. Hyaline cartilage is the most common type of cartilage in the body and is found in the larynx, nose, ribs and trachea. A very thin layer of 'articular' hyaline cartilage is also found on bony surfaces at joints. The word hyaline means 'glass-like' and this type of cartilage is smooth, slippery and semitransparent, with a bluish tint. A membrane called the perichondrium surrounds it and provides it with nutrients, as this cartilage tissue has no blood vessels of its own. When cartilage is damaged, it doesn't heal as well as most other tissues due to the lack of blood supply and the fact that chondrocytes do not replicate or repair themselves very quickly.

The body's membranes are thin sheets of tissue that cover the body, line body cavities, and cover organs within the cavities of the body. They are composed of both epithelial and connective tissue and include mucous membranes (secrete mucous), serous membranes (secrete fluid e.g. around lungs), synovial membranes (secret fluid and found in joints) and the meninges covering the brain and spinal cord.

'Fascia' is a new trending word in the health and fitness industries these days, and those who study fascia have found that all of the body's connective tissue - solid and liquid - and internal epithelium is not just a system of separate units and coverings, but actually one continuous structure that exists from head to toe, so that each part of the entire body is connected to every other part. It envelops, separates, or binds together muscles, organs and other soft structures of the body.

Described as being like the yarn in a sweater or a spider's web, fascia appears to be an interwoven system of fibrous connective tissue throughout the body, providing a framework that helps support and protect individual muscle groups, nerves, blood vessels, organs and the entire body as a unit. "Fascia is the missing element in the movement/stability equation," says Tom Myers, author of the acclaimed book "Anatomy Trains". Myers was among the first medical professionals to challenge the ignorance of fascia in the human body and says: "while every anatomy book lists around 600 separate muscles, it is more accurate to say that there is one muscle poured into six hundred pockets of the fascial webbing." Myers also states: "Fascia forms a whole-body, continuous three-dimensional matrix of structural support around our organs, muscles, joints, bones and nerve fibres. This multidirectional, multidimensional fascial arrangement also allows us to move in multiple directions".

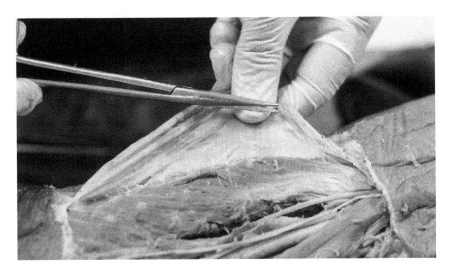

4.7 Fascia

Biotensegrity has been defined as the "new science of body architecture" and includes the latest research into the fascia. Biotensegrity, or tensegrity in biology, is described as the tensional network of the human body. With the explosion of interest in fascia, many therapists and body workers are now studying this subject, and according to some, injury, tightness or restrictions in one area of the body can lead to a problem in a completely different area, so it's important to see where our problems really lie. It is thought that physical trauma, long-term unprocessed emotions, chronic stress, or over-stretching may all lead to a build-up of excess fascia, affecting body shape and health. Treating the root cause may help prevent other issues from developing further down the line, but treating only the problem area may lead to worse symptoms later on. Bearing in mind that we all started out as a single cell that rapidly divided and then differentiated into different cell types during our time in the uterus, it makes sense that all the cells and tissues of the body are interconnected rather than isolated parts.

5. Skin

The skin is an organ that provides an outer protective wrapping for the body, acting as a waterproof, airtight and flexible barrier between the environment and internal organs. Skin, hair and nails are often collectively referred to as the 'integumentary system' - a protective outer covering. The skin is the largest body organ - with a surface area of around two square metres - and accounts for about 16% of body weight. Its thickness varies, with eyelids having the thinnest skin and soles of the feet the thickest. Skin can absorb small molecules like those found in aromatherapy essential oils, as well as other chemical substances such as steroid creams, hormone replacement therapy creams and 'stop smoking' patches.

Human skin is composed of two layers - the outer epidermis and the dermis underneath. Beneath the dermis is the subcutaneous layer (hypodermis), which is normally thicker in females than in males. This is composed of fatty tissue as well as elastic fibres, making it flexible as well as reducing heat loss and protecting underlying organs from injury. The subcutaneous layer also attaches the skin to underlying bone and muscle, as well as supplying it with blood vessels and nerves.

The outer epidermis is made up of five layers or 'strata'. The deepest layer, the stratum germinativum or basal layer, is attached to the dermis from which it receives nutrients through tiny blood capillaries. Here the cells are living and dividing. As new cells are produced, older cells are gradually pushed upwards, taking on average 28 days to reach the upper layers of the epidermis - but this time period increases with age. Melanin - a pigment that protects the skin from the harmful effects of ultra violet sunlight - is formed in special cells called 'melanocytes' in this layer.

Structure of the Epidermis

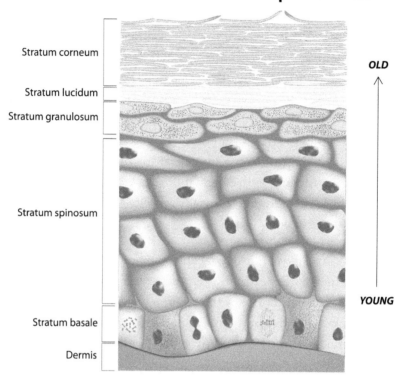

5.1 Layers of the epidermis

The stratum spinosum or prickle-cell layer houses the cells immediately above the basal layer. These rows of cells are still living and capable of mitosis. However, their membranes are beginning to split, giving them a prickly appearance when viewed under a microscope.

In the 3-5 rows of the stratum granulosum or granular layer, the cells become flattened and the nuclei begin to disintegrate as the cells lose fluid and fill with granules of a substance called keratohyalin. This is the first stage in their transformation into a tough, fibrous, waterproof protein called keratin.

The cells in the stratum lucidum or clear layer are transparent, small, tightly packed and have no nucleus. This layer is very thin in facial skin but thicker on the soles and palms, and is thought to be the barrier zone controlling transmission of water through the skin.

The stratum corneum - the 'horny' outermost epidermal layer - is composed of 25-30 layers of keratinised cells packed tightly together, the outer layers of which are constantly being shed and replaced from below. Keratin keeps the skin waterproof, preventing the body from becoming waterlogged and keeping out harmful chemical substances. Intact skin also prevents the entry of pathogens - e.g. bacteria - that could cause infection. According to US dermatologist Albert Kligman, M.D., Ph.D. (1919-2010) "Whenever you see inflamed skin, regardless of cause, the stratum corneum is leaky and permeable. But, if you repair the stratum corneum, that tells the underlying tissues that they don't have to keep reacting like there's danger in the environment."

Human Skin Anatomy

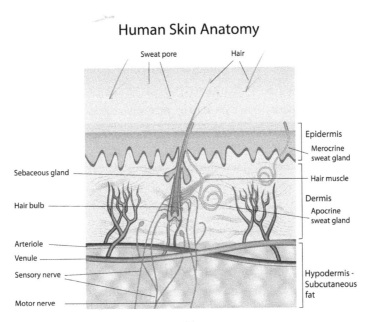

5.2 Human skin anatomy

61

The dermis is the layer of skin beneath the epidermis and above the subcutaneous layer. It is the thickest layer of the skin and contains flexible connective tissue composed of collagen that provides strength, and elastin that gives the skin its resilience and elasticity. Fibroblast cells manufacture the proteins, collagen and elastin. With age, these cells reduce their production, leading to a loss of strength and elasticity in the skin. According to some skin experts, excess sugar molecules in the body can damage the collagen and elastin through a process known as 'protein glycation.' Renegade sugars in the system can bind to these proteins, causing them to become weak, stiff and less supple, and this shows up on the skin's surface as wrinkles, sagginess and a loss of radiance – a good reason to follow a healthy diet!

Stretch marks (striae) are stripe-like skin marks that develop in the dermis when the skin is stretched and small tears occur in the connective tissue. Many women experience stretch marks during pregnancy as the skin stretches to make room for the developing baby. Stretch marks sometimes appear due to weight gain or loss, and teenagers often develop stretch marks after a sudden growth spurt. Corticosteroid creams, lotions and pills can cause stretch marks by decreasing the skin's ability to stretch. Cushing's syndrome and other adrenal gland disorders can cause stretch marks by increasing the amount of cortisone in the body.

Other cells found in the dermis include mast cells that secrete histamine in allergic reactions, and cells called histiocytes (macrophages) that become active when stimulated by infection and attack bacteria and other foreign matter in the skin. The dermis contains nerve endings for touch, pain, heat, cold and pressure. They send messages to the central nervous system about what is going on outside the body and on the surface of the skin. The dermis is composed of two layers: the papillary dermis and the reticular dermis. The papillary dermis is the more superficial of the two and lies just beneath the epidermal junction. The reticular dermis is the deeper and thicker layer of the dermis that lies above the subcutaneous layer of the skin.

Sweat glands are tube-like ducts that rise up through the dermis and epidermis, ending at the surface of the skin to form pores. Apocrine sweat glands in the underarms become active at puberty, secreting fatty substances as well as salt and water that react to air and can cause body odour (bromhidrosis) if a person is not careful with hygiene. Secretions from these glands occur most frequently during periods of emotional stress or sexual excitement. Chemicals called pheromones that act as catalysts of sexual attraction are secreted onto the skin through the apocrine glands - sometimes called human scent glands. Eccrine sweat glands that excrete waste through sweating are found all over the body, with many on the palms and soles. This watery sweat cools on evaporation, helping to regulate body temperature. Different factors can affect eccrine sweat glands and increase their sweat production, sometimes causing hyperhidrosis. These include emotional issues, temperature, exercise, certain diseases and illnesses, hormonal problems like an overactive thyroid or certain drugs (e.g. dementia drugs, antidepressants) that can affect the hypothalamus - an area of the brain that helps to regulate body temperature. Some people suffer from decreased sweating (anhidrosis) due to nerve damage, genetics or other causes.

Sebaceous glands in the dermis open into hair follicles. These are more numerous on the scalp and face, particularly the forehead, chin and nose. They secrete sebum, the skin's natural oil that moisturises and conditions skin and hair. Sebum and perspiration mix on the surface of the skin to form the 'acid mantle', a very fine, slightly acidic film that acts as a barrier to bacteria, viruses and other potential contaminants that might penetrate the skin. Human skin has an average pH value of between 4 and 6, with facial skin typically having a pH value of between 4.5 and 5.5, which is slightly acidic. Harsh skin washing products can disrupt the acid mantle, so it's best to seek out gentler products without ingredients like sodium lauryl sulphate, which is a powerful degreaser. Sebum production increases after puberty, as the hormones oestrogen and testosterone activate the sebaceous glands. Excess sebum may result in comedones (blackheads), milia (whiteheads) or acne if the sebaceous glands become inflamed. Sebum production decreases with age, particularly in females whose oestrogen supplies diminish after menopause.

UV rays from sunlight change cholesterol molecules (7-dehydro cholesterol) in the skin into vitamin D3 (cholecalciferol). This passes into the bloodstream and is further synthesised - first in the liver where it is converted into a pre-hormone called calcidiol, and then in the kidneys, where it finally forms a hormone called calcitriol that is used for bone maintenance and aiding the absorption of calcium and phosphorus in the intestines. Vitamin D3 is important for keeping bones and teeth strong and has numerous other health benefits, including improving mood and depression and supporting the immune system. In the UK, we can only make adequate vitamin D3 in the skin from late March/early April to September, as the sun is not strong enough here during the winter months. To compensate, it is advisable to eat plenty of vitamin D rich foods such as oily fish and eggs, and also take a daily vitamin D supplement during the winter months.

The dermis also contains fine blood and lymph vessels that carry nutrients and allow removal of waste from the skin. When the body heats up (e.g. during exercise), blood vessels in the dermis dilate, allowing extra blood to the surface of the skin to lose heat and cool the body. When it's cold, the blood vessels constrict as blood moves inwards to keep vital organs functioning and maintain normal body temperature. Stress reactions also cause blood vessels in the skin to constrict as blood is diverted to the heart, lungs and muscles in 'fight or flight' situations. This reduces the supply of oxygen and nutrients to the skin and can account for stress-related skin and hair disorders. In Raynaud's disease arterioles in the extremities constrict in response to cold temperatures, causing numbness and pain.

Hair follicles - downward growths in the dermis - are found all over the body except on the lips, soles and palms. Cells move up the follicle from the hair bulb at its base, changing in structure to form a hair. Tiny muscles called 'erector pili' (or arrector pili) attached to all hair follicles cause hairs to stand erect when it is cold, trapping heat near the surface of the skin to warm up the body. Aggression or fright can also contract these muscles leading to the appearance of 'goose bumps'.

Skin varies in colour, texture and condition from one person to another, and it can tell much about a person's physiological and psychological state. Physiological signs may appear as colour (redness or pallor), areas of puffiness, dry or greasy patches, spots etc. while psychological signs may be reflected in muscular tightness as well as lines and wrinkles from stress and worry.

The changes that occur in facial skin with age are due to subtle alterations in anatomical structure as well as by modifications to the skin itself. Skin becomes slacker due to loss of collagen, elastin and underlying fat, and this can lead to the formation of lines and wrinkles. It also becomes more transparent due to thinning of the epidermis, and is more easily bruised due to thinner blood vessel walls. The shrinking of facial bones plays a surprisingly significant part in facial ageing, according to U.S. Plastic Surgeon Dr. David Kahn, M.D. who says: "As we age, not only do we lose fat in our faces but our bones actually change in contour, often making us look older than we feel. As bones shrink, the skin cannot tighten around the skeleton causing drooping and wrinkles that can age the face." According to a study carried out by Dr. Kahn and colleagues, facial bones remodel themselves with time, dissolving, shrinking and leaving empty space.

In addition, people lose skin elasticity with age. The study also found that women had a significant decrease in facial bone volume at a younger age than men, causing women to see the signs of ageing sooner. According to Dr. Kahn, this earlier change in bone structure may be why many women seek facial cosmetic enhancement at a younger age than men.

Sun damage also plays a major role in skin ageing. Ultraviolet (UV) radiation is part of the electromagnetic light spectrum that reaches the earth from the sun. There are three different types of UV classified as UVA, UVB and UVC. UVC is mostly absorbed by the ozone layer and does not reach the earth, but UVA and UVB penetrate the atmosphere and play an important role in premature skin ageing. Sunburn is a reaction to UV overexposure caused by the sun and/or sunbeds. The superficial layers of the skin release chemicals that cause blood vessels to expand and leak fluid, causing swelling, pain and redness. Without sun protection, UV radiation starts to penetrate deep into the layers of the skin, damaging skin cells. UVB are the burning rays that reach the outer layers of the skin, causing sunburn and skin cancer in some cases. UVA rays penetrate deeper into the skin and also contribute to burning, wrinkling, premature ageing and skin cancers. UVA rays can reach the skin through clouds, smog or glass.

When skin is injured, an automatic series of events - often referred to as 'the cascade of healing' - takes place. The four overlapping phases in this cascade are haemostasis, inflammation, proliferation and maturation. Haemostasis begins at the onset of injury, and aims to stop bleeding through the blood clotting system, which is described in detail in Chapter 10. During the inflammatory phase, white blood cells called neutrophils enter the wound to destroy bacteria and remove debris. They are closely followed by cells called macrophages that continue clearing debris and attracting other immune cells and chemicals to the wound to facilitate tissue repair. This phase can last four to six days and is often associated with oedema, erythema (reddening of the skin), heat and pain. During the proliferative stage, shiny, red 'granulation tissue' fills the cleaned out wound bed with connective tissue, and new blood vessels are formed. The wound margins contract and pull toward the centre of the wound, while epithelial cells arise from the wound bed and spread across it until the wound is covered with epithelium. The proliferative phase can last anywhere from four to twenty four days. During the maturation phase, the new tissue slowly gains strength and flexibility. The collagen fibres reorganise, the tissue remodels and matures, and there is an overall increase in tensile strength - though never quite as good as the pre-injured strength. This phase varies greatly depending on the size and type of wound, and can last anywhere from twenty-one days to two years.

Factors that can influence the wound healing process include moisture, hygiene, infection, age, nutritional status and general state of health. When the right healing environment is established, the body works in wondrous ways to heal and replace damaged tissue, although in most cases, some scarring can result.

Keloid scars come from an overgrowth of scar tissue and tend to be larger than the original wound. They may take weeks or months to develop fully and are more common among people with dark skin. There may be genetic links i.e. a person is more likely to have keloids if one or both parents have them. Although keloids aren't harmful, sometimes they can be sore or itchy. Keloids can be surgically removed but the scar tissue may grow back again, and it sometimes grows back larger than before. Keloids are easily confused with another more common type of scar called hypertrophic scars. These are flat scars that can range from pink to brown in color. They are usually smaller than keloid scars and often disappear over time.

Types of scars

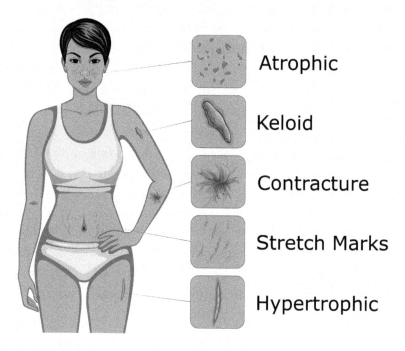

Atrophic

Keloid

Contracture

Stretch Marks

Hypertrophic

5.3 Scar types

Scar formation - which can be external or internal - is a natural process of wound healing. Scar tissue contains more fibrous tissue and collagen deposits than normal skin, making it structurally and functionally different. The injury or surgery may have resulted in nerve damage, causing numbness or sensitivity in the area. As skin is healing after an operation or accident, different layers under the skin can stick together as the body rushes to close and heal the wound. In some cases, scar tissues link to form adhesions, which are bands of scar tissue. The adhesions can connect internal parts, which may restrict movement or may hinder organs from performing their intended functions. Nowadays there are various treatments options available that can help to manage scars and the adhesions that may accompany scar tissue.

There is a generally accepted method of classifying skin according to the balance of sebum and water in the tissues, although skin may change its type and condition from time to time. In normal skin, the oil glands produce sebum at a moderate rate, resulting in a balanced skin that is neither too oily nor too dry. Dry skin is usually due to sebaceous glands not producing enough sebum to keep the skin naturally lubricated. It often appears dull and may feel dry, itchy and sometimes sensitive. Oily skin is caused by over-active sebaceous glands producing excess sebum, resulting in skin that has a greasy, coarse texture, appears shiny, and frequently has large unevenly sized pores. Oily skin types are prone to developing acne, as sebum becomes trapped inside the pores leading to spots and blackheads. Despite these drawbacks, oily skin generally remains younger looking and more supple over time than other skin types.

Most people have at least two different types of facial skin at any given time. Combination skin is characterised by an oily 'T-zone' area with larger pores covering the forehead, nose and chin, while skin around the cheeks, eyes and mouth is normal or dry. This is the most common adult skin type. Dehydrated skin is a condition where skin lacks water rather than oil. It can appear to have fine lines and creases, and may flake or look rough. Any skin type can become dehydrated due to environmental factors such as sun exposure, air conditioning, air travel and central heating - all of which can draw moisture out of the skin. It is even possible to have an underlying oily skin with dehydration on the top layers. In the skincare world, this is known as 'transdermal water loss'. To prevent this it is advisable to drink plenty of water, avoid spending too much time in centrally heated or air-conditioned environments, and always protect the skin from the sun. Skincare products containing humectants help to draw moisture to the epidermis, either from the air if it is humid enough, or from the underlying dermis in low-humidity conditions, while occlusive ingredients simultaneously keep pollutants, toxins and harmful bacteria out. Some skincare products containing substances such as beeswax, shea butter, avocado oil and other vegetable oils, not only provide valuable nutrients to the skin, they also serve as emollients that are considered slightly occlusive, and can help to slow down the rate of transdermal water loss.

Any skin can become sensitive, which is more of a skin condition than a skin type. Sensitive skin reacts badly to emotional turmoil, stress, environmental conditions and hormonal changes, and often requires special treatment to remain in good condition. Sensitive skin is also prone to react to cosmetics containing alcohol, synthetically manufactured ingredients, fragrance and artificial colours - usually appearing red and blotchy - and benefits greatly from natural, gentle skin care products and treatments.

Skin naturally becomes drier with age, and mature skin can become dry and tight, with a rough, wrinkled texture and a dull appearance. The hormonal changes that accompany ageing can accentuate this, particularly in females, as sebaceous glands slow down sebum production in response to a drop in oestrogen. Small wrinkles commonly referred to as 'crow's feet' appear around the outer corners of the eyes. Excessive exposure to the sun, as well as cigarette smoke, can damage the cells that produce collagen and elastin, prematurely ageing the skin. Mature skin needs plenty of care and nourishment with good quality natural products to keep it in optimum condition.

The pigments responsible for varying skin colours are melanin, which absorbs UV light to turn the skin brown, carotene, which gives the skin a yellowish colour, and haemoglobin, which gives red blood cells their colour. White skin (Caucasian) is often dry and thin, burns easily in the sun, bruises more easily, and signs of ageing appear earlier. This category also includes those with ruddy, freckled complexions and red hair. Skin cancers are most common in this skin type. Those with southern European/Mediterranean skin have oily, olive, dark complexions with signs of ageing appearing later. Darker and thicker scars are more common, wrinkles appear later, and there is a decreased risk of skin cancer. In those with African/African-American/Australian Aboriginal skin, signs of ageing appear later and there is very little wrinkling, but the formation of keloid scars is quite common. Pigmentation changes may occur, but skin cancers are rare. In those with Asian/Oriental skin, signs of ageing appear later and fine wrinkling is uncommon. Pigmentation changes may occur but skin cancers are rare.

Birthmarks and other pigmentation disorders affect many people. Loss of melanocytes in areas of the skin results in vitiligo, a condition that produces white patches on the skin. Vitiligo affects all skin types, but is more noticeable in people with darker skin, and can also affect the hair and the inside of the mouth. The cause is not clear, but it is associated with a disorder of the immune system, family history (heredity), emotional stress, physical trauma, or stress to the skin like severe sunburn or exposure to industrial chemicals.

Melasma - also called chloasma - which is associated with hormonal changes, causes brown pigmentation marks, often on the face. Melasma is sometimes referred to as the mask of pregnancy, because the splotches typically show up around the upper lip, nose, cheekbones and forehead in the shape of a mask during pregnancy. It can affect other areas of the body, and skin that is already more pigmented such as nipples, freckles etc. may become even darker during pregnancy. This also tends to happen in areas where friction is common e.g. the underarms and inner thighs. The same increased production of melanin that causes the facial splotches of melasma also causes the dark line - linea nigra - that pregnant women may notice running down the belly.

Albinism is a rare, genetic disorder characterised by a total or partial lack of melanin in the skin and hair, and sometime affecting the eyes. People with albinism are sensitive to the effects of the sun, and have an increased risk of developing skin cancer.

Dermatosis papulosa nigra (DPN) is a harmless skin condition that tends to affect people with darker skin. It consists of small, dark bumps that usually appear on the face and neck. A lentigo is a pigmented, flat or slightly raised lesion with a clearly defined edge. Unlike ephilides (freckles), lentigines do not fade in the winter months. There are several kinds of lentigo and the name originally referred to its resemblance to a small lentil. Age spots - also called sunspots, liver spots and solar lentigines - are small, flat, dark patches on the skin that usually appear on areas exposed to the sun - such as the face, hands, shoulders and arms - and are more common in older people.

As well as disorders of melanocytes, there are other disorders that may not have any health implications, but can be disfiguring and cause distress. Vascular naevi (hemangiomas) are malformed, dilated blood vessels that appear as red or purple blotches on the skin, and can appear anywhere on the body. They include strawberry birthmarks that are usually harmless and typically fade by the time a child reaches the age of ten. Port-wine stains - so called because they look like wine has been spilled on the skin - are birthmarks that appear most often on the face, head, arms or legs, but can be found anywhere on the body. These red marks - caused by overly dilated capillaries - are rarely harmful and they don't usually signal any major health problem. They usually start out being flat and smooth, but over time they may become thicker or slightly bumpy, and may be prone to bleeding when scratched or injured.

All skin is subject to problems at one time or another, regardless of skin colour or ethnic background. Blemishes, scarring, wrinkles, skin discolorations, disorders, sensitivity and sun damage can affect everyone to some degree, although darker skinned people have more protection from the damaging effects of the sun than those with fair skin. Skin diseases and disorders vary greatly in symptoms and severity. They can be temporary or permanent and may be painless or painful. Some may be genetic or caused by bacterial, viral, fungal or parasitic infections. Some are due to allergies or autoimmune conditions. The skin may reflect signs of systemic diseases, while other skin disorders are topical, affecting the skin only. See the references for websites with pictures of all skin diseases and disorders mentioned in this chapter.

Systemic lupus erythematosus is an inflammatory, autoimmune disease that occurs when the body's immune system attacks its own tissues and organs. Inflammation caused by lupus can affect the skin, joints and organs inside the body. Discoid lupus affects only the skin, causing a red, scaly, rash with raised borders on areas of the body that are exposed to sunlight. A butterfly-shaped rash on the face that covers the cheeks and bridge of the nose is a common feature. Lupus can cause the scalp hair to gradually thin out, and some people lose clumps of hair. Loss of eyebrow, eyelash, beard and body hair also is possible. In most cases, the hair will grow back when the lupus is treated, but some people with lupus develop round (discoid) lesions on the scalp that can scar the hair follicles, causing permanent hair loss.

Scleroderma is an autoimmune disease in which the skin thickens, hardens and tightens due to an overproduction and accumulation of collagen. Sometimes other parts of the body are affected and joint pain may result. Scleroderma affects women more often than men, and most commonly occurs between the ages of 30 and 50. As well as immune system problems, genetics and environmental triggers such as exposure to harmful chemicals, certain viruses or some medications may also be involved. While there is no cure for scleroderma, a variety of treatments can ease symptoms and improve quality of life. These include medications to suppress the immune system and treat specific symptoms.

Lichen planus is another autoimmune disease that causes inflammation on the skin or inside the mouth. On the skin, it causes a rash that is usually itchy, and inside the mouth it may cause burning or soreness. The most common symptoms on the skin are shiny red or purple bumps that are firm and may itch. Fine white lines or scaly patches may also accompany the bumps. They can occur anywhere, but are most common on the wrists, arms, back, shins and ankles. Sometimes the bumps may appear in an area where the skin has been scratched or burned. As the skin bumps fade, dark patches may be left, but these eventually fade away. Lichen planus inside the mouth looks like lacy patches of tiny white dots on the inside of the cheeks or on the tongue. It may not cause any other symptoms, but in severe cases, redness and sores can develop. Lichen planus can also affect the nails, causing thinning, ridges, splitting and nail loss on fingers and toes. If it affects the scalp, redness, irritation and tiny bumps can form, and in some cases, hair may start to thin and patches of hair loss may occur. Lichen planus in the genitals can cause red, painful areas. Medical advice regarding treatment for lichen planus should be sought.

Xanthomas (Greek for 'yellow') are fatty deposits under the skin or around tendons. They are fairly common - especially among older people - and can range in size from tiny to large (7 centimetres or more). There are different types, depending on where they are, what causes them and what they look like. Typically the lumps or nodules occur on elbows, knees and other joints, as well as on the eyelids. Xanthomas are usually a sign that a person has high cholesterol or high triglycerides (fats in the blood). People with diabetes are prone to develop certain kinds of xanthomas because they often have lipid abnormalities. The lumps don't usually itch or cause pain, and sometimes they disappear spontaneously. A dermatologist can remove them using surgery, laser therapy or a topical acid, but they may return after treatment. The best course of action is to get blood lipids under control.

Psoriasis is a non-contagious skin condition resulting from increased epidermal cell turnover. It has no exact cause, but in many cases it is thought to be due to genetics or an autoimmune condition, whereby the immune system attacks the body's own skin cells, causing a speeding up of the skin production process from around one month to three or four days. There are different types of psoriasis, with plaque psoriasis being the most common. This causes red, inflamed, itchy patches, often covered with whitish-silver scales or plaques. These plaques are commonly found on the elbows, knees and scalp. There may also be pitting of the nails and swollen or painful joints due to psoriatic arthritis. Most sufferers go through cycles - with severe symptoms for a few days or weeks, and then remissions and relapses. Common triggers for outbreaks include stress, alcohol, injury to the skin, infection e.g. sore throat, and some medications e.g. antimalarial medication, lithium or high blood pressure medication.

Psoriasis has no cure and treatments aim to reduce inflammation, slow the growth of skin cells and remove plaques. Ultraviolet or natural light appears to benefit sufferers and is helpful in reducing symptoms of mild to moderate psoriasis. Eating a healthy diet and avoiding foods that may cause inflammation - e.g. red meat, refined sugar, processed foods, dairy products - may help reduce symptoms in some sufferers. Guttate psoriasis is another form that is common in childhood and causes small pink spots on the torso, arms and legs. These spots are rarely thick or raised like plaque psoriasis. Pustular psoriasis is more common in adults and causes white, pus-filled blisters and broad areas of red, inflamed skin on the hands or feet, but it can be widespread. Erythrodermic psoriasis is a severe and very rare type of psoriasis that often covers large sections of the body at once and gives the skin a sunburned appearance. Scales that develop often slough off in large sections or sheets, and sufferers may have a fever or become very ill.

The word eczema comes from the Greek word 'ekzein', which means 'to boil' and this perfectly describes the irritation and redness caused by this condition. Eczema is a term for a group of medical conditions that causes the skin to become inflamed or irritated. The most common type of eczema is known as atopic eczema or atopic dermatitis. Atopic refers to a genetic tendency to develop allergic diseases such as asthma and hay fever. Eczema is a common skin condition, especially in children. It is thought to be due to 'leakiness' of the skin barrier, which causes it to dry out and become prone to irritation and inflammation by many environmental factors. Some people with eczema have food sensitivities - e.g. dairy products - that can make the condition worse.

The exact cause of eczema is unknown but in some people with severe atopic dermatitis, it is due to inheritance of a faulty gene called the FLG gene that provides instructions for making a large protein called filaggrin that is found in epidermal cells. Filaggrin helps structural proteins in the outermost skin cells to form tight bundles, flattening and strengthening the cells to create a strong barrier. It is also involved in the production of molecules that are part of the skin's 'natural moisturising factor' - the acid mantle - that helps maintain hydration as well as the correct acidity (pH) of the skin. Eczema often affects body creases, but any part of the body can be affected, and it is almost always itchy. Sometimes the itching will start before the rash appears. Affected areas usually appear very dry, thickened or scaly. In fair-skinned people, these areas may initially appear red and then turn brown. Among darker-skinned people, eczema can affect pigmentation, making the affected area lighter or darker.

Allergic contact dermatitis occurs when the skin comes in direct contact with an allergen e.g. detergents, jewellery made with nickel, or plants like poison ivy. It usually manifests as red, bumpy, scaly, itchy or swollen skin at the point of contact. Perioral dermatitis is a rash that occurs around the mouth and mainly affects women and children. The rash is bumpy and scaly in appearance, and there may be itching and pain along with fluid discharge. It can occur as a reaction to steroid creams, cosmetics, sun creams, hormonal fluctuations or weather effects e.g. strong winds or UV light.

Urticaria (hives) is an inflammation of the skin triggered when the immune system releases histamine. This causes small blood vessels to leak, leading to swelling in the skin. Swelling in deep layers of the skin is called angioedema. Acute urticaria occurs after eating a particular food or coming in contact with a particular trigger, and can also be triggered by heat or exercise as well as medications, foods, insect bites or infections. Chronic urticaria is rarely caused by specific triggers and should be medically investigated to rule out a serious internal disease.

Bacteria are microscopic, single-cell organisms that live almost everywhere. Some are airborne, while others live in water or soil. Not all bacteria are harmful - some 'friendly' bacteria live in the digestive system, aiding digestion and producing vitamins, and plants need bacteria in the soil in order to grow. Some bacteria live on the skin and cause no harm, but other 'pathogenic' bacteria can cause skin infections e.g. staphylococcus and streptococcus. Pathogenic bacteria cause disease in two ways; they may gain access to the tissues and multiply to damage their surroundings, or they may release toxins that poison remote parts of the body. Bacterial skin infections are treated with oral or topical antibiotics, depending on the strain causing the infection.

Acne is a common bacterial skin condition that occurs when hair follicles become plugged with oil and dead skin cells. It often causes whiteheads, blackheads or pimples, and usually appears on the face, forehead, chest, upper back and shoulders. Acne is common among teenagers, due to activity of the sebaceous glands that are stimulated by the hormones oestrogen and testosterone. However, it can affect people of all ages. Depending on its severity, acne can cause emotional distress and skin scarring, so early treatment intervention is advisable.

Cellulitis is a spreading bacterial infection of the skin. It begins as redness and tenderness and develops into hot swollen areas that are slightly pitted. It can occur after being bitten by dogs or humans, or following an injury in dirt or water. Cellulitis occurs most often on the legs, but it can appear anywhere on the body. Left untreated, the infection can spread to the lymph nodes and bloodstream, and rapidly become life threatening.

Folliculitis is a bacterial infection of hair follicles that causes red, swollen, pimple-like bumps on the skin. Improperly treated pools or hot tubs can harbour bacteria that cause folliculitis. 'Sycosis barbae' is inflammation of the hair follicles in the beard area. Boils (furuncles) are deep bacterial skin infections that start in hair follicles as firm, red, tender bumps that progress until pus accumulates underneath the skin. They can be due to poor hygiene or a weak immune system. A carbuncle is a red, swollen, painful cluster of boils that are connected to each other under the skin. A carbuncle is most likely to occur on a hairy area of the body such as the back or nape of the neck, but it can also develop in other areas of the body such as the buttocks, thighs, groin or armpits.

Impetigo is a common and highly contagious skin infection that mainly affects children. It usually appears as red sores on the face - especially around the nose and mouth - and can affect other areas such as the hands and feet. The sores burst and develop honey-coloured crusts. A less common form of impetigo called bullous impetigo, features larger blisters that occur on the trunk of infants and young children.

A more serious form of impetigo called ecthyma penetrates deeper into the skin, causing painful fluid or pus-filled sores that can turn into deep ulcers. Ecthyma most often affects buttocks, thighs, legs, ankles and feet. Occasionally, the local lymph nodes become swollen and painful.

Methicillin Resistant Staphylococcus Aureus (MRSA) is a type of staphylococcus aureus bacteria resistant to certain antibiotics including methicillin and more common antibiotics. Most often, it causes mild infections on the skin, such as sores, boils or abscesses, but it can also cause more serious skin infections or infect surgical wounds, the bloodstream, the lungs or the urinary tract, and in some cases it can be life-threatening. Because it is hard to treat, MRSA is sometimes called a 'super bug.' While some antibiotics do work, MRSA is constantly adapting and mutating, and researchers developing new antibiotics are having a hard time keeping up. MRSA is spread by contact, and infections are common among those with weak immune systems who are in hospitals, nursing homes or other health care environments. Infections can appear around surgical wounds or invasive devices like catheters or implanted feeding tubes.

Pressure sores - sometimes called bed sores, or decubitus ulcers - occur on areas of the skin that are under pressure from lying in bed, sitting in wheelchairs, wearing a cast or being immobile for a long period of time. The pressure restricts blood flow, and results in dead skin that breaks off forming sores or ulcers that can become infected. Changing the affected person's position regularly, using supportive items like pillows or foam pads to reduce pressure, keeping the skin clean and dry, and tending to any wounds promptly, can help prevent serious infections.

Viruses are much smaller than bacteria and cannot reproduce on their own. Instead, viruses reproduce by infecting a host cell and using the host's DNA or RNA replication systems to make copies of itself. Just one virus can turn into lots of viruses and cause disease and illness.

Viral skin infections are most commonly seen in immunocompromised individuals, or they may occur due to allergic problems.

Warts are skin growths caused by the human papillomavirus (HPV). There are more than 60 kinds of HPV, some of which cause warts on the skin. HPV stimulates a quick growth of cells on the skin's outer layer e.g. the common warts that appear on the hands. Some types of HPV cause warts to appear in the genital area and certain forms of the virus can cause cervical cancer. Plantar warts (verrucas) appear on the soles of the feet. Verruca filiformis or 'filiform wart' is a long slender wart projecting from the skin's surface, like a stalk with finger-like projections. They are often found on the neck or face and sometimes on the eyelids. A doctor may burn them off with electricity, freeze them with cryotherapy, or remove them through excision.

A seborrheic keratosis – sometimes referred to as a senile wart - looks like a waxy or wart-like growth that typically appears on the face, chest, shoulders or back in elderly people. They are usually brown due to the presence of melanin and so can be mistaken for moles. They are often confused with warts but they are neither viral nor contagious, and the term 'seborrheic wart' is based on their appearance rather than being medically correct. They may be removed for cosmetic reasons or if they become irritated by clothing.

Molluscum contagiosum - a type of poxvirus - causes small, benign, raised bumps with a tiny indentation in the centre on the upper layers of the skin - often on the face. The bumps are usually painless and disappear spontaneously, rarely leaving scars. If they are scratched or injured, the infection can spread to surrounding skin. The bumps can remain from two months to four years. Molluscum contagiosum is spread by direct contact with someone who has the condition or by touching an object contaminated with the virus, such as a towel or a piece of clothing. Though most common in children, molluscum contagiosum can affect adults as well, particularly those with weakened immune systems.

Herpes is an infection caused by the herpes simplex virus (HSV). Oral herpes (herpes simplex type 1) causes cold sores around the mouth or face. Genital herpes (herpes simplex type 2) is a sexually transmitted disease that affects the genitals, buttocks or anal area. People who become infected with HSV will have the virus for the rest of their lives. Even if it does not manifest symptoms, the virus will continue to live in an infected person's nerve cells and some people may experience regular outbreaks. Others may only experience one outbreak after they have been infected and then the virus may become dormant. Even if the virus is dormant, certain stimuli such as stress, sun exposure or illness can trigger an outbreak.

The varicella zoster virus causes chicken pox - a highly infectious disease that is accompanied by a blistery rash. The infection can occur in any age group, but is most commonly seen in children under the age of ten. Once infected, the person becomes immune to this disease - however it can manifest in adulthood as shingles. It has an incubation period of 14-16 days and is spread through direct contact with the infected person. Overcrowding promotes the spread of chicken pox very rapidly.

Herpes zoster - also known as shingles - is a common viral infection that occurs in people who have earlier been infected by the chicken pox virus. It occurs most commonly in those aged 50-80 years. Shingles usually occurs when the body's immunity is weak, and this can lead to reactivation of the varicella zoster virus that caused chicken pox. It is associated with a painful rash along with blister formation. It can affect any part of the body including the face, lips, eyes, lower limbs, genitals etc. Multiple, clustered blisters usually appear along a particular dermatome (nerve track) on one side of the body. The disease is contagious when the blisters are weeping. Later the blisters dry out and form scabs that are gradually shed from the body. The pain of shingles is referred to as 'post-herpetic neuralgia' and this can last for a long time after the rash has disappeared.

Pityriasis rosea is a viral rash that is characterised by a single, large, pink, scaly plaque called the 'herald patch' or 'mother patch', followed by smaller, oval-shaped, red patches - mainly on the chest and back. One to two weeks following its initial appearance, smaller pink lesions develop on the trunk, arms and legs, followed by a large number of oval spots, ranging in diameter from 0.5 centimetre to 1.5 centimetres. The individual lesions usually form a symmetrical 'Christmas tree' pattern on the back. It does not involve the face, scalp, palms or soles. Pityriasis rosea may be very itchy, but in most cases it does not itch and it usually clears up in about six to twelve weeks. Pale marks or brown discolouration may persist for a few months in darker-skinned people, but eventually the skin returns to its normal appearance. Second attacks are uncommon, but another viral infection may trigger a recurrence years later.

Fungal skin infections usually occur due to moisture in the environment or weakness in the body's immune system. A mild temperature and moisture provide the best environment for a fungus to grow, and so these infections are seen most commonly in the axilla, mammary folds, toe webbings, and vagina or groin regions of the body. Topical anti-fungal creams are usually given for application at the affected site. Natural approaches include dietary changes that can help alleviate fungal infections as well as antifungal aromatherapy oils that should be used under professional guidance.

There are several fungal infections from the ringworm family and the medical terms are 'tinea' or 'dermatophytosis'. Ringworm gets its name from the distinctive ring-like pattern the red spots often form on the skin – and there are no worms involved! Athlete's foot (tinea pedis) is a fungal infection of the foot that is commonly found in those who wear tight shoes. It can affect the toes, toenails or the webbing between the toes, and can spread to affect the entire foot. Ringworm of the nails doesn't create a ring-like pattern. Instead, it turns the nails thick, yellow and brittle. Tinea capitis (scalp ringworm) manifests as an itchy, scaly, pink rash on the scalp that can cause patchy hair loss. Tinea corporis (body ringworm) manifests as itchy, round patches with pink, scaly borders and clear centres. Tinea cruris (jock itch) is a common fungal skin infection in the groin area, affecting men more than women. Adolescents and those suffering from diabetes mellitus or obesity are also highly susceptible. It can cause severe skin lesions and infection due to vigorous itching that can tear the skin. Ringworm spreads easily from person to person, especially in communal areas like locker rooms and swimming pools. The fungus can linger on floors as well as on towels, bedding, headwear, combs and brushes.

Parasitic infections are not life threatening, but can be contagious and very uncomfortable. Lice (pediculosis) are small, wingless, blood-sucking parasites that can infect the hair (pediculosis capitis), body (pediculosis corporis) or pubic hair (pediculosis pubis). Scabies is a skin infestation caused by the sarcoptes scabiei itch mite. The mites reproduce on the surface of the skin, burrow into it and lay eggs, causing an itchy, red rash to form on the skin. The infestation may be transmitted through intimate contact or infested clothing or bedding. Treatment consists of medication that kills the mites and their eggs. Bedbugs are small, reddish-brown, parasitic insects that bite the exposed skin of humans and animals and feed on their blood. They hide in the cracks and crevices of beds, box springs, headboards, bed frames and other objects around a bed. Frequent airing, cleaning and vacuuming is recommended to prevent them multiplying.

Cutaneous larva migrans (CLM) is a skin condition caused by several species of parasite. It is also referred to as 'creeping eruption' or 'larva migrans', and is one of the most common skin conditions in tropical climates. Infection can happen when the skin comes into contact with the larvae in contaminated soil or sand. When contact is made, the larvae burrow into the upper layer of the skin. Signs and symptoms include red, twisting and spreading lesions, itching, stinging, swelling, pain and discomfort. CLM can occur anywhere on the body, although it most often occurs on areas exposed to contaminated soil or sand - such as the feet, buttocks, thighs and hands.

Lyme disease is an increasingly common infectious disease caused by the bacteria 'borrelia burgdorferi' that is transmitted to humans by a bite from an infected blacklegged tick - also known as a deer tick. The tick becomes infected after feeding on infected deer, birds or mice. The disease got its name from the town of Old Lyme, Connecticut where it was first recognised in 1975, and it is now the most common tick-borne illness in Europe and the USA. Those who live or spend time in wooded areas known for transmission of the disease, and those with domesticated animals that visit wooded areas, have a higher risk of getting Lyme disease. Signs and symptoms vary in severity from person to person, but it usually manifests on the skin as a flat, circular rash that looks like a red oval, and it can appear anywhere on the body. Other manifestations include fatigue, joint pain and swelling, muscle aches, headache, fever, swollen lymph nodes, sleep disturbances and difficulty concentrating.

Lyme disease is best treated in the early stages and usually involves a 10 to 14-day course of oral antibiotics to eliminate the infection, after which the condition of most patients improves. However 10-20% of treated patients may have lingering symptoms of fatigue, musculoskeletal pains, disrupted sleep and lack of their normal mental functions. Being 'tick aware' and taking precautions such as keeping to footpaths and avoiding long grass, wearing appropriate clothing, considering the use of repellents and making a habit to carrying out a 'tick check can help prevent infection. If bitten by a tick, it should be removed as soon as possible using fine-tipped tweezers or a tick removal tool.

Burns are injuries to the skin caused by heat, sunlight, chemicals, electricity or radiation, and they differ according to the cause and degree of the burn. First-degree burns are shallow, superficial burns affecting the epidermis with redness and sometimes swelling. Second-degree burns extend into the dermis and usually have blistering and thickening of the skin. Third-degree burns involve injury to all layers of the skin - including the subcutaneous layer - causing redness, swelling, blistering, blackness, scarring, and usually require skin grafts. Scalding can cause all three burns, depending on how hot the liquid is and how long it stays in contact with the skin. There are also fourth-degree burns that include all of the symptoms of a third-degree burn, but also extend beyond the skin into tendons and bones. Chemical and electrical burns require immediate medical attention because they can affect the inside of the body, even if skin damage is minor.

BURN

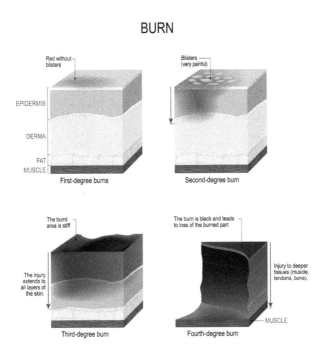

5.4 Skin burn classification

The sun, as well as exposure to UV radiation from tanning lamps and sunbeds, can cause many different skin disorders. Some are common and harmless, while others like skin cancers can be life threatening. Skin cancers are generally due to long-term UV exposure, and fair-skinned people are more susceptible - though any skin type can be affected. Skin cancer treatments include surgery, radiation, chemotherapy and immunotherapy - described in Chapter 11.

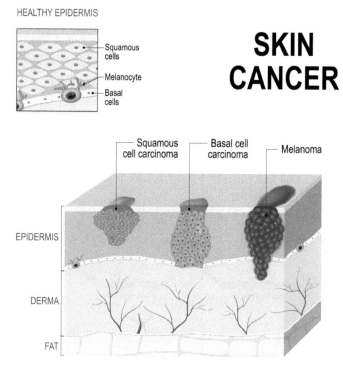

5.5 Skin cancers

Basal cell carcinoma is the most common type of skin cancer and begins in the basal cells of the epidermis. Although basal cell carcinomas can affect anywhere on the body, they are usually found on the face where they typically grow slowly over months or years and can vary in size. The most common type is a small translucent growth, sometimes with rolled edges and small blood vessels on the surface. They can also be brown like a little mole, or be skin coloured and look like a waxy scar. They may become an open sore (sometimes called a 'rodent ulcer'), bleed, and never quite heal. This type of skin cancer rarely metastasises and can be surgically removed by a dermatologist. Avoiding the sun and using sunscreen will help protect against basal cell carcinoma.

ABCDE
rule for the early
detection of melanoma

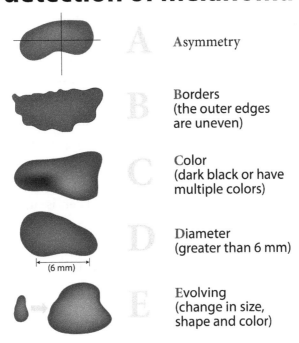

A — Asymmetry

B — Borders
(the outer edges
are uneven)

C — Color
(dark black or have
multiple colors)

D — Diameter
(greater than 6 mm)

(6 mm)

E — Evolving
(change in size,
shape and color)

5.6 ABCDE of Melanoma

Melanoma - the most serious type of skin cancer - develops in melanocytes - the cells that produce melanin. Melanomas can appear anywhere on the body, but most often develop in areas that are exposed to the sun, such as the back, legs, arms and face. Melanomas can also occur in areas that don't receive much sun exposure, such as the soles of the feet, palms of the hands and fingernail beds. These hidden melanomas are more common in people with darker skin. The first melanoma signs and symptoms are often a change in an existing mole, or the development of a new pigmented or unusual-looking growth on the skin. Exposure to ultraviolet (UV) radiation from sunlight or tanning lamps and sunbeds increases the risk of developing melanoma. If detected early, melanoma can be treated successfully, but it can spread quickly and become malignant and so requires prompt medical attention.

Squamous cell carcinoma is a common form of skin cancer that develops in squamous cells that make up the middle and outer layers of the skin. Squamous cell lesions can develop in scars, skin sores and other areas of skin injury, and the skin around them typically shows signs of sun damage such as wrinkling, pigment changes and loss of elasticity. They can appear as thick, rough, scaly patches that may crust or bleed. They can also resemble warts, or open sores that don't completely heal. Sometimes squamous cell carcinomas show up as growths that are raised at the edges with a lower area in the center that may bleed or itch. This type of skin cancer is not usually life threatening, though if not treated, it can be aggressive and grow or spread to other parts of the body, causing serious complications. Avoiding UV exposure helps reduce the risk of squamous cell carcinoma and other forms of skin cancer.

Proper skin care and a healthy lifestyle can keep skin looking good whatever our age. Cleansing and moisturising with good quality, gentle ingredients, balanced nutrition, hydration, adequate sleep, exercise, fresh air and avoidance of cigarette smoke and other pollutants will all help to maintain the health and vitality of this wonderful protective organ that we are blessed with.

6. Hair

For many of us, hair is our 'crowning glory' and is often viewed as a reflection of our identity. Many people spend lots of time and money trying to achieve the perfect hairstyle, and the old saying 'bad hair day' can be very real if our hair doesn't look its best. Although I'm guilty of spending hours in front of the mirror preening my locks, I know that the main function of my hair is protection - guarding my scalp from cold temperatures, injury and the sun's rays, my eyes from foreign particles, and my ear canals and nostrils from invading insects and inhaled particles. In her book 'Survival of the Prettiest', Nancy Etcoff points out that hair is also one of the most powerful sexual signals in humans, and that the stimulating effect of hair is so profound that many cultures throughout history have either made women cover their heads after marriage or even cut off their hair.

Every hair on the body is composed of a shaft, most of which projects above the surface of the skin, with the root below. The shaft of coarse hairs like those on the scalp consists of three parts - medulla, cortex and cuticle. The medulla in the centre is composed of large cells containing keratin and air spaces. The medulla is found only in large thick hairs e.g. on the scalp, rather than the arms and other areas where hairs tend to be lighter and less dense. The cortex, forming the bulk of the hair, is composed of long cells containing keratin and also melanin, which determines hair colour. Hair turns grey and eventually white as the pigment glands decrease their production of melanin and eventually shut down. The outer hair cuticle is made from 6 to 11 layers of overlapping, semi-transparent keratin scales that make the hair waterproof and allow it to be stretched. Someone with thick, coarse hair will have more overlapping layers than someone with fine hair. The keratinised scales point upwards and overlap like slates on a roof, while beneath the skin, the outer layer interlocks with the downward-pointing, scale-like cells lining the inner root sheath of the hair follicle - also called a cuticle - securing the hair in place. Hair

conditioning products do their work by smoothing out the scaly cells
of the hair cuticle.

HAIR ANATOMY

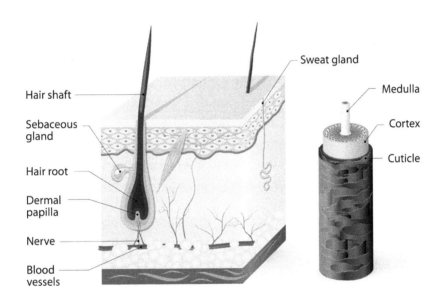

6.1 Hair anatomy

The hair root, which penetrates into the dermis - and in some cases
into the subcutaneous skin layer - also contains a medulla, cortex and
cuticle continuous with the hair shaft. Surrounding the root is the hair
follicle that is formed by the basal or germinating layer of the
epidermis growing down into the dermis and creating a pit. The inner
root sheath or lining of the hair follicle is comprised of three parts:
Henle's layer (named after German anatomist Friedrich Gustav Jakob
Henle), Huxley's layer, (named after English biologist Thomas Henry
Huxley) and the cuticle. The cuticle - which is the part closest to the
hair - is made from dead hardened cells that give the hair added

protection and its scale-like cells interlock with the scale-like cells of the hair root as already described. Surrounding the inner root sheath is the external or outer root sheath that is separated from the surrounding connective tissue by a glassy 'vitreous' membrane. The dermis grows upwards into the base of the hair follicle to form an area called the dermal 'papilla' (meaning 'projection'), filled with loose connective tissue and blood capillaries to nourish the growing hair. A helpful visual is to imagine the hair follicle as a vase with an indented base and the hair itself as the stem of a flower.

Hair growth originates from the central area (matrix) of the bulb, an area of active growth where cells are alive and dividing. These cells are pushed upwards, where they gradually fill with keratin to produce a hair that eventually projects from the open end of the follicle when older hairs are shed. Electrolysis and laser treatments destroy the hair bulb to prevent re-growth of hairs.

A sebaceous gland lies within each hair follicle, producing sebum - the skin's natural oil - from a duct that opens into the hair follicle about halfway down from the skin surface. The follicle also has a bulge directly below the sebaceous gland in the outer root sheath. It contains stem cells that divide and regenerate new hair follicles and sebaceous glands, and participates in healing the epidermis after a wound. The bulge also provides the insertion point for the tiny erector pili muscles that contract to make hairs stand on end when we are cold or frightened.

Hair grows in repeated cycles. One cycle can be broken down into three phases and each hair passes through the phases independent of neighbouring hairs i.e. they are never all at the same stage.

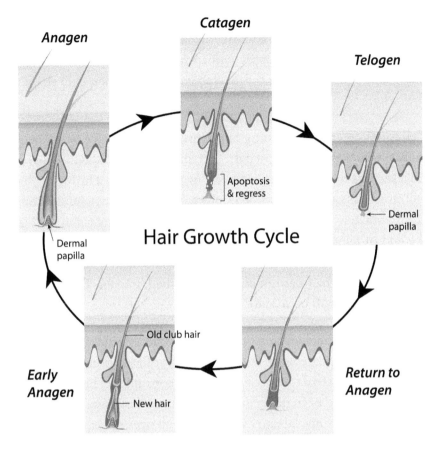

Anagen

Catagen

Telogen

Apoptosis & regress

Dermal papilla

Dermal papilla

Hair Growth Cycle

Old club hair

Early Anagen

New hair

Return to Anagen

6.2 Hair growth cycle

Anagen is the 'active' or growth phase, accounting for about 85% of hairs at any one time, with different hairs at different stages of growth. Anagen can vary from between two and seven years for scalp hair, one or two months for eyebrows, and between three and six weeks for eyelashes. In early anagen, a new hair bulb surrounds the nutrient providing papilla, and a hair begins to grow from living cells in the matrix. This active growth phase ends when the hair begins to separate from the papilla and no longer receives nutrients.

Catagen is the 'changing' or transitional phase, and lasts about one or two weeks. Only 1% of hairs are at this stage at any given time. The hair is now fully grown and cell division has stopped. The hair has separated from the papilla and the follicle begins to shrink, cutting the hair off from its blood supply and from the cells that produce new hair. Hairs at this stage are called 'club hairs' due to their club shape at the base.

Telogen is the 'tired' or resting phase, and lasts about five or six weeks during which no growth occurs, but the hair stays attached to the follicle while the papilla stays in a resting phase below. The resting hair will either fall out or be pushed out by a new hair growing underneath. Approximately 10-15% of hairs are in this phase at any given time. At the end of telogen, the hair follicle re-enters anagen when the papilla and base of the follicle join together again and a new hair begins to form. If the old hair has not already been shed, the new hair pushes it out and the growth cycle starts again.

As a foetus in the womb, a human is covered in a fine, soft, downy hair called lanugo. Between 36 and 40 weeks of gestation, most of this falls off and some of it the foetus actually consumes! This is stored in the intestines and excreted in the meconium, or first bowel movement. In premature infants, lanugo can be found all over the body but is lost soon after birth and replaced by new hair that is stronger and more pigmented. The soft, downy and almost invisible hair found all over the body - except for the lips, palms and soles - is called vellus hair. The hairs of the scalp, eyebrows, eyelashes, axillary and pubic regions are called terminal hairs. Compared to vellus hairs, they are longer and coarser with deeper follicles.

Studies indicate that hair generally grows faster during spring and summer and slower during winter months. It is normal to lose between 80 and 100 scalp hairs daily, but losing more than this can lead to hair thinning due to a variety of causes.

Dietary factors adversely affecting hair health are often deficiencies of protein and iron. Protein is essential for cell growth and repair, while iron produces haemoglobin in the blood, carrying oxygen for growth and regeneration of all body cells. In Traditional Chinese Medicine, hair is seen as an extension of the blood and so reflects its state. Other factors are essential fatty acids (EFA's) and vitamins B complex and C, which nourish hair follicles. Smoking destroys vitamin C and nicotine causes blood vessels to constrict, making it harder for nutrients to reach the skin and hair and for waste to be eliminated.

The terms 'alopecia' or 'effluvium' refer to hair loss, which can sometimes be sudden and severe. Hair loss can be due to an autoimmune condition, where the body is attacking its own hair follicles. Anagen alopecia refers to the shedding that arises during the anagen (growth) stage of the hair cycle. The main causes of anagen alopecia are radiation, chemotherapy, infection, drugs or toxins. There can be a sudden shedding of patches of hair (alopecia areata) or all of the hair on the scalp (alopecia totalis), and often from the entire body - including eyebrows, eyelashes and body hair (alopecia universalis). The bald patches on the scalp can be random and sometimes red and scaly.

Telogen alopecia is a form of temporary hair loss that usually happens after stress, a shock or a traumatic event. Normally 10% of a person's hair is in the telogen or resting phase and some shedding naturally occurs during this phase. Telogen alopecia occurs when there is a higher than average amount of hair shedding i.e. 30% or more. Hair shedding occurs all over the scalp, resulting in a reduced volume of hair. Common triggers include childbirth, trauma, illness, bereavement, sudden weight loss, new medication or hormonal changes. In around a third of those affected, no cause can be found and the hair usually grows back normally once the trigger is removed or resolved. Traction alopecia is hair loss caused by repeatedly pulling on the hair. This condition can result from regularly wearing the hair in a tight ponytail, bun or braids - especially if chemicals or heat are also used.

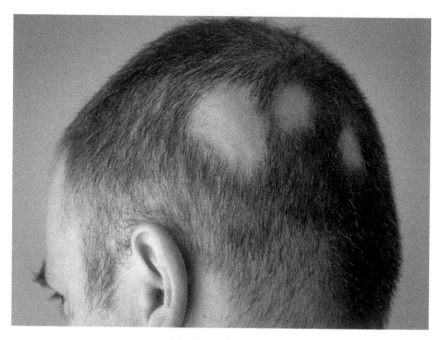

6.3 Alopecia areata

Androgenic alopecia - male pattern baldness - can be passed on through successive generations. Although it affects both men and women, women are less likely to develop full-blown androgenic alopecia because the gene reacts to male hormones such as testosterone, which is higher in males. Oestrogen, the equivalent dominant hormone in women, keeps the action of the gene in check until menopause, but after that a woman who carries the inherited gene may suffer hair loss.

Hair is sensitive to changes in thyroxin levels and gradual hair loss can result from an underactive thyroid. Hair can become greasier at puberty and during menstruation, while a drop in oestrogen levels at menopause can lead to dry, coarse, brittle hair. There may be temporary hair loss during pregnancy or after delivery, due to a drop in oestrogen levels.

Hirsutism refers to excessive hair growth in women in places where it normally does just for men e.g. upper lip, chin, chest, stomach or back. The hair is often dark and coarse, instead of the light, fine 'peach fuzz' that covers most of the body. It can be genetic or caused by high levels of testosterone that can result from disorders like polycystic ovaries or Cushing's syndrome. Some drugs can change hormone levels in the body leading to hirsutism e.g. anabolic steroids or drugs that spur hair growth e.g. Rogaine (minoxidil).

Drugs that may cause temporary hair loss include chemotherapy for cancer treatment, anaesthetics, anticoagulants to thin the blood, retinoids to treat acne and skin problems, beta-adrenergic blockers to control blood pressure, and oral contraceptives. No one should stop taking prescribed medication without medical advice, but dietary changes and some well-chosen supplements can really make a difference to good hair and scalp condition.

Shock, as well as prolonged stress, has been known to cause hair to fall out as blood vessels in the skin constrict, starving the hair of vital nutrients. With extreme trauma, this can happen overnight. Hair is one of the first places the body shows distress, and under stress it is easy to let basic health habits go, eating badly and lacking sleep. Tension in the scalp muscles can restrict the flow of oxygen and nutrients to the hair follicles, with an adverse effect on hair growth.

Perming and dyeing as well as overuse of hair dryers and straighteners can damage the hair making it dry and brittle. Frequent use of shampoos and hair treatments full of strong detergents and chemicals can dry out the scalp. Treated water in swimming pools can also dry and irritate the scalp. Hair is most fragile when wet, and should not be vigorously brushed but carefully combed through with a wide-toothed comb and left to dry naturally if possible.

Seborrheic dermatitis – also known as dandruff - is a common skin condition that mainly affects the scalp. It causes scaly patches, red skin and scaly white or grayish flakes of dead skin cells that are shed. Seborrheic dermatitis can also affect oily areas of the body, such as the face, sides of the nose, eyebrows, ears, eyelids and chest. In infants, the condition is known as cradle cap and causes crusty, scaly patches on the scalp. The exact cause is unclear but may be due to skin cells that grow and die off too fast. A common fungus called malassezia that feeds on the natural oils on the scalp also contributes to dandruff. This fungus lives on the scalp of most healthy adults without causing any problems, but in some people, the immune system may overreact to that fungus, causing dandruff.

An ingrown hair occurs when a shaved or tweezed hair grows back into the skin. It can cause inflammation, pain and tiny bumps in the area where the hair was removed. Ingrown hairs most commonly affect the beard area - including the chin, cheeks and neck. They can appear on the scalp in those who shave their heads, or in the armpits, pubic area and legs. Sycosis barbae is a bacterial infection that leads to inflammation and irritation of the hair follicles (folliculitis) in the chin or bearded region in men. To avoid infection always use clean implements for hair removal, shave or tweeze in the direction of the hair growth and clean the skin afterwards.

Pediculosis capitis is an infection with head lice. It is a very common infestation that is spread by contact e.g. sharing combs and brushes, wearing infested clothing such as hats, scarves, hair ribbons etc. or lying on a bed or pillow that has recently been in contact with an infected person. Louse eggs - nits - hatch into baby lice called nymphs and then into adult lice. Pediculosis corporis is the name given to body lice. Body lice infestation can be found in people living in crowded, unsanitary conditions where clothing is not regularly changed or washed.

Scalp hair can be straight, curly, wavy or kinky, and it all depends on the shape of the follicle from which it grows - the rounder the follicle, the straighter the hair will be. Hair can be dry, oily or in-between. Dry hair is usually due to under-active sebaceous glands, but dryness can also be caused by other factors like overexposure to the sun and harsh hair care products. Accumulated sebum can lead to dryness by blocking pores and preventing sebum getting to the surface. Curly hair is usually dry because oils produced in the scalp don't travel as easily down a curly hair shaft as they do with straight hair. Oily hair - usually accompanied by oily skin - is due to excess sebum leaving the scalp and hair oily.

Fine hair is not necessarily thin hair, although the two often come together. Thin hair means there are not a lot of strands on the scalp, but some people have thick hair that's considered 'fine' because it's silky and smooth, without the curls or roughness that provide texture. Fine hair grows from smaller, narrower follicles. It tends to lack volume, so conditioners and other products are best applied to the ends rather than roots to avoid weighing down the hair.

A good haircut will keep scalp hair healthier by removing dead or frayed hair, and a good hair stylist should be able to tell if your hair needs more moisture, more hydration or more nutrients, and recommend the right products to achieve these goals.

7. Nails

Nails are accessory organs of the skin made from sheets of hardened cells called 'keratinocytes', filled with keratin. Fingernails and toenails help us dig, climb, scratch, grab and manipulate small objects. They guard against injuries, protecting our fingers and toes from getting cut or scraped during daily activities.

Nails are constantly growing, but their growth rate varies, depending on the health of the circulation and the ageing process - they grow more slowly as we get older. On average, fingernails grow at a rate of three millimetres per month, while toenails grow much more slowly at just one millimetre per month. It takes a toenail twelve to eighteen months to grow from root to free edge (tip), while a fingernail takes six months to grow from root to tip.

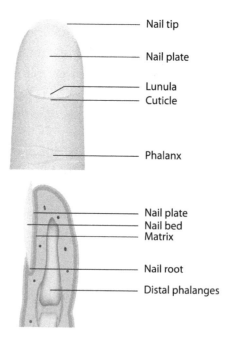

7.1 Nail anatomy

The nail structure is divided into six parts – the root, nail plate, nail bed, eponychium (cuticle), paronychium (skin overlapping sides of nail plate) and hyponychium (part of finger just underneath edge of nail). Each of these parts has a specific function and if a component of the nail structure is disrupted, the nail can look abnormal.

The nail plate is the actual nail itself, made of translucent keratin, and its pinkish appearance comes from blood vessels underneath. The underside of the nail plate has grooves that run along the length of the nail and help anchor it to the nail bed underneath.

The root of the nail is also known as the germinal matrix, and its edge appears as a white crescent called the lunula (half moon). The nail root lies below the skin underneath the nail and extends several millimetres into the finger. The nail bed is the soft, pink tissue that sits underneath the nail and supports it while it grows. It extends from the edge of the nail root, or lunula, to the hyponychium and contains blood vessels, nerves and melanocytes that produce melanin. As the nail grows from the root, it moves down along the nail bed and adds material to the underside of the nail, making it thicker.

The eponychium - commonly known as the cuticle - is situated between the skin of the finger and the nail plate. It fuses these structures together and provides a waterproof barrier. The paronychium is the skin of the finger that overlaps onto the sides of the nail plate and this is the site of hangnails, ingrown nails and nail infections. A hangnail is a piece of skin that appears jagged and torn and generally appears on the fingers, though it's also possible to have one around a toenail. The hyponychium is the seal underneath the extended 'free' edge of the nail plate, and its purpose is to prevent pathogens from infecting the nail bed.

Trauma to the fingertip and nail remains the most common of all hand injuries, and nails can also say a lot about a person's state of health.

Factors that affect nail growth positively include good nutrition and a good blood supply. Factors that can negatively affect nail growth include poor health and nutrition, overexposure to chemicals and detergents, poor manicure or pedicure techniques, injuries to the nail bed, and the ageing process.

'Onychosis' is the technical term for a nail disease – it comes from the Greek 'onych' (pronounced 'on-eek'), meaning nail or claw. Nails can be affected by many skin conditions and can indicate internal imbalances, neglect or stress. A dermatologist is best placed to diagnose and recommend treatment of nail diseases. You will most likely know the common names for some of the following nail diseases and disorders. I have also listed the medical terms for these conditions, as those of you who are students may need to know this information for your exams. Check online for images, so you can recognise what nails with these conditions look like.

Beau's lines are horizontal ridges or grooves on the nail plate and can reflect temporary retardation of growth due to illness or nutritional deficiency e.g. zinc. Vertical ridges or grooves can occur due to uneven growth, and are associated with ageing. Severe ridges can be due to injury to the nail matrix through poor treatments or exposure to chemicals and detergents, and can also be caused by poor circulation or psoriasis. Nails affected by psoriasis may become thicker, develop pinprick holes, change colour or shape, and can also feel tender and sore.

Koilonychias are spoon shaped, thin, concave nails (usually of the hand) resulting from abnormal growth. This condition can be genetic, or may be due to iron deficiency anaemia or an overactive thyroid.

Pitting of the nails is characterised by depressions in the surface of the nail due to defective development of the layers in the superficial nail plate. It is common in those with psoriasis and can also be associated with other conditions, including connective tissue disorders. Generally, any condition that causes a superficial and localised inflammation of the skin can also affect the nails and result in nail pitting.

Nail discoloration - in which nails appear yellow, green or white - can result from different infections and conditions of the skin. Tinea unguium - ringworm of the nail – also called onychomycosis - is a common fungal infection causing thickened deformed nails. It can appear on the fingernails, but is more common on toenails because the fungus that causes onychomycosis thrives in environments that are damp and dark. The infected nail usually appears yellow and may separate from the nail bed, crumble or flake off. Another species of fungi that can affect the nails is trichophyton rubrum, which also causes athlete's foot. This type of fungus has a tendency to infect the skin as it requires keratin for growth, and is therefore known as a dermatophyte. Pseudomonas is a type of bacteria that can infect the nail bed, giving the nails a greenish colour. Red or black nails may result from blood under the nails (haematoma) as a result of trauma e.g. a bruise or an ingrown toenail. Leukonychia are white spots or streaks resulting from trauma, air bubbles or poor health, and these spots usually grow out of the nail in time. Cyanosis is when the fingernails appear blue due to lack of oxygen in the blood, making the skin or membrane below the skin turn a purplish-blue color. This can indicate an underlying medical condition affecting the lungs, heart, blood cells or blood vessels, and if persistent it should be medically investigated. Cold temperatures can also cause fingernails to turn blue as blood vessels in the extremities constrict, making it difficult for the right amount of oxygen-rich blood to get to the nails.

Paronychia is a bacterial infection of the skin surrounding the nail, causing it to become red, swollen and painful. It is a common infection resulting from injury, nail biting or poor manicure techniques. Onychia is inflammation of the nail bed with the development of pus and loss of the fingernail or toenail. The inflammation can be due to bacterial infection resulting from an injury to the nail.

Onychauxis is abnormal thickening of the nail plate on fingers or toes. It can be hereditary or caused by trauma to the nail, fungal infections or neglect. Over time, the nails may become curled and turn white or yellow. Chronic thickening can lead to onychogryphosis (ram's horn nail) where toenails thicken and become hooked. This may be due to nail bed damage and can be painful and injure adjoining toes. Onychogryphosis is often found in older people who may be unable to look after their toenails.

Onychocryptosis is an in-growing nail, where the sides of the nail penetrate the skin, causing it to become red, shiny and painful to touch. It is most common on the big toe and can be due to improper nail cutting or badly fitting shoes.

Onycholysis is separation of the nail plate from the nail bed and can be due to an overactive thyroid, fungal infection, psoriasis, iron deficiency, trauma or infection. Exposure to some medicines e.g. psoralens (light sensitive drugs used to treat certain skin conditions), or strong antibiotics from the tetracycline or fluoroquinolone groups can cause the nail to react to sun exposure by lifting away from its bed. Once the cause is found, treating the underlying issue will help resolve the nail lifting when a new nail grows.

Onychorrhexis refers to dry, brittle, splitting nails and is common in old age or in those with arthritis or anaemia. It can be due to poor treatment techniques and excess soaking of the hands in water or detergents.

Onychoschizia, commonly known as nail splitting and also known as onychoschisis or lamellar dystrophy, is a condition that causes horizontal splits within the nail plate. Frequent wetting and drying of the hands is the most common cause of nail splitting. It can also be caused by harsh nail cosmetics, medical problems e.g. a skin disease such as psoriasis, or malnutrition.

Onychatrophia, also known as atrophy, is when a fully-grown nail wastes away, loses its shine and healthy look, shrinks in size and eventually falls off. It can have various causes including bacterial or fungal infection, or untreated psoriasis.

A whitlow is a painful and highly contagious infection that usually affects the fleshy area of the fingertip, but it can affect the toes. It is caused by the herpes simplex virus (that causes cold sores) and is also known as herpetic whitlow. It appears as an abscess in the soft tissue near a fingernail or toenail, and can occur when broken skin comes in direct contact with body fluids infected with the herpes simplex virus.

A form of skin cancer called melanotic whitlow or subungual melanoma has a similar appearance as whitlow, except that the affected area of the finger is a darker colour. A melanotic whitlow can appear in the skin at the border of, or beneath the nail, and requires prompt medical attention.

Habit-tic is a condition that is often the result of nervous habits, including picking at, playing with, or stroking the nails constantly e.g. thumbnails are often damaged by another nail or the person repetitively picks or pushes back the cuticles. Onychophagia is the medical term for nail biting and is classified as an impulse control disorder, which means that those who suffer from it cannot control their urge to bite their nails. It can lead to infections, pain in the fingers and torn skin around the fingernails.

Fingernails and toenails need good care and attention, so as well as ensuring you have a healthy diet to nourish the nails from within, here are a few tips to keep them looking their best.

Keep nails dry and clean to prevent bacteria from growing underneath. Repeated or prolonged contact with water can contribute to split fingernails, so wear protective gloves when washing up, cleaning or using harsh chemicals. When cutting nails, always use a sharp manicure scissors or clippers and disinfect all equipment before use. Trim nails straight across, then round the tips in a gentle curve. Applying a nail hardener can help strengthen nails. When using a hand cream, rub it into fingernails, toenails and cuticles, too.

8. The Skeletal System

The skeletal system is the body's basic framework, providing structure, protection and movement. The 206 bones of the body also produce blood cells, store important minerals, and release hormones necessary for bodily functions. The skeleton is composed of two parts. The axial skeleton comprises the skull, the 33 bones of the vertebral column (spine), 12 pairs of ribs and the sternum. The appendicular skeleton includes the shoulder girdle (scapula and clavicles), upper limbs, pelvic girdle and lower limbs.

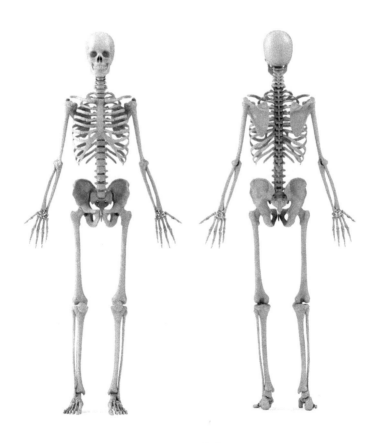

8.1 Human skeleton

The bones of the body are classified into different groups. The long bones of the legs and arms are the body's levers that allow movement. The short bones of the wrists (carpals) and ankles (tarsals) are strong and compact, while flat bones like the scapulae and some of the skull bones help to protect underlying structures. Some bones like the vertebrae and zygomatic bones (cheekbones) have irregular shapes, while sesamoid bones like the kneecap (patella) are located within tendons.

There are different types of bone tissue. Compact bone tissue is hard and dense and makes up the outer layer (cortex) of most bones and the main shaft of long bones. Nerves and blood vessels live inside this tissue, running through longitudinal tunnels in the bone called 'Haversian canals' - named after British physician Clopton Havers who did pioneering research on the microstructure of bone in the 17th century. Each Haversian canal generally contains nerve fibres and capillaries. Tiny transverse branches called Volkmann's canals - named after German physiologist Alfred Volkmann (1800-1878) - interconnect the Haversian canals with each other, and with the periosteum - which is the skin that covers bone. Larger blood vessels run through smooth-walled holes called 'nutrient foramina' found in the compact bone.

Spongy or cancellous bone is lighter tissue with many spaces and a sponge-like appearance. It is composed of an irregular latticework of thin plates of bone called trabeculae, and within these are lacunae or spaces, containing osteocytes. Spongy bone is found at the ends of long bones e.g. the head of the femur, as well as at the centre of other bones. The medullary cavity - the central space inside long bones - is lined with a thin vascular membrane called the endosteum and bone marrow is stored here. Red bone marrow contains hematopoietic cells that are responsible for generating red blood cells, white blood cells and platelets (thrombocytes) for blood clotting. In infants, most bones - including the fingers - are filled with red bone marrow. With age, hematopoietic bone marrow is replaced by fatty, adipose marrow – usually called yellow bone marrow. By adulthood, hematopoietic bone marrow is largely confined to the skull, vertebrae, ribs, clavicles, sternum, pelvis and top of the femur. By old age, most of the bone marrow is yellow.

BONE STRUCTURE

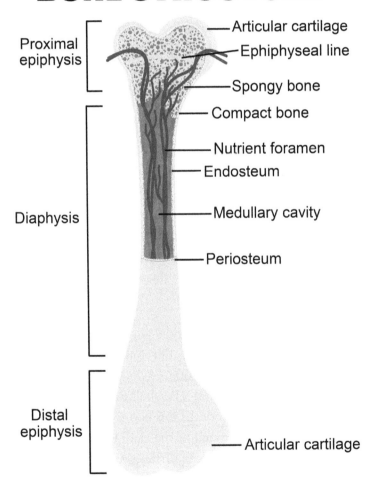

8.2 Bone structure

There are three types of cells in bone tissue - osteoclasts, osteoblasts and osteocytes. Osteoclasts break down old bone tissue, allowing osteoblasts – the bone making cells - to replace it with new material. Together, these cells facilitate bone mending and bone growth. Osteocytes are considered as mature osteoblasts and they do not secrete bone matrix, but they maintain bone metabolism, exchange nutrients and eliminate waste.

Long bones grow in size by the use of 'growth plates', which are cartilage 'epiphyseal' discs, separating the diaphysis - shaft of the bone - from the epiphysis - ends of the bone that are covered with a thin layer of smooth hyaline cartilage. A membrane called the periosteum, mostly made of elastic fibrous material such as collagen, covers the diaphysis of the bone. The periosteum also contains nerves and blood vessels. The inner layer of the periosteum contains osteoblasts, and is most active in foetal life and early childhood when bone formation is at its peak, or any time a bone is fractured. Long bones grow by depositing new bone matrix on the diaphysis side of the epiphyseal disc, causing bones to lengthen as we grow. Between the ages of 18 to 25, the epiphyseal discs harden and are replaced by bone, and no more growth occurs. Other bone types grow by osteoblasts depositing new bone tissue to the outside and osteoclasts taking excess bone tissue away from the inside.

The terms 'osteogenesis' or 'ossification' are often used to describe the process of bone formation. During development as an embryo, the skeleton is made of cartilage and connective tissue. This is replaced by bone as we develop in the uterus. The skull first forms as connective tissue, and after about three months this connective tissue is gradually replaced by bone. By birth, much of the skull is bone, apart from the fontanels (soft spots) where bones of the skull haven't fused yet. A newborn has fontanels on the top, back, and sides of the head, and fusion of the skull bones is not complete until about the age of two years. The same thing occurs with the rest of the skeleton, however this forms initially as cartilage, and is later replaced by bone. The skeleton does not complete its ossification until we stop growing. Bones continue to develop throughout adult life, for repair of fractures and for remodelling to meet changing lifestyles e.g. weight-bearing or high-impact exercise promotes the formation of new bone.

GROWING BONES

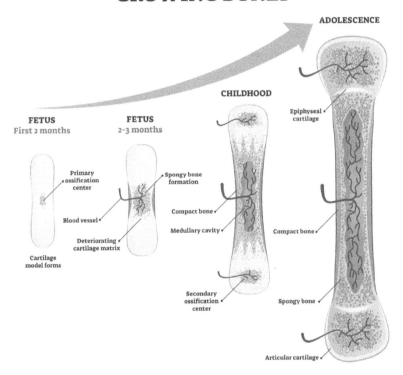

8.3 Bone growth

A fracture is the medical term for a broken bone due to injury or disease. There are different types of fractures, but the main categories are displaced, non-displaced, open and closed. Displaced and non-displaced fractures refer to the alignment of the fractured bone. In a displaced fracture, a bone snaps into two or more parts, and the two ends do not line up straight. In a non-displaced fracture, a bone cracks either part or all the way through, but maintains its proper alignment. A simple or closed fracture is when a bone is broken in one place and has not damaged the tissue around it, while a compound or open fracture is when a broken bone damages or pierces the skin. An open fracture carries the risk of a deep bone infection. A comminuted fracture is when a bone is broken in several places, while an incomplete fracture of a long bone is called a greenstick fracture and is common in children whose bones are still quite pliable. An impacted fracture occurs when the broken ends of a bone are jammed together by the force of an injury. If the broken bone damages tissue or organs around it, it is called a complicated fracture.

BONE FRACTURES

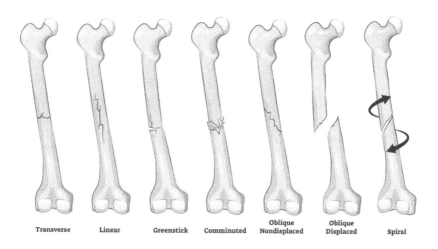

| Transverse | Linear | Greenstick | Comminuted | Oblique Nondisplaced | Oblique Displaced | Spiral |

8.4 Bone fractures

Stress fractures are tiny cracks in bone caused by repetitive force, often from overuse e.g. repeatedly jumping up and down or running long distances, and are most common in the weight-bearing bones of the lower leg and foot. Stress fractures can also develop from normal use of a bone that's weakened by a condition such as osteoporosis.

Fractures can be linear i.e. parallel to the bone's long axis, transverse i.e. at a right angle to the bone's long axis, or oblique i.e. diagonal to a bone's long axis (more than 30°). A spiral fracture occurs when a long bone is broken by a twisting force e.g. an arm caught in a rotating machine. Some fractures require surgery or metal plates, while others may need a cast or a brace. If a limb is irreparably damaged, a prosthesis may be needed. A prosthesis is an artificial substitute for a missing body part. The artificial parts that are most commonly thought of as prostheses are those that replace lost arms and legs, but artery and heart valve replacements as well as artificial eyes and teeth are also termed prostheses.

Stages Of Healing Bone Fracture

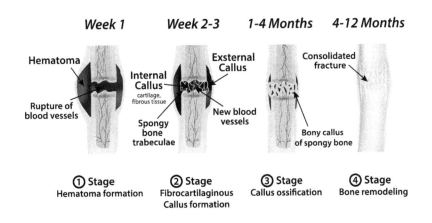

8.5 Stages of bone healing

For the first two weeks, healing of a damaged bone is much the same as healing of any other tissue. The site of the fracture contains clotted blood (haematoma) and the broken ends of the bone that die off. The site is invaded by white blood cells and osteoclasts that remove damaged bone. Between two and six weeks, callus forms at the site of the haematoma. Callus is made of fibrous tissue that hardens the clot and is similar to cartilage in density. The callus forms both internally and externally to the fracture. Between six and twelve weeks, ossification occurs - this is where callus is replaced with bone, though there is no real distinction between compact and cancellous bone at this stage. Following this stage, differentiation of the fracture site occurs. This is where the compact bone and cancellous bone re-form, and the bone regains its full strength. This usually occurs between six and twelve months after the fracture, but takes longer with age.

Ageing causes loss of minerals from bones (e.g. calcium, magnesium) as well as loss of collagen, leading to bones becoming brittle and susceptible to fractures. Osteoporosis - meaning 'porous bone' - is a common age-related problem, particularly for menopausal women, as reduced oestrogen levels affect the absorption of calcium. While steroid medicines can be lifesaving treatments for some conditions, they can also cause bone loss and osteoporosis. These medicines are often referred to as steroids, glucocorticoids or corticosteroids. Viewed under a microscope, healthy bone looks like a honeycomb, but with osteoporosis, the holes and spaces in the honeycomb are much larger than in healthy bone, as osteoporotic bones lose density or mass. As bones become less dense, they weaken and are more likely to break. A bone density scan is used to check for osteoporosis.

Osteopenia usually precedes osteoporosis and is defined as when bones are weaker than normal, but not so far gone that they break easily, which is the hallmark of osteoporosis. Weight-bearing physical activity causes new bone tissue to form, and this makes bones stronger. In fact, bones and muscles both become stronger when muscles push and tug against bones during physical activity. Some examples of weight-bearing physical activities include walking, running and lifting weights. Such exercises, along with dietary advice and medication for bone building, are usually prescribed to those affected by osteopenia and osteoporosis.

Osteomalacia refers to a softening of the bones, most often caused by severe vitamin D deficiency. The softened bones of children and young adults with osteomalacia can lead to bones bowing during growth, especially in the weight-bearing bones of the legs. This condition is called rickets. Osteomalacia in older adults can lead to fractures. Treatment for osteomalacia involves supplementation with vitamin D and calcium, both of which are needed to harden and strengthen bones, as well as looking for any other underlying causes of the condition.

Osteogenesis imperfecta is a genetic disorder in which bones fracture easily, sometimes for no apparent reason. It can also cause weak muscles, brittle teeth, a curved spine and hearing loss. The disease affects the production of collagen, a protein that helps make bones strong. Symptoms can range from mild to severe and vary from person to person. A person may have just a few or as many as several hundred fractures in a lifetime. There is no cure but symptoms can be managed, and treatments include exercise, pain medication, physical therapy, braces and surgery.

Paget's disease is a chronic disorder that can result in enlarged and misshapen bones. The excessive breakdown and formation of bone tissue causes affected bones to weaken, resulting in bone pain, misshapen bones, fractures, and arthritis in joints near the affected bones. It generally affects just one or a few bones, as opposed to osteoporosis, which can affect all the bones in the body. It is not known exactly what causes Paget's disease and in some cases where the disease runs in families, it is thought to be genetic. The disease is more common in older people and those of northern European heritage. Scientists are studying the possibility that a slow-acting virus may cause Paget's disease.

Arthrology is the study of joints and there are three main types in the body. Immovable or fibrous joints are those that do not allow movement, or allow for only very slight movement at joints. They are held together structurally by thick, fibrous, connective tissue containing collagen. These joints are important for stability and protection. Examples include the narrow fibrous joints (sutures) connecting bones of the skull. Slightly movable or cartilaginous joints permit some movement, but provide less stability than immovable joints and the bones are connected by cartilage - a tough, elastic connective tissue that helps to reduce friction between bones. Hyaline cartilage and fibrocartilage are the two types of cartilage found in cartilaginous joints. Hyaline cartilage is very flexible and elastic, while fibrocartilage is stronger and less flexible. Cartilaginous joints formed with hyaline cartilage can be found where the ribs connect with the sternum. These bars of costal, hyaline cartilage provide elasticity and flexibility to the walls of the thorax, allowing the lungs to expand and contract during breathing. A thin layer of hyaline cartilage also covers the ends of bones where they meet at joints. Intervertebral discs located between the spinal vertebrae and the joint between the two pubic bones (the symphisis pubis) are examples of slightly movable joints composed of fibrocartilage.

Freely movable or synovial joints allow for greater mobility, but are less stable than fibrous and cartilaginous joints. They have a synovial cavity or space between the adjacent bones, filled with synovial fluid, a thick liquid that allows the bones to move freely and prevents friction between them. An articular capsule composed of fibrous connective tissue surrounds the joint and connects to adjacent bones. The inner layer of the capsule is lined with a synovial membrane that produces the synovial fluid. Within the articular capsule, the rounded ends of adjacent bones are covered with smooth hyaline cartilage, which is reputed to be more slippery than ice! The articular hyaline cartilage absorbs shock and provides a smooth surface for fluent movements.

Bones at synovial joints are usually supported by structures outside of the joint such as ligaments, tendons and bursae - which are small fluid-filled sacs that reduce friction at joints.

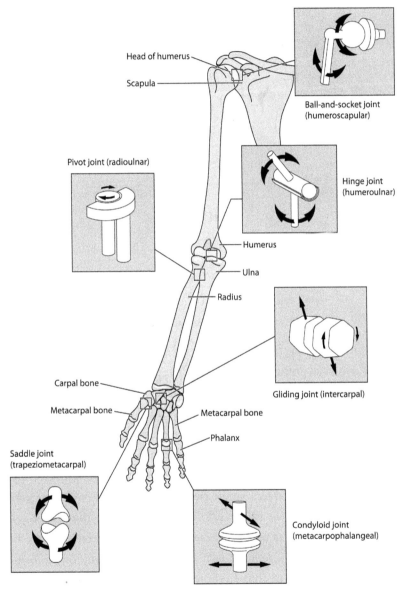

Head of humerus

Scapula

Ball-and-socket joint (humeroscapular)

Pivot joint (radioulnar)

Hinge joint (humeroulnar)

Humerus

Ulna

Radius

Gliding joint (intercarpal)

Carpal bone

Metacarpal bone

Metacarpal bone

Phalanx

Saddle joint (trapeziometacarpal)

Condyloid joint (metacarpophalangeal)

8.6 Types of joints

SYNOVIAL JOINT

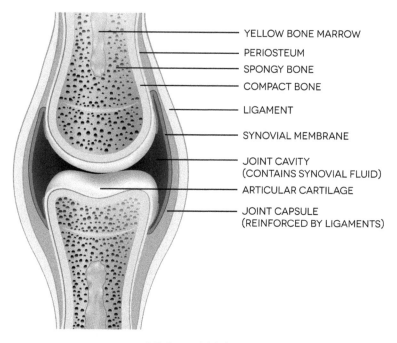

YELLOW BONE MARROW
PERIOSTEUM
SPONGY BONE
COMPACT BONE
LIGAMENT
SYNOVIAL MEMBRANE
JOINT CAVITY
(CONTAINS SYNOVIAL FLUID)
ARTICULAR CARTILAGE
JOINT CAPSULE
(REINFORCED BY LIGAMENTS)

8.7 Synovial joints

Synovial joints allow for different types of body movements, and six types of synovial joint are found at different locations in the body. They include pivot, condyloid, hinge, saddle, plane (gliding), and ball and socket joints. Pivot joints permit rotational movement around an axis e.g. the joint between the first and second cervical vertebrae near the base of the skull allows the head to turn from side to side. Hinge joints permit bending and straightening movements like a door hinge, with movement limited to a single direction. Examples of hinge joints include the elbow, knee, ankle and the joints between the phalanges - the bones of the fingers and toes. Condyloid joints allow bending and straightening, side-to-side and circular movements. One of the bones has an oval-shaped end that fits into a slight depression on another bone e.g. the joint between the radius bone of the forearm and bones of the wrist. A saddle joints allows movement in various directions e.g. the trapeziometacarpal joint at the base of the thumb, connecting the trapezium - one of the carpal or wrist bones - and the metacarpal bone of the thumb. Here the bones fit up against each other like a saddle fits over the back of a horse. Plane joints allow bones to slide past each other in a gliding motion. The bones at plane joints are of a similar size and the surfaces where the bones meet are nearly flat e.g. the joints between the bones of the wrist (carpals) and the ankle (tarsals), as well as between the collarbone and shoulder blade. Ball-and-socket joints allow the greatest degree of movement e.g. bending and straightening, side-to-side, circular and rotational movements. The end of one bone is rounded like a ball and fits into the cupped end or socket of another bone e.g. the hip and shoulder joints.

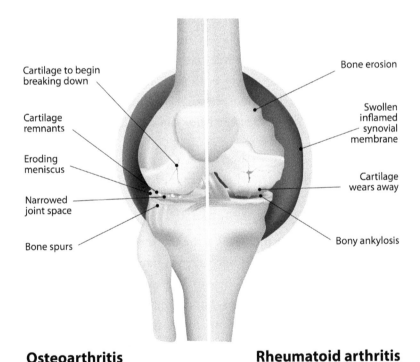

Osteoarthritis

Cartilage to begin breaking down

Cartilage remnants

Eroding meniscus

Narrowed joint space

Bone spurs

Rheumatoid arthritis

Bone erosion

Swollen inflamed synovial membrane

Cartilage wears away

Bony ankylosis

8.8 Osteoarthritis & rheumatoid arthritis

'Itis' means 'inflammation' and 'arthr' means 'joint' and the term 'arthritis' refers to joint inflammation with swelling and tenderness in one or more joints. The main symptoms of arthritis are joint pain and stiffness that typically worsens with age, and the most common types are osteoarthritis and rheumatoid arthritis. Osteoarthritis causes the slippery hyaline cartilage that covers the ends of bones where they form a joint to break down, and is generally due to wear and tear and the ageing process. Rheumatoid arthritis is a disease in which the immune system attacks the joints, beginning with the joint lining. In people with rheumatoid arthritis, the body interprets the synovial lining of the joints as a threat similar to a virus or bacteria and mounts an attack, causing fluid to accumulate within the joint. This leads to swelling, pain, inflammation and morning stiffness that can last an hour or more. It tends to affect the smaller joints such as those in the hands and feet first, though in severe cases it can affect all joints as well as other connective tissue in the body. Rheumatoid arthritis affects joints symmetrically, while osteoarthritis usually affects joints asymmetrically, but it can affect both sides in some cases. Both types of arthritis are more common in women than men and more prevalent in older adults, but rheumatoid arthritis can develop at any age and can run in families.

Uric acid crystals that form when there is excess uric acid in the blood can cause a type of arthritis called gout. Gout is characterised by sudden, severe attacks of pain, swelling, redness, and tenderness in the joints, often the joint at the base of the big toe. Gout tophi are lumps that are often noticed on a joint that is attacked by gout. In severe cases tophi can form in bone or cartilage elsewhere in the body e.g. they can be found on the elbows, hands, feet, or the outer edge of the ear. Tophi tend to be easy to spot thanks to their size, but some smaller tophi can only be detected with an MRI or other imaging test. Tophi sometimes disappear when uric acid levels are controlled, and in some cases they are surgically removed. The body produces uric acid when it breaks down purines, substances that are found naturally in the body. Purines are also found in certain foods, such as organ meats and seafood. Other foods can promote higher levels of uric acid e.g. alcoholic drinks - especially beer - and drinks sweetened with fruit sugar (fructose).

Infections or underlying disease, such as psoriasis or lupus, can cause other types of arthritis e.g. psoriatic arthritis is a form of arthritis that affects some people who have psoriasis. It is thought to be an autoimmune condition and can cause swollen, stiff and painful joints e.g. fingers and toes, as well as foot pain, lower back pain and pitting of the nails. Synovitis is inflammation of the synovial tissue lining a joint. This condition can cause joint pain and swelling and is seen with a variety of inflammatory conditions such as rheumatoid arthritis. Treatments vary depending on the type of arthritis, and the main treatment goals are to reduce symptoms and improve quality of life.

Ligaments are bands of tough elastic tissue around joints, connecting bone to bone, giving the joints support and limiting their movement, while a tendon is a fibrous cord of tissue that connects muscle to bone. Ligaments are found around the knees, ankles, elbows, shoulders and other joints. A sprain is an injury to a ligament i.e. one or more ligaments is stretched or torn, while a strain is an injury to a muscle or tendon. Stretching or tearing ligaments can make joints unstable and can happen as a result of a sports injury, an awkward movement, an accident or wear and tear. Abnormal, excessively supple collagen in the ligaments can lead to hypermobile joints, and these are more likely than normal joints to get injured if they are over stretched.

A ganglion cyst is a small sac of fluid that forms over a ligament or tendon. Inside the cyst is a thick, sticky, jellylike material that may feel firm or spongy. Ganglion cysts most commonly occur on the back of the hand at the wrist joint, but they can also develop on the palmar side of the wrist or other areas, and often disappear spontaneously. In the past, home care has included topical plaster, heat and poultices, as well as the use of a heavy book like the Bible to physically smash the cyst – giving them the name 'bible bumps'. This method is not recommended and may do more harm than good.

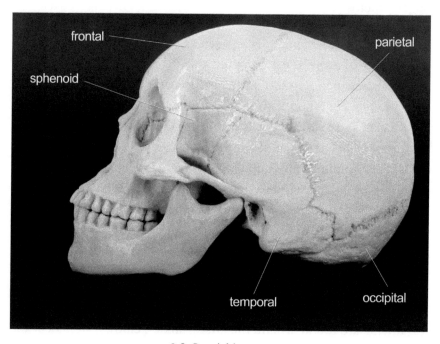

8.9 Cranial bones

Now let's look at the actual bones that make up the skeleton. The skull is composed of twenty-two bones, with eight bones forming the dome-shaped cranium and fourteen bones forming the face. The cranial bones include the following:

One frontal bone forms the forehead, eye sockets and part of the nose.

One occipital bone is located at back of the skull with a large opening called the foramen magnum through which the spinal cord passes to join the brain.

Two parietal bones form the sides and roof of the cranium.

Two temporal bones are located on each side of the head, with openings to the middle and inner ears.

One butterfly-shaped sphenoid bone forms the floor of the cranium and the temples.

One ethmoid bone at the roof of the nose forms the supporting structures of the nasal cavities.

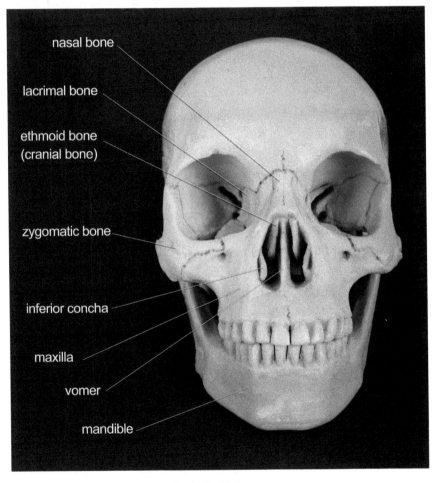

nasal bone

lacrimal bone

ethmoid bone
(cranial bone)

zygomatic bone

inferior concha

maxilla

vomer

mandible

8.10 Facial bones

The facial bones include the following:

One mandible forms the lower jaw and is connected to the temporal bone at the hinge-like temporomandibular joint (TMJ), where the mandible and temporal bone meet.

Two maxillae form the upper jaw, the front part of the hard palate (roof of the mouth), part of the walls of the nose and part of the floor of the eye sockets.

Two palatine bones form the back part of the hard palate, part of the walls of the nose and part of the floor of the eye sockets.

Two small nasal bones form the bridge of the nose - the rest of the nose is cartilage.

Two zygomatic bones form the cheeks and sides of the eye sockets.

Two tiny lacrimal bones are located on the inside walls of the eye sockets. A groove between the lacrimal bones and the nose forms a canal through which tears flow across the eyeballs into the nasal cavity – this accounts for a runny nose when we cry!

Two scroll-shaped inferior conchae or turbinate bones form a curved ledge along the inside walls of the nasal cavity, encouraging the turbulent circulation and filtration of inhaled air before it passes into the lungs.

One vomer joins the ethmoid bone to form the nasal septum, separating the two nostrils.

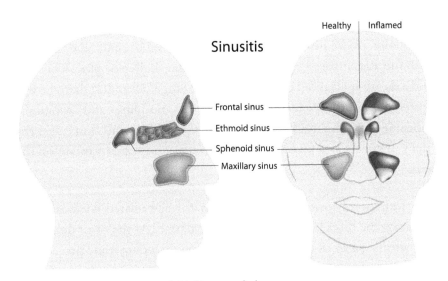

Sinusitis

Frontal sinus
Ethmoid sinus
Sphenoid sinus
Maxillary sinus

8.11 Paranasal sinuses

The paranasal sinuses are cavities located inside some of the bones of the skull. As well as giving resonance to the voice, the sinuses warm and moisten inhaled air and reduce the weight of the skull. Like the nose, they are lined with very fine, hair-like cilia whose function is to move mucus produced by the sinuses towards tiny holes called ostia that provide drainage into the nose. Two maxillary sinuses are located in the cheeks, while the ethmoid sinuses are located around the bridge of the nose, behind and between the eyes. Both the maxillary and ethmoid sinuses are present at birth, while the frontal sinuses in the forehead do not develop until around seven years of age. The sphenoid sinuses, located deep in the face behind the nose, do not develop until adolescence.

The spine or backbone is composed of thirty-three bones called vertebrae. By adulthood, five bones at the base of the spine have fused into one bone called the sacrum, and the four tailbones have also fused together to form the coccyx. This is one reason why we lose flexibility with age. The seven bones in the neck are called cervical vertebrae ('cervix' is Latin for neck) and are often referred to as C1-C7. The atlas (C1) is the first cervical vertebra and is named after the Atlas of Greek mythology who carried a globe on his shoulders, because it supports the 'globe' of the head i.e. the skull. C2 is called the axis, and together with the atlas it forms a joint connecting the skull and spine. The atlas and axis are specialised to allow a greater range of motion than normal vertebrae, and are responsible for the nodding and rotational movements of the head. The axis has a tooth-like projection called the 'dens' that acts as a pivot, allowing the atlas and head to rotate on the axis.

Cervical spondylosis is a general term for age-related wear and tear affecting the discs between the neck vertebrae. As the discs dehydrate and shrink, signs of osteoarthritis develop, including bony projections called bone spurs along the edges of the bones. Cervical spondylosis is very common and worsens with age. More than 85% of people over the age of 60 are affected by some degree of cervical spondylosis. Most people experience no symptoms, but when symptoms do occur, they typically include pain and stiffness in the neck.

Whiplash is a common neck injury that occurs following a sudden acceleration-deceleration force that causes rapid forward and backward movement of the head and neck, most commonly from motor vehicle accidents when a car is impacted from the rear. It can cause damage to the soft tissues - ligaments, tendons and muscles - that hold the cervical vertebrae together.

Spine and structure of segments

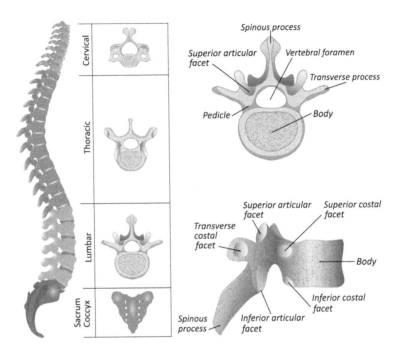

8.12 Bones of the spine

The twelve thoracic vertebrae (T1-T12) are attached to the ribs and five large lumbar vertebrae (L1-L5) form the lower back. Each of the vertebral bones is separated from its neighbour by a doughnut shaped disc filled with a jelly-like fluid that allows movement and cushions shock. Behind each of the discs, and between every pair of vertebral bones, is a foramen (hole) through which spinal nerve roots exit to the arms, chest and legs.

Facet joints are the small, cartilage-covered points of contact where each individual vertebra meets the one above and below it. They enable the spine to flex during movement and also limit its range of motion. However, if the cartilage wears thin, pain can occur. The wear and tear of ageing, excess body weight or injury to the spine are risk factors for facet joint damage. Along the midline of the spine are spinous processes - the bumps that can be felt along the back of the neck, thoracic spine and lower back.

Although they do not actually 'slip,' a disc may bulge, split or rupture causing the disc cartilage and nearby tissue to herniate and allowing the central gel portion of the disc to escape into the surrounding tissue. This is often referred to as a slipped or herniated disc, and the protruding, jelly-like substance can put pressure on the spinal cord or on an adjacent nerve. This can cause pain, numbness or weakness, either around the damaged, herniated disc or anywhere along the area supplied by that nerve. A damaged facet joint can also put pressure on a nerve.

When there is damage to a disc, to one of the facet joints, or to a vertebral bone, there can be too much movement in the area and that can be painful. Fusion surgeries, where the bones are welded together, are sometimes recommended when there is excessive movement.

The spine houses and protects the spinal cord, which begins at the base of the brain and runs down the spine to the lower back. Between every two vertebral bones, two nerves exit the spinal canal - one on the left and another on the right - with each nerve going to a specific area of the body. The spine is supported by strong ligaments and by powerful 'erector spinae' muscles running in bands on either side of the vertebrae.

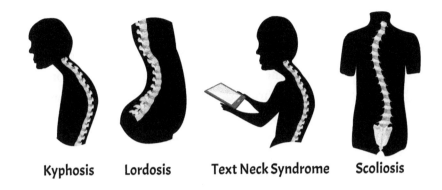

Kyphosis **Lordosis** **Text Neck Syndrome** **Scoliosis**

8.13 Spinal deformities

A healthy spine when viewed from the side has gentle curves that help it absorb stress from body movements and gravity. When viewed from the back, the spine should run straight down the middle of the back, but when abnormalities of the spine occur, the natural curvatures of the spine are misaligned or exaggerated in certain areas. Lordosis - also called swayback - is when the spine curves significantly inward at the lower back. Kyphosis is an abnormally hunched and rounded upper back, while scoliosis refers to a sideways curve of the spine - often an S-shaped or C-shaped curve. Spinal abnormalities can be congenital i.e. present at birth or hereditary, environmental i.e. caused by work or lifestyle, or traumatic i.e. due to an injury. Text neck syndrome and SMS thumb are modern day problems due to overuse of hand held devices, resulting in repetitive stress injury while using mobile phones or other electronic devices for prolonged periods of time.

Spinal stenosis is a medical condition in which the spinal canal narrows, compressing the spinal cord and nerves. It occurs most often in the lower back and the neck, and is most commonly caused by wear-and-tear changes in the spine related to osteoarthritis. Some people with spinal stenosis may have no symptoms, while others may experience pain, tingling, numbness and muscle weakness. In severe cases, doctors may recommend surgery to create additional space for the spinal cord or nerves.

'Ankylosis' means stiffening and immobility of a joint and 'spondylitis' means inflammation in the spinal vertebrae. Ankylosing spondylitis (AS) is a rare type of arthritis that causes inflammation, pain and stiffness in the spine. This lifelong condition - also known as Bechterew's disease and Marie Strumpell disease - usually starts in the lower back, often in the sacroiliac joint where the sacrum and pelvis meet. It can spread up to the neck or damage joints in other parts of the body, and can affect places where tendons and ligaments attach to bones. It can even cause the vertebrae to fuse together. About 40% of people with AS have a painful, inflammatory eye problem called uveitis that can blur vision and make the eyes sensitive to bright light. There is no cure for AS, but medication and exercise can ease pain and help keep the back strong.

The hyoid bone is a small horseshoe-shaped bone located in the front of the neck between the chin and the thyroid cartilage, and it aids with swallowing and tongue movements. It is secured to the thyroid cartilage by ligaments and is at the level of the third cervical vertebra, attached indirectly by tendons to muscles of the tongue, the floor of the mouth and the anterior neck.

The thorax refers to the 12 pairs of ribs, the sternum and the thoracic vertebrae. The three parts of the sternum are the manubrium (upper part), the body and the xyphoid process, which is the pointed end – 'xyphoid' is Greek for 'sword like'. All 12 ribs articulate posteriorly with the 12 thoracic vertebrae. The first 7 ribs - called true ribs - articulate anteriorly with the sternum via the costal cartilage. The next 5 are called false ribs, as they are not directly attached to the sternum. The last 2 pairs are called floating ribs as they do not articulate with the sternum, but are attached to the abdominal muscles. Some people have an extra cervical rib above the normal first rib on one side. This extra rib arises from the seventh cervical vertebra. In some people this can cause a condition called thoracic outlet syndrome if the rib compresses the brachial plexus - the group of nerves going down the arm. This can cause pain and 'pins and needles' in the arm on the affected side. Treatment can include painkillers, physiotherapy, and sometimes surgery to relieve the compression.

RIB CAGE

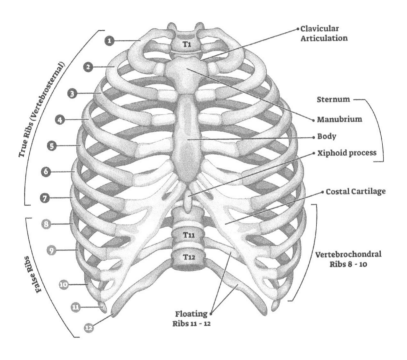

8.14 Ribcage

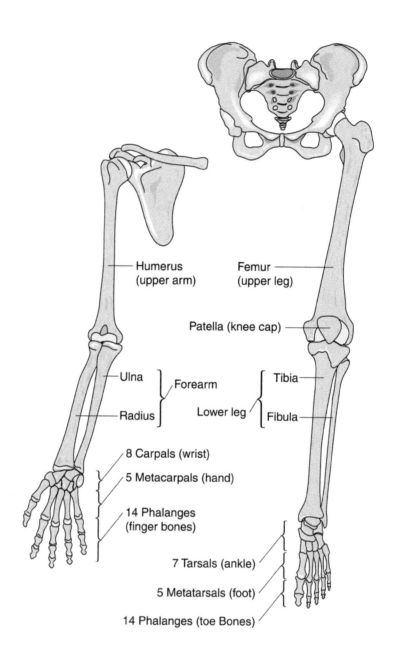

Humerus
(upper arm)

Femur
(upper leg)

Patella (knee cap)

Ulna

Forearm

Tibia

Radius

Lower leg

Fibula

8 Carpals (wrist)

5 Metacarpals (hand)

14 Phalanges
(finger bones)

7 Tarsals (ankle)

5 Metatarsals (foot)

14 Phalanges (toe Bones)

8.15 Bones of the upper and lower limbs

The shoulder girdle is the bony arch made up of two clavicles (collarbones) and two scapulae (shoulder blades), all held together by ligaments. There are three joints in the shoulder girdle. The acromioclavicular joint is formed by the articulation of the clavicle with the acromion - the highest point of the scapula. This joint allows the scapula to rotate on the clavicle. The sternoclavicular joint is formed by the articulation of the clavicle with the manubrium - the upper part of the sternum. The humerus or upper arm bone sits in a socket of the scapula called the glenoid cavity to form the glenohumeral joint – a ball and socket synovial joint and the most moveable joint in the body.

The humerus connects with the radius (thumb side) and ulna (little finger side) of the forearm at the elbow joint. The olecranon process is the prominent bony projection of the ulna bone that can be felt at the elbow. It is a common site of elbow fractures and is sometimes called the 'funny bone', because when it is struck, a sharp, tingling sensation can be experienced along the forearm and hand due to pressure on the ulnar nerve that runs over this bone under the skin.

Hands are composed of various bones, muscles and ligaments that allow for a large amount of movement and dexterity. The human thumb is longer compared to finger length, than the thumb of any other primate, and this long thumb and its ability to easily touch the other fingers allows humans to firmly grasp and precisely manipulate objects of various shapes and sizes. Hands can grip with strength and with fine control so that many actions can be performed, from throwing a ball to fine motor movements such as writing, sewing or playing a musical instrument. The hands and feet together contain more than half the bones in the body, with 26 bones in each foot and 27 bones in each hand.

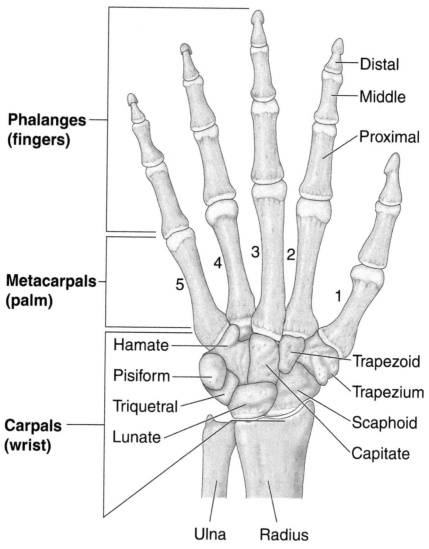

Phalanges (fingers)

Metacarpals (palm)

Carpals (wrist)

Distal

Middle

Proximal

5 4 3 2 1

Hamate
Pisiform
Triquetral
Lunate

Trapezoid
Trapezium
Scaphoid
Capitate

Ulna Radius

8.16 Bones of the hand

Eight small carpal bones form each wrist, five metacarpal bones form each palm, and fourteen phalanges make up the fingers and thumb of each hand - three in each finger and two in each thumb. The carpal bones are arranged in two rows of four. The proximal row of carpal bones includes the scaphoid, lunate, triquetral (triquetrum) and

134

pisiform bones. The distal row includes the trapezium, trapezoid, capitate and hamate. The most commonly injured carpal bone is the scaphoid, located near the base of the thumb. Carpal tunnel syndrome - also called median nerve compression - is a condition that causes numbness, tingling or weakness in the hand, due to pressure on the median nerve, which runs down the arm and through a passage in the carpals, ending in the hand. The median nerve controls the movement and feeling of the thumb and the movement of all fingers except the little finger. Repetitive wrist movements like using a keyboard - particularly when the hands are lower than the wrists - can cause carpal tunnel syndrome. It can also occur during pregnancy due to fluid retention that can cause swelling and increase pressure on the median nerve.

The pelvic girdle is formed by two large hipbones - sometimes called the innominate bones or 'os coxae' - that articulate with the axial skeleton via the sacrum. Each hipbone is made up of three parts. The ilium is the flared upper portion that articulates with the sacrum at the sacroiliac (SI) joints. Injury, arthritis or inflammation can often affect the SI joints. Trauma - such as a fall or other injury - can damage the ligaments supporting the joints leading to pain and discomfort. Pregnancy hormones that relax the ligaments in readiness for childbirth can sometimes cause a slight dislocation of the joints, or the extra weight can lead to wear and tear. The SI joints can also be affected by arthritis (e.g. osteoarthritis, psoriatic arthritis, ankylosing spondylitis), leading to sacroiliitis, which is inflammation of the SI joints. This can cause pain in the buttocks or lower back and can extend down one or both legs. Prolonged standing or stair climbing can worsen the pain. The ischium is the lower part that we sit on (ischial tuberosity), and two pubic bones form the lower anterior part.

The symphisis pubis is a joint made of hyaline cartilage and fibrocartilage located between the left and right pubic bones near the midline of the body, in front of the bladder. Symphysis pubis dysfunction (SPD) is a relatively common disorder when the ligaments that normally keep the pelvic bones aligned during pregnancy become over relaxed and stretchy too soon before birth (as delivery nears, things are supposed to start loosening up). This in turn can make the symphysis pubis unstable, causing strange sensations and sometimes quite severe pelvic pain. A male pelvis is smaller and narrower than a female pelvis, with thicker bones designed to support a heavy body build and a stronger muscle structure, while a female pelvis is wider and roomier for the purpose of childbearing.

The acetabulum is the socket of the hipbone into which the head of the femur sits to form the hip joint. Those suffering from osteoarthritis of the hip joint may require hip replacement surgery (arthroplasty) if the pain interferes with daily activities and other treatments haven't helped, or are no longer effective. During hip replacement surgery, a surgeon removes the damaged sections of the hip joint, and replaces them with parts usually constructed of metal, ceramic or very hard plastic. The artificial joint (prosthesis) helps reduce pain and improve function.

The lower limb includes the femur (thighbone), which forms the lateral and medial tibia-femoral hinge joints at the knee with the tibia - the weight-bearing bone of the lower leg, commonly called the shinbone. These are the joints that are usually involved in knee replacement surgery, with either one side (partial knee replacement) or both sides (full knee replacement) needing surgery. During surgery, an orthopedic surgeon carves away the damaged areas of bone and replaces them with metal or plastic. Osteoarthritis is the most common reason for knee replacement surgery, and this can be due to ageing, overuse, obesity, hormonal disturbances or a congenital abnormality.

Located between the tibia and femur are menisci - small fibrocartilage discs that provide cushioning as the knee is flexed and extended. The patella (kneecap) forms the gliding patellofemoral joint with the femur. Some daily activities that work the patellofemoral joints include walking up or down hill, going up or down stairs, kneeling, squatting or getting up from a seated position. In some people this can lead to chondromalacia, which is the breakdown of cartilage on the underside of the kneecap. In its most chronic form, this condition may require surgery and is a common injury in runners, soccer players, skiers and cyclists.

Pre-patellar bursitis - also known as 'housemaid's knee' - is caused by inflammation of the small bursa or fluid-filled sac in front of the kneecap, located between the skin and the patella. It most commonly occurs in people who spend long periods of time kneeling.

When the knee joint is affected by arthritis - particularly an inflammatory arthritis such as rheumatoid arthritis - abnormal amounts of fluid can build up and the knee can become swollen. Injury to the ligaments or meniscus - the cartilage in the knee - can also cause swelling.

The fibula is the long, thin, lateral bone of the lower leg. It runs parallel to the tibia and helps to stabilise the ankle and support the muscles of the lower leg. The fibula is sometimes harvested for tissue to graft onto other bones in the body e.g. it can be grafted onto the mandible to replace bone lost during oral cancer surgery. Skin and blood vessels covering the fibula are grafted along with the bone tissue to maintain blood supply to the bone and to close the wound in the face. The remaining tissue in the leg is sutured together to heal around the donor site. The medial and lateral malleoli are the 'bumps' on either side of the ankle. The end of the tibia forms the medial malleolus, while the end of the fibula forms the lateral malleolus.

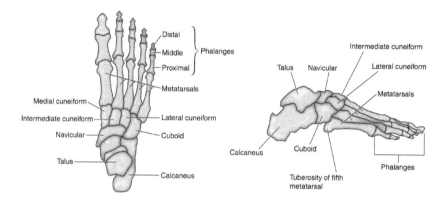

8.17 Bones of the foot

The ankle joint is composed of the tibia, fibula and talus, which together form a tight synovial hinge joint that allows plantarflexion (toes down) and dorsiflexion (toes up) of the foot. The talus is one of the seven tarsal bones that form the back of the foot. The other tarsals are the calcaneus (heel bone), the navicular, the cuboid and three small cuneiform bones. The tarsals have fairly flat surfaces that allow them to glide past one another, providing lateral mobility to the foot and allowing it to bend and adjust to the body's balance. The calcaneus is the largest bone in the foot and absorbs the most shock and pressure. Heel spurs can sometimes develop as an abnormal growth of this bone. Most commonly, these spurs are calcium deposits that form when the plantar fascia – the thick connective tissue that supports the arch on the bottom (plantar side) of the foot - pulls away from the heel area, causing a bony protrusion.

Twisting motions that can occur when the foot is planted awkwardly, when the ground is uneven, or when an unusual amount of force is applied, can easily injure the ankle joint. When an ankle is injured with a sprain, tendon injury or fracture, inflammation occurs. Blood vessels become 'leaky' and allow fluid to ooze into the soft tissue surrounding the joint. White blood cells responsible for inflammation migrate to the area and blood flow also increases. Signs and symptoms of an injured ankle include swelling, pain and redness. Unless the injury is severe, the best course of action is rest, ice, compression and elevation of the joint (R.I.C.E.)

PATHOLOGIES OF FOOT

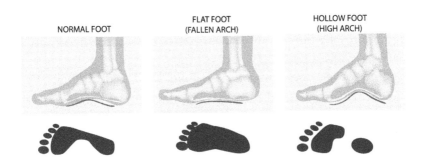

8.18 Arches of the foot

Anterior to the tarsals are the five long metatarsal bones and the fourteen phalanges of the toes. The phalanges, metatarsals and tarsals form the longitudinal and transverse arches of the foot to divide the body weight across the entire foot, and act as a spring to absorb and release the force of the body's weight on the ground. Flat feet or 'pes planus' is a condition in which the foot does not have a normal arch when standing. If the whole foot is touching the floor when you stand up, you have flat feet. There are many causes of flat feet including pregnancy, obesity or repetitive pounding on a hard surface that can weaken the arch. Often people with flat feet do not experience discomfort. However, when symptoms develop and become painful, walking becomes awkward and causes increased strain on the feet and calves. Orthotic devices such as shoe inserts, as well as stretching exercises and rigid soled shoes can often help this condition.

A bunion is a common problem affecting the foot. This is a bony bump that forms on the joint at the base of the big toe when it pushes against the adjacent toe, forcing the big toe joint to become larger and stick out. The skin over the bunion is often red and sore. Wearing tight, narrow shoes can cause bunions or make them worse. Bunions also can develop as a result of an inherited structural defect, stress on the foot, or a medical condition such as arthritis. Treatment options vary depending on the severity of the bunion and how much pain it causes and include nonsurgical treatments that may relieve the pain and pressure of a bunion and/or surgery to correct the deformity.

A hammertoe is a deformity of the second, third or fourth toes, where the toe is bent at the middle joint so that it resembles a hammer. If the hammertoes are flexible they can be easily corrected, but if left untreated, they can become fixed and may need surgery. The most common complaint with hammertoes is rubbing and irritation from footwear on top of the bent toe.

Other common foot problems include corns, which are areas of thickened skin generally found on the top of the toes due to shoe irritation, or in between the toes due to irritation and friction from a bony prominence. Calluses are thick, hardened layers of skin that develop when the skin tries to protect itself against friction and pressure. They vary in size and shape, are generally larger than corns, and are often found on the ball of the foot.

Another not so common foot problem that affects the nervous system rather than the skeletal system is Morton's neuroma, which occurs when the tissue inside the foot gets thicker next to a nerve leading to one of the toes. The pressure irritates the nerve causing pain, usually between the third and fourth toes. Women are more likely than men to get Morton's neuroma, and high-heeled shoes are among the main culprits because they put pressure on the feet.

Regular weight bearing exercise, eating a balanced diet with calcium rich foods, getting adequate vitamin D, avoiding cigarette smoke and limiting alcohol consumption can all help to maintain healthy bones.

Wearing a seat belt when driving and a helmet when cycling as well as appropriate headgear when engaged in active sports can help protect our valuable skeletal system from injury and damage.

9. The Muscular System

The muscular system is involved with all movement of the human body, both external and internal, and consists of skeletal, smooth and cardiac muscle. Muscle tissue is specialised elastic tissue with several properties including excitability (the ability to respond to stimuli), contractibility (the ability to contract), extensibility (the ability to be stretched without tearing) and elasticity (the ability to return to its normal shape).

Types of Muscle

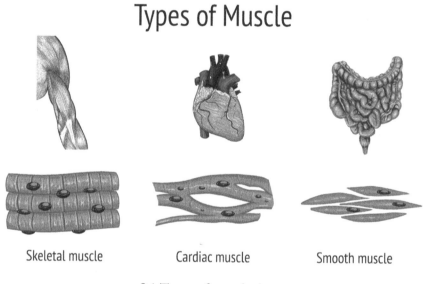

Skeletal muscle   Cardiac muscle   Smooth muscle

9.1 Types of muscle tissue

Skeletal muscle tissue - often referred to as voluntary or striated/striped muscle - is attached to the bones of the skeleton and is involved in the movements of everyday living. The percentage of muscle mass in the human body depends upon gender, age and physical fitness. For males, the average muscle mass is between 38% and 54%, while for females the range is between 28% and 39%. Skeletal muscle tissue is composed of approximately 75% water, 20% protein and the remaining 5% is composed of fats, mineral salts and glycogen (stored glucose from carbohydrate metabolism).

Contractions of skeletal muscles help return blood to the heart and move lymphatic fluid (more about that later on!) Muscles stabilise joints, maintain body posture and aid with homeostasis by helping to regulate body temperature. Muscle contraction requires energy and produces heat as a byproduct of metabolism. In extreme cold, muscles help to warm the body by contracting quickly, causing us to shiver.

Skeletal muscle anatomy has traditionally been studied as a collection of individual components, with each one designed to move a specific part of the body, and in many gyms you can find exercise machines designed to isolate a single body part - and sometimes a number of separate machines to 'train' the same body part. However, progressive health and fitness professionals are increasingly viewing the body as a single, integrated structure, through developing a greater understanding of the body's largest type of connective tissue, fascia - the web-like connective tissue that gives the entire body form and structure. David Lesondak, author of 'Fascia: What it is and Why it Matters' says: "In the same way that an orange rind creates organized sections of juicy pulp, fascia forms a pocket around each of our 600+ muscles and 200+ bones. Collectively, fascia forms a 3D, full-length body-stocking that keeps everything separate and at the same time connected."

One concept proposes a series of chain-like 'slings' that crisscross the body like seams on a patchwork quilt. These chains composed of muscles, tendons, ligaments and fascia all function together to create and support optimal movement patterns in the body. For example, the posterior oblique sling (POS) is a chain that runs across the back and into the gluteal region, and is formed by the latissimus dorsi on one side and the gluteus maximus of the opposite side, along with the thoracolumbar fascia in between. This deep fascial tissue crosses the entire lower back area and connects the shoulder to the opposite hip. The POS is regarded as an essential part of walking, and is the reason that as you step forward with one foot the arm on the opposite side swings forward. These slings cross over and create an X across the lower back that helps to provide lower back stability as well as supporting lower extremity movements. The POS travels over the sacroiliac joints, a common source of lower back pain - therefore strengthening the POS can be beneficial in minimising the stress on these joints. Other 'slings' or 'chains' of muscle and fascia include the anterior oblique system - two intersecting slings that run diagonally across the front of the torso and connect the external and internal obliques with the opposing leg's adductors and intervening anterior abdominal fascia; the deep longitudinal system that runs vertically along the back and down the legs and connects the erector spinae muscles, multifidus, thoracolumbar fascia, sacrotuberous ligament (anchors sacrum to pelvis) and the biceps femoris of the hamstrings group; and the lateral system that connects smaller muscles around the pelvis and groin i.e. gluteus medius and minimus, tensor fascia latae and iliotibial band (IT band).

Prominent anatomist and body worker Tom Myers developed the myofascial meridians as another way of explaining the role of the fascial system in relation to human structure and function. Myers' book 'Anatomy Trains' has become a leading resource in the study of the fascial network. According to the Anatomy Trains concept, there are 12 specific fascial lines throughout the body. Even though 12 lines have been identified, they are also interconnected to form an uninterrupted continuum within the body, and enclose organs, muscles, tendons, ligaments and other tissues that are included in the line. Currently there is no clear-cut definition of fascia, or exactly which tissues make up the fascial network, and it is still an emerging area of anatomical study. An understanding of how the myofascial network functions as a wholly integrated system is now feeding into training for fitness instructors, massage therapists and body workers of all kinds, and is worth bearing in mind and investigating further as you read this chapter. Fascia-related modalities include structural integration, fascial manipulation, myofascial release, fascial stretch therapy and myofascial trigger point therapy. While these approaches have some differences, they all use a combination of hands-on fascial manipulation combined with slow stretching and other movements to free up restrictions within the body.

Although skeletal muscles come in different shapes and sizes, the main structure of skeletal muscle tissue remains the same. A myofibril refers to an individual muscle cell or fibre composed of repeating contractile sections called sarcomeres containing actin and myosin protein filaments that are responsible for muscle contractions. A bundle of individual muscle fibres is called a fascicle, and a muscle itself is divided into sections containing a number of fascicles. A layer of connective tissue called the epimysium covers each muscle and protects it from friction against other muscles and bones.

A helpful image that I came across in my studies is to imagine looking into a container full of drinking straws – this is like a muscle and the straws are the dozens of long cylindrical muscle fibres (muscle cells or myofibrils) bundled together. Another connective tissue layer called the perimysium surrounds each bundle of fibres (fasciculi) and each individual muscle cell or fibre is covered with a thin layer of connective tissue called the endomysium, containing blood capillaries. The endomysium, perimysium and epimysium continue at the end of the muscle to form a tendon that merges into the periosteum or skin of a bone to form a strong attachment. All of these membranes can be regarded as part of the body's fascial network. Beneath the endomysium and surrounding the muscle fibre is the muscle cell membrane or sarcolemma - a fine transparent tubular sheath. Beneath this is the sarcoplasm - the muscle cell's cytoplasm - containing glycogen and fats for energy as well as the mitochondria that produce the muscle cell's energy. Under a microscope, skeletal muscle fibres look stripy. Actin and myosin protein filaments that run across the muscle fibres in transverse bands form these stripes or striations.

When a muscle contracts, the actin filaments slide between the myosin filaments causing the fibres to shorten and thicken (check out sliding filament theory if you want to know more!)

Structure of Skeletal Muscle

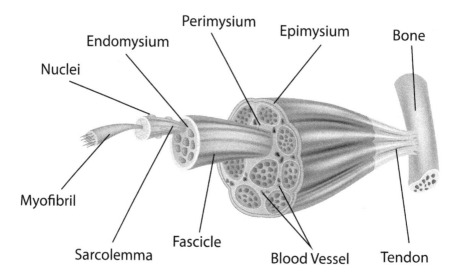

9.2 Skeletal muscle anatomy

Most skeletal muscles are attached to bones by tendons, and as muscles contract they exert force on the bones, helping to support and move the body. In most cases, one end of the muscle - the origin - is fixed in its position, while the other end - the insertion - moves during contraction. The insertion is usually distal - further away from the trunk - while the origin is proximal - closer to the trunk - relative to the insertion. The thickest part of a muscle - usually in the middle - is called the muscle belly. Muscles work in groups rather than individually when a part of the body moves. During any particular movement, individual muscles will play different roles, depending on their origin and insertion. These roles can be described as agonist or prime mover, which is the muscle that does most of the movement, antagonist - the muscle that relaxes and slows down or stops the movement of the agonist, and the synergist that assists the agonist to function effectively. For example, when the elbow is flexed to bring food to the mouth, the biceps brachii on the anterior forearm is the agonist, the triceps on the posterior is the antagonist and the brachioradialis and brachialis on the anterior are the synergists, helping the biceps brachii to do its work.

Skeletal muscles allow us to perform many body movements. Flexion and extension are movements forward and backward from the body, such as bending and straightening the elbow. Abduction and adduction are side-to-side movements, such as moving the arms laterally when doing star jumps. When we spread our fingers out and look at the palm of our hand that's supination, and when we turn the palm over to look at the back of our hand, that's pronation. Elevation and depression are up-and-down movements e.g. shrugging the shoulders, while moving the jaw back and forth in a jutting motion is protraction and retraction of the mandible. The foot is inverted when it is turned inward to look at the sole and everted to put the sole of the foot back on the ground and turn it laterally (outward) away from the midline.

Some people slightly invert or evert their feet when walking, and this can be noticed on footwear after a while. If the lateral side of the tread appears to be more worn than the medial side, that usually means that more pressure is being exerted on the outside of the foot when that person is walking and/or running, and is an indicator that foot inversion patterns are an issue. With eversion of the foot, the medial side of the tread will appear more worn down. Strengthening the foot inversion and eversion muscles can help stabilise the foot and remedy these issues. Walking on the heels dorsiflexes the feet and plantar flexion is going on tiptoe. Rotation of the head occurs when it is turned from side to side, and circumduction occurs when the arm is swung in a large circle from the shoulder joint. Internal rotation is a very common movement occurring in the shoulder, hip and knee. For example, when the knees are turned towards each other in a standing position, the hips and legs are rotating internally. External rotation is in the opposite direction, so when the knees turn away from each other in a standing position, the hips and legs are being externally rotated.

Contractions of skeletal muscles can be isotonic or isometric. An isotonic contraction is when a muscle shortens, at least one joint moves, and the body moves. The resistance can come from lifting something or from pulling up the body. Isometric muscle contractions such as pushing against a fixed resistance like a doorframe, do not involve any joint or body movement. Even though there is no movement, muscles are still working and contracting. Also known as muscle cramps, spasms occur when a muscle involuntary and forcibly contracts and cannot relax. These are very common, can affect any muscle and usually involve part or all of a muscle, or a group of muscles. The most common sites for muscle spasms are the thighs, calves, foot arches, hands, arms, abdomen and sometimes along the ribcage. When occurring in the calves, they are known as 'charley horses.' They have various causes including insufficient stretching before physical activity, muscle fatigue, exercising in heated temperatures, dehydration and electrolyte imbalances e.g. potassium, magnesium or calcium.

Adhesions can form in muscles, ligaments or tendons, and can even form between a muscle and a nerve causing tingling in the hands or feet. Adhesions act like glue in a muscle preventing it from stretching or contracting properly, and resulting in weaker and less flexible muscles. This can alter the normal function of a joint and cause pain. Adhesions can form from over-use, repetitive actions, and sustained positions like standing and sitting. They can also form from trauma e.g. a car accident, fall or a tear.

All muscle movement is controlled by the nervous system. A conscious impulse to move causes neurons (nerves) within the motor area of the brain to send signals to corresponding parts of the spinal cord. Motor neurons in the spinal cord then carry the signal to the muscles. Nerves communicate with muscles through 'neurotransmitters', which are chemicals stored in the ends (terminals) of the nerves. Electrochemical signals produced in nerves travel towards the nerve terminals, stimulating a neurotransmitter called acetylcholine (ACh) to be released into a tiny gap called the synaptic cleft between the nerve and muscle, thus causing the muscle to move. Calcium, sodium and ATP are also involved in the process of making muscles contract.

Botox (botulinum toxin) - a neurotoxin produced by the bacterium clostridium botulinum - works by disrupting the neurotransmitter release that allows neurons to communicate effectively with muscles. Botox is used medically to treat certain muscular conditions, and cosmetically to reduce the appearance of wrinkles by temporarily paralysing muscles - usually in the face. Botox got its name from 'botulus', the Latin for 'sausage', as it was first discovered in the 18th century in poorly prepared sausages that killed those who ate them by causing respiratory failure. Nowadays botox is synthetically produced in a highly controlled laboratory setting, and administered in tiny amounts by trained professionals. It is often used to treat medical conditions such as excessive sweating, chronic migraine headaches, eyelid spasms, crossed eyes, hypersalivation, dystonia, Bell's palsy and other conditions. Generally, the effects of botulinum toxin therapy wear off after three to four months – this is the case for medical as well as cosmetic purposes. Therefore, it is only a temporary solution for its many different uses.

Muscle tone has been described in a multitude of ways, and a common understanding of the term is the natural and continuous slight contraction of muscles. Even when we are asleep, our muscles maintain a slight degree of tone. Muscle tone prepares the body for action, maintains balance and posture, generates heat that keeps muscles healthy, and allows for a quick, unconscious reaction to any sudden internal or external stimuli. If muscles are not used, they can atrophy (waste) or atony - loss of muscle tone - can set in. Spasticity refers to excessive muscle tone that increases in response to fast stretching of muscles. This muscle tightness results from interruption to the brain and spinal cord's control of movement, and is one of several motor control problems that can occur as a result of brain malformation or injury e.g. cerebral palsy. Treatments include muscle relaxant medication, physical and occupational therapy, surgery e.g. tendon release and botulinum toxin therapy – especially for limb spasticity.

Dystonia is a disorder involving excessive muscle activity and can affect almost any part of the body - even the vocal cords. The disorder can occur at any point from childhood to old age. 'Focal' dystonia affects one part of the body - e.g. neck or head - while 'generalised' dystonia can affect many parts of the body. Signs and symptoms include contractions, cramping, twisting and tremors. Treatments for dystonia include medication, behavioural modification, deep brain stimulation and botulinum toxin therapy.

Keeping fit with exercise can help skeletal muscles strengthen and grow as a result of demands placed upon them. This also applies to facial muscles, which are best exercised rather than being paralysed by Botox! When under the stress of contractions during exercise, the actin and myosin protein filaments within muscle cells shatter and break down. During rest (between workouts) these filaments are repaired back to their pre-workout state. However, the stress also creates a need for the muscle cells to lay down additional protein, so they become better prepared for similar stress levels. The extra protein makes the cells stronger as there are more protein strands working to pull a load. The additional protein also causes the cells to hold more water, thus they thicken and enlarge. This naturally occurring process in which protein is produced to repair muscle damage caused by intense exercise is called 'muscle protein synthesis'. Increasing protein intake immediately following exercise can enhance muscle protein synthesis. The amino acids derived from protein will then be shuttled to the muscles, replacing any lost to exercise. Amino acids, which are covered in detail in Chapter 2, are the building blocks of protein and muscle tissue. They also play a major part in physiological processes relating to energy, recovery, mood and brain function.

During exercise, blood flow to the heart increases as muscle contractions compress veins and assist with blood flow. The heartbeat increases and more blood is circulated, bringing more oxygen to the muscles. With increased demand for energy, glycogen (stored glucose) in the muscles is converted back to glucose and released into the bloodstream. The rate and depth of breathing increases as lactic acid in the blood stimulates the respiratory centre in the brain. If muscles continue to contract without rest, oxygen may run out leading to lactic acid buildup that causes a burning sensation, and the muscles may start to quiver. With rest and deep breathing, a fresh supply of oxygen will stop the production of lactic acid. As lactic acid is water-soluble, the more hydrated the body is, the less likely a person is to feel a burn from lactic acid buildup while exercising. Stretching also helps to release lactic acid, alleviating any burning sensations or muscle cramps. Exercise also has psychological benefits, causing the brain to produce endorphins – body chemicals that act as natural painkillers.

Body types, which are classified as ectomorph, mesomorph and endomorph, can influence how a person responds to exercise, as each body type builds muscle, burns fat and gains muscle tone at different rates. An ectomorph is a typical 'skinny' person with a small body frame and bone structure and lean muscle mass. They find it hard to gain weight and have a fast metabolism that burns up calories quickly. A mesomorph has a large bone structure, large muscles and a naturally athletic physique. They are naturally strong and find it quite easy to gain and lose weight and to build muscle. The endomorph body type is solid, soft and rounded, and they gain fat easily due to a slow metabolism. Endomorphs are usually of a shorter build with thick arms and legs and strong muscles, especially in the upper legs. Many people are a combination of these three body types, and professional fitness trainers should be able to advise on the best exercise regime for each individual.

Although exercising is important for a healthy body, too much exercise, done too quickly, can become a problem. Lifting weights that are too heavy, as well as doing too many repetitions and exercising too quickly without proper warm up and cool down sessions, are the leading causes of muscle injuries. Doing the same motion over and over can damage muscles, tendons and nerves and lead to repetitive strain injury (RSI), the main causes of which are manual labour, office work and the use of modern technological devices.

Injuries caused by muscle overuse are referred to as trauma injuries and there are two categories: macrotrauma are major injuries that usually occur in conjunction with a traumatic or forceful blow or an event such as an accident - e.g. ankle sprain, joint dislocation, ruptured tendons - while microtrauma are smaller and more common muscle injures as a result of overuse. Microtrauma injuries include things like tendonitis and carpal tunnel syndrome - a common microtrauma injury caused by overuse. Shin splints, which manifest as pain along the front of the tibia in runners, golfer's elbow (medial epicondylitis) and tennis elbow (lateral epicondylitis), are more painful options that can have lasting side effects.

Myositis refers to inflammation of muscles, and this can occasionally be caused by overly-vigorous exercise leading to muscle pain (myalgia), inflammation, swelling and weakness that may last for hours or days after a workout. Myositis symptoms after exercise or injury nearly always resolve completely with rest and recovery. More common causes of myositis are viral infections e.g. the common cold or flu, autoimmune conditions e.g. rheumatoid arthritis or lupus, and the side effects of some medications e.g. statins. Treatment of myositis varies according to the cause.

Sprains and strains can sometimes occur due to unduly strenuous or incorrect exercising as well as accidents and injuries. The difference between them is that a sprain injures ligaments - the bands of tissue that connect bones together - while a strain involves an injury to a muscle or tendon - the band of tissue that attaches a muscle to a bone. Sometimes muscle rupture can occur if a muscle is over-strained due to being subjected to a load beyond its strength. This leads to swelling, bruising or redness at the site of injury. The vast majority of ruptures are partial muscle ruptures, which usually occur at the junction between the muscle tendon and the muscle belly, as this is the weakest point. Muscle ruptures in children and adolescents are rare compared with adults. The recommended treatment for strains or ruptures is rest - to allow healing to occur, ice - to reduce swelling and ease pain, compression - to provide support, and elevation - to help swelling go down by raising the inflamed area. (RICE = Rest, Ice, Compression, Elevation)

Over-exercising can release excessive amounts of the hormone cortisol, accelerating the breakdown (catabolism) of a dangerous excess of proteins in the body. It can also cause muscle fatigue, leaving muscles feeling weak, tired and sore. Infections and illnesses e.g. influenza, can also cause temporary muscle fatigue - usually through muscle inflammation. Even though recovery is usual, if the inflammation is severe the weakness can last quite a while. Some health conditions can also prompt muscle fatigue, including muscular dystrophy - a group of inherited diseases that damage and weaken muscles over time due to lack of a protein called dystrophin that is needed for normal muscle function. The absence of this protein can cause problems with walking, swallowing and muscle coordination. There are more than 30 different types of muscular dystrophy that vary in symptoms and severity e.g. Duchenne muscular dystrophy is the most common type among children - mainly boys.

As well as muscle dysfunction due to overuse, stress can have a negative effect on muscle function. Muscle tension can be caused by the physiological effects of stress and can lead to episodes of back pain. Stress can alter the body's nervous system by constricting blood vessels and reducing blood flow to the soft tissues, including muscles, tendons and nerves in the back. This can lead to a decrease in oxygen and a build up of biochemical waste products in the muscles, resulting in muscle tension, spasm and back pain. Muscle tension is usually treated using nonsurgical options to relax the muscles including massage, exercise, water therapy and heat therapy.

Stress also affects the cardiac muscle in the heart and the smooth muscle in blood vessels as it activates the sympathetic nervous system's fight-or-flight response, which is discussed in more detail in Chapter 14. This response is the body's primitive, built-in mechanism for safely escaping a life-threatening emergency. In a state of stress, adrenaline is released, causing the cardiac muscle to work harder as heart rate increases to enable more blood to be pumped to the big muscles needed to run, climb and make our way to physical safety. In turn, the smooth muscle in the walls of certain blood vessels constricts as blood flow is diverted from 'non-essential' organs and systems - e.g. from the liver, brain, reproductive system, urinary system, integumentary system, digestive tract - to the big muscle groups and body systems that are involved in the fight-or-flight response. The blood also clots more easily, so that we don't bleed to death, in case we are injured during our 'escape'.

For short durations, this stress response is most important and potentially life saving, but when it occurs too often or goes on for too long as a result of the frenzy of modern life, we end up in a state of sympathetic nervous system overdrive. Constantly diverting blood flow from the digestive system to major muscle groups leads to improper digestion of food, thereby failing to convert it into nutrients. Certain nutrients like magnesium, which the body uses to run the intracellular machinery that prepares it for combat or escape, can be depleted. The arteries can get worn down from the heart constantly beating harder and faster than it needs to in a normal state.

In prolonged states of stress, cortisol levels in the body increase and this causes a breakdown of muscle protein (catabolism). The amino acids from this broken down protein are released into the bloodstream and are used by the liver to synthesise glucose for energy - a process called gluconeogenesis. This raises blood sugar to ensure the brain has adequate glucose for energy. Cortisol is necessary and plays a role in many functions in the body. However, excesses and deficiencies of cortisol can lead to various physical abnormalities and disease states.

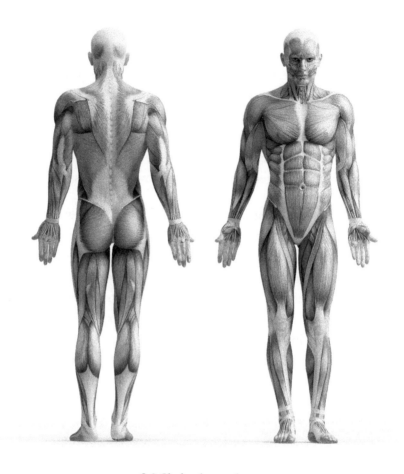

9.3 Skeletal muscles

Skeletal muscles are really the body's 'meat' and are composed of two main types of fibres. Slow twitch fibres are small red fibres that are resistant to fatigue and used for posture and endurance activities. They are packed with blood capillaries and mitochondria, and good for activities like long distance running or cycling, as they can work for a long time without getting tired. Fast twitch fibres are large white fibres suitable for short, fast movements such as punching and throwing. They have very few mitochondria and few blood capillaries and are good for rapid movements like jumping to catch a ball or sprinting, as they contract quickly. They also tire quickly as they consume lots of energy. If you eat chicken you can think of the dark and white meat you find when you cook it. The dark meat in the chicken legs is composed of mainly slow twitch fibres for walking and standing, while the white meat in the wings and breast is largely made up of fast twitch fibres for brief bursts of flight. Most skeletal muscles are composed of a mixture of slow and fast twitch fibres. The calf muscles and muscles of the back involved in maintaining posture contain mainly slow twitch fibres, while arm muscles contain more fast twitch fibres. The muscles that move the eyes are composed mainly of fast twitch fibres.

There are around 200 main skeletal muscles that do the obvious movements of the body, while another 100 or so control movements of the face, hands and feet. About 400 more, such as some tiny facial muscles, tongue muscles, muscles that move the eyeballs and some of the muscles of the pelvic floor, are so small and obscure that only medical specialists ever need to know about them.

In reading the descriptions of skeletal muscles on the following pages, it may be helpful to refer to the relevant muscle anatomy images. You can find clear images in Chris Jarmey's "Concise Book of Muscles" which is listed in the references.

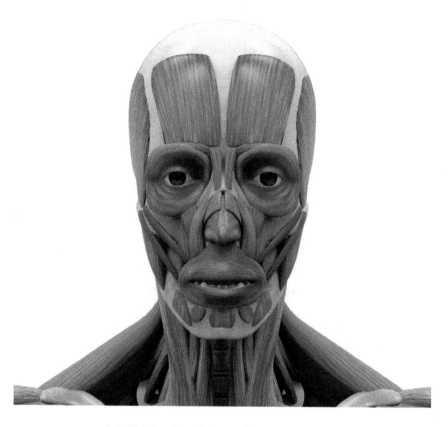

9.4 (1) Muscles of the scalp, neck and face

Here is a brief summary of some important skeletal muscles:

On top of the skull lies a strong tendon called the galea aponeurotica ('galea' means helmet in Latin and 'aponeurotica' means a flat tendon). Attached between this tendon and the skin above the eyes is the frontalis muscle that draws the scalp forward, raises the eyebrows and wrinkles the forehead. At the back of the skull lies the occipitalis muscle between the occipital bone and galea aponuerotica, drawing the scalp backwards. Sometimes these muscles are considered together as the occipitofrontalis. The tiny procerus muscle wrinkles at the bridge of the nose to express disgust, while the corrugator supercili muscles raise the eyebrows and 'corrugate' the brow to express worry, anger or concentration. The circular orbicularis oculi muscles surround the eyes, enabling blinking and closing of the eyes. A tiny muscle on each eyelid - the levator palpebrae - lifts the eyelids to open the eyes.

9.4 (2) Muscles of the scalp, neck and face

On the sides of the nose, the nasalis muscles compress and dilate the nostrils when sniffing or sneezing and the circular orbicularis oris surrounds and closes the mouth and shapes the lips for speech. The zygomaticus muscles run from the zygomatic bones (cheekbones) to the corners of the mouth, drawing upwards when smiling. The levator anguli oris is also involved in drawing back the corners of the mouth, while the levator labii superioris - thin bands of muscle running from eyes to mouth - elevate the upper lip when smirking. The triangular shaped depressor anguli oris muscles (sometimes called the triangularis) pull down the corners of the mouth to express sadness. The buccinator muscles in the cheeks enable sucking and blowing motions, while the risorius muscles draw the corners of the mouth out to the sides when grinning. On the chin, the mentalis muscle pulls the skin up when pouting and turns the lower lip outwards.

The muscles used for chewing are referred to as the muscles of mastication. The most important of these are the strong masseter muscles running from the maxilla (upper jaw) and zygomatic arch (cheekbone arch) to the mandible (lower jawbone), and they can be felt on each side of the jaw when the teeth are clenched. The temporalis muscles that cover the temporal bones above the ears, work with the masseter muscles to open and close the mouth. Both of these muscles can become very tight - especially when a person is stressed - and massage in this area can be very beneficial. The deepest muscles in the cheeks are the wing-shaped pterygoids that raise the mandible and allow it to move from side to side.

The broad, flat platysma covers the front of the neck, depressing the mandible and drawing the lower lip down when pouting. The deep scalene muscles at the sides of the neck are an important part of the neck anatomy, with several important structures such as the subclavian arteries and veins, the phrenic nerve which contracts the diaphragm, and the nerves that run down the arms (brachial plexus) located between and around them. As the scalenes attach to the first and second ribs they assist with respiration and they also help to flex the neck. The rope-like sternocleidomastoid muscles run up the sides of the neck and flex the neck as well as rotating the head. When leaning back to look upwards, the trapezius muscle contracts. This kite-shaped muscle covers the whole of the upper back, from the occipital bone along the cervical and thoracic vertebrae, and also attaches to the clavicle, acromion (highest point on the shoulder blade) and the spine of the scapula. Beneath the trapezius are the rhomboids muscles, running between the spine and the shoulder blades. These muscles often ache due to the long hours many people spend hunched over a computer, and are greatly alleviated by massage.

The muscles of the arm and hand are specifically designed to meet the body's needs for strength, speed and precision while completing many complex daily tasks. Capping the top of each shoulder is the triangular deltoid muscle that contracts when the arm is lifted away (abducted) from the body, while the biceps and triceps of the upper arm enable flexion and extension at the elbow. A small fluid-filled sac called the sub deltoid bursa is located between the shoulder joint and the deltoid muscle, reducing friction in the shoulder and allowing the joint to move more easily. If this bursa becomes inflamed, damaged or irritated, it can lead to deltoid bursitis.

Four deep muscles and their tendons form a nearly complete circle around the shoulder joint, providing strength and stability to keep the humerus in place. These are the 'rotator cuff' muscles - supraspinatus, infraspinatus, teres minor and subscapularis. This is a common site of injury for sports people such as basketball players or shot putters.

Most of the muscles that move the wrist, hand and fingers are located in the forearm. These thin, strap-like muscles extend from the humerus, ulna and radius and insert into the carpals (wrist bones), metacarpals (palm bones), and phalanges (finger bones) via long tendons. The muscles on the anterior forearm - such as the flexor carpi radialis and flexor digitorum superficialis - flex the hand at the wrist as well as flexing each of the phalanges. Golfer's elbow (medial epicondylitis), an irritation on the inner side of the arm and elbow at the origin of the flexor muscles can be caused by any activity that requires repeated twisting or flexing of the wrist such as playing golf.

On the posterior forearm the extensor muscles - such as the extensor carpi ulnaris and extensor digitorum - extend the wrist and fingers. The extensor muscles run in long, thin straps from the humerus to the metacarpals and phalanges. They are generally weaker than the flexor muscles that they work against, as can be felt in the ease of opening a hand compared to gripping something firmly.

Tennis elbow (lateral epicondylitis) is an overuse and muscle strain injury that results in inflammation at the outside of the elbow and forearm where the extensor muscles are attached. With repeated use, the extensor muscles can be overworked, becoming inflamed and painful. Plumbers, carpenters, painters and cooks, as well as tennis players, are prone to tennis elbow due to the repetitive nature of their occupations. Seasonal activities such as raking, gardening and cutting wood can also cause tennis elbow.

The thenar muscles are three short muscles located at the base of the thumb and are responsible for the fine movements of the thumb. The bellies of these muscles produce a bulge, known as the thenar eminence.

Trigger finger and Dupuytren's contracture are problems that can affect the fingers. Trigger finger - also known as stenosing tenosynovitis - occurs due to inflammation of one of the tendons that flex the fingers, causing tenderness and pain. This condition limits movement of the affected finger and can make it difficult to straighten and bend. Gentle stretching and avoiding certain activities that involve bending the finger can help alleviate symptoms.

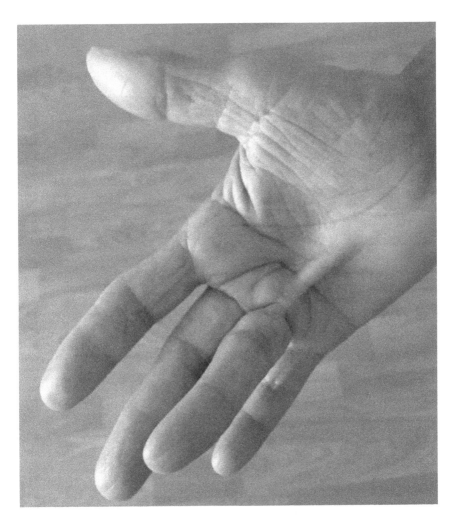

9.5 Dupuytren's contracture

In the case of Dupuytren's contracture, the fascia on the palm of the hand thickens and draws in, causing the affected finger to bend toward the palm and small hard knots can form just under the skin at the base of the finger. The ring and little fingers are most commonly affected and the condition is often painless but uncomfortable. Unlike a finger that is bent due to trigger finger, a finger bent by Dupuytren's contracture is unable to straighten, even with help from the other hand. It is named after French anatomist Guillaume Dupuytren who first described this condition in 1833. Treatment depends on the severity of the condition and can include stretching exercises, heat, ultrasound or a cortisone injection that can help local inflammation. In some cases, surgery may be needed to release and restore function in the affected finger.

A ribbon-shaped group of muscles called the erector spinae - also known as the sacrospinalis group of muscles - runs all the way from the ilium and sacrum bones in the pelvis to the occipital bone at the base of the skull, extending the spine to maintain erect posture. The splenius cervicus and splenius capitis that extend the neck and turn and twist the head when driving are part of this group.

The pectoralis major and minor muscles - commonly referred to as the 'pecs' - are the muscles that create the bulk of the chest. A developed pectoralis major is most evident in males, as the breasts of a female hide these muscles. The pectorals are mainly used to control arm movements, with the contractions of the pectoralis major pulling on the humerus to create lateral, vertical or rotational movements. The pectoral muscles also play a part in deep inhalation by pulling on the ribcage to create room for the lungs to expand.

The muscles of the thoracic wall are mainly involved in breathing, and include the internal and external intercostal muscles that are located in spaces between the ribs. The intercostal muscles help move and stabilise the chest wall during various movements of the trunk. They connect one rib to another and aid in breathing by expanding and contracting the ribs effectively. The diaphragm is a dome-shaped muscle - like an open umbrella - that forms a partition between the thorax and abdomen. It has a central tendon that pulls down during inhalation to increase lung volume, and it relaxes back to its dome shape to push air out of the lungs during exhalation. It has several openings for structures that have to pass from the thorax to the abdomen - these include the oesophagus, aorta and inferior vena cava.

A hiatal/hiatus hernia happens when the upper part of the stomach bulges through the esophageal opening of the diaphragm.

The abdomen - unlike the thorax and pelvis - has no bony reinforcements or protection. The abdominal wall consists entirely of four muscle pairs - often referred to as the 'abs' - arranged in layers along with the fascia that envelops them. The deepest are the transversus abdominus muscles that run horizontally across the abdomen and help to maintain good posture as well as assisting with forced expiration, sneezing and coughing. The internal and external obliques form the next two layers and their fibres run diagonally in opposite directions. They support the abdominal organs and help to bend and rotate the trunk. The topmost layer - the rectus abdominis - is divided into sections by tendinous bands and gives support to the lumbar spine as well as the internal organs. A well-developed rectus abdominis is associated with the 'six pack' muscles seen in conditioned athletes.

The 'linea alba' or white line is the central tendinous band, composed mainly of collagen connective tissue that runs down the midline of the rectus abdominus, from the xiphoid process of the sternum to the pubic symphysis joint between the two pubic bones. The linea alba often darkens during pregnancy in response to hormonal changes, acquiring the name 'linea nigra' or black line. The exact cause of the linea nigra is unknown, but one theory is that melanocyte-stimulating hormone created by the placenta is a contributing factor. This hormone is also believed to cause the darkening around the nipples that occurs during pregnancy.

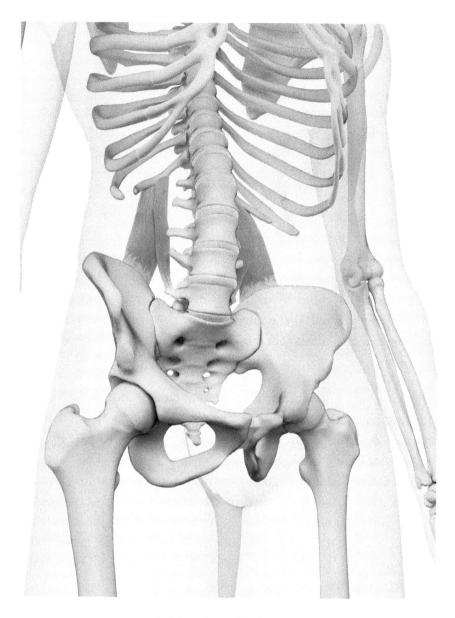

9.6 Quadratus lumborum

The term 'core muscles' refers not just to the abdominal and back muscles, but to all muscles that attach to the spine. When the core muscles are strong, they provide stability to the entire torso. Weakness of the core muscles can lead to excess lumbar curvature (lordosis) and an inability to stabilise the lower back and pelvis when lifting one leg off the ground. The quadratus lumborum (QL) is the deepest core muscle in the abdominal region. It is located in the lower back on either side of the lumbar spine, starting at the lowest rib and ending at the top of the pelvis. It is quite common to have pain here because this muscle is used when sitting, standing and walking, and is regarded as one of the prime sources of lower back pain. Some gentle side stretching while standing or sitting can help stretch the quadratus lumborum. Strong core muscles are important in supporting the digestive organs, and weak abdominal muscles can contribute to hernia occurrence.

A hernia is when an organ or part of an organ is displaced and squeezes through a weak spot in the muscle or tissue that holds it in place. For example, if part of the intestines squeeze through into the groin area, this is called an inguinal hernia - these are more common in men because of a natural weakness in this area. Other types of hernia are incisional (intestine pushes through the abdominal wall at the site of previous abdominal surgery), femoral (outer groin - intestine enters the canal carrying the femoral artery into the upper thigh), umbilical (part of the small intestine passes through the abdominal wall near the navel) and hiatal (when the upper stomach squeezes through the hiatus - an opening in the diaphragm through which the oesophagus passes). Anything that causes an increase in pressure in the abdomen can cause a hernia e.g. lifting heavy objects without stabilising the abdominal muscles, diarrhoea or constipation, persistent coughing or sneezing and obesity.

Two muscular sheets – the levator ani (largest component), the coccygeus muscle and their associated fascia form the pelvic floor. These pelvic floor muscles span the bottom of the pelvis and support the pelvic organs. Having strong pelvic floor muscles gives control over the bladder and bowel. Weakened pelvic floor muscles can mean that internal organs are not fully supported and a person may have difficulty controlling the release of urine, faeces or flatus (wind). Common causes of a weakened pelvic floor include childbirth, obesity and the associated straining of chronic constipation. Pelvic floor exercises are designed to improve muscle tone and prevent the need for corrective surgery.

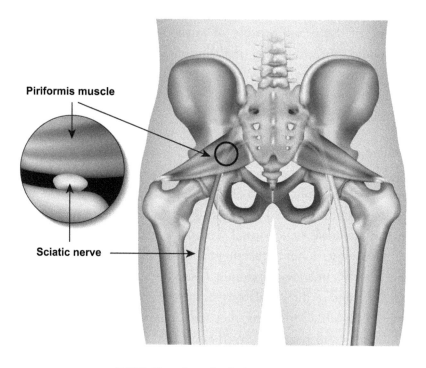

9.7 Piriformis and sciatic nerve

The muscles that move the thigh originate on the pelvis and insert onto the femur. The gluteal muscles (glutes) are three muscles that make up the buttocks: the gluteus maximus, gluteus medius and gluteus minimus. They originate from the ilium and sacrum and insert onto the top of the femur, and aid with standing up from a sitting position, climbing stairs and standing erect. The gluteus maximus, which forms the bulk of each buttock, is also attached to the iliotibial band (IT band or iliotibial tract). This is an elongated strip of fascia

168

extending from the iliac crest down the lateral part of the thigh to a bony projection on the outside of the tibia called the lateral condyle. It contains a small area of muscle called the tensor fascia lata that supports the IT band and helps to stabilise the pelvis. The IT band provides stability to the knee and assists with flexion and extension of the knee joint. Activities that bend the knee repeatedly can sometimes injure the IT band, leading to a nagging pain on the outer part of the knee.

The piriformis is a small muscle located deep in the buttock, beneath the gluteus maximus. It starts at the lower spine and connects to the upper surface of the femur, and helps in rotating the hip and turning the leg and foot outwards. The large sciatic nerve running down each leg travels directly beneath the piriformis, and in some people the nerve can run straight through the muscle. Piriformis syndrome is a condition in which the piriformis muscle goes into spasm causing buttock pain. This can irritate the nearby sciatic nerve and cause pain, numbness and tingling along the back of the leg and into the foot. The best remedy for this is an ice pack or sometimes a heat pack, as well as gentle massage and gentle stretching.

The hip flexors are several muscles that bring the legs and trunk together in a flexion movement. The major hip flexor muscles are the psoas and iliacus - often referred to as the iliopsoas. A small muscle called the pectineus that lies at the top of the inner thigh - often referred to as the groin muscle – also flexes the hip, as does the rectus femoris - one of the four quadriceps muscles. The sartorius is a long, narrow, ribbon-like thigh muscle beginning at the anterior superior iliac spine on the lateral edge of the hip bone, extending obliquely down the front and side of the thigh, and attached to the inner and upper portion of the tibia just below the knee. It helps to flex and rotate the hip and flex the knee e.g. sitting in a cross-legged position. This position was often adopted by tailors who sewed by hand - hence, the sartorius is called the 'tailor's muscle'.

The main action of the quadriceps muscles that are located at the front of the thigh is to straighten the leg at the knee. The Latin translation of 'quadriceps' is 'four headed,' as this group (sometimes referred to as the 'quads') contains four separate muscles: vastus lateralis, vastus medialis, vastus intermedius and rectus femoris. Each of the vastus muscles - which are partially covered by the rectus femoris - originates on the top of the femur, while the rectus femoris originates on the ilium (hipbone).

All four muscles insert into the tibial tuberosity via the patella, where the quadriceps tendon becomes the patellar ligament. The tibial tuberosity is a bony bump on the front of the tibia, just below the knee. Osgood-Schlatter syndrome is a painful knee condition caused by stress on the quadriceps tendon, and manifests as inflammation of the patellar ligament at the tibial tuberosity. It is associated with repeated physical activity involving the quadriceps e.g. football. It mainly affects adolescents and often occurs during a growth spurt. This condition usually resolves with rest, stretches and pain relief.

The hamstrings are three muscles that originate at the ischial tuberosity - the part of the pelvis you can feel when you sit down - and they run along the back of the leg until they connect with the tibia just below the back of the knee. They include the semimembranosus (medial side), biceps femoris (lateral side) and semitendinosus (in the middle). When walking or running, the hamstrings work to extend the hips and flex the knees.

The adductors are a group of thin muscles located along the medial side of the thigh, although they all originate in different places at the front of the pelvis. Their main function is to adduct the femur at the hip joint - when we step into or out of a car, we abduct the first leg and adduct the second one to bring the legs together. The adductor group includes the pectineus, adductor brevis, adductor longus, adductor magnus (the largest one) and the gracilis.

The gracilis, semitendinosus and sartorius (sometimes collectively referred to as the 'guy ropes') form a common tendon called the 'pes anserinus' (meaning 'goose foot') that inserts onto the front inside surface of the proximal tibia. The name 'goose foot' comes from the three-pronged appearance of the conjoined tendon as it inserts onto the tibia. Sitting underneath this conjoined tendon is the pes anserine bursa, a small sac filled with fluid that helps to reduce friction between the tendon and the tibia as the knee moves. Pes anserine bursitis causes inflammation and pain on the inner side of the knee, approximately 2-3 centimetres below the knee joint. It usually develops gradually, and tends to get worse with activities such as stair climbing and running. It commonly affects athletes due to repetitive use, or those who are overweight. It can also be due to tight hamstring muscles, arthritis, or trauma to the area. Rest, application of ice, and/or anti-inflammatory medication may be prescribed to help alleviate this condition. A physical therapist can assess for any areas of weakness and tightness that may be contributing to the problem, and may prescribe stretches, strengthening exercises, or surgery in rare cases.

The front of the shin holds the tibialis anterior, the extensor digitorum longus, the extensor hallucis longus and the peroneus tertius muscles. These muscles pull the toes and feet upwards in dorsiflexion. The tibialis anterior also helps to turn the foot inwards. You can feel these muscles contract by placing your hand just to the outside of your tibia and pulling your foot up. The outside of the lower leg contains the peroneus longus and peroneus brevis muscles that pull the toes and feet outwards. They also help with pointing the foot (plantarflexion). To feel these muscles contract, place your hand on the outside of your shin and turn your foot out.

At the back of the lower leg are the large calf muscles - the gastrocnemius and soleus. The gastrocnemius is shorter and thicker, and is the most visible of the calf muscles. The soleus lies underneath, and in this area there is also a smaller muscle called the plantaris. These three muscles attach to the Achilles tendon and all aid with plantarflexion of the feet. The Achilles tendon is one of the strongest tendons in the body and is crucial in helping to facilitate all movements of the feet. Injuring the Achilles can be one of the most crippling foot injuries and is usually followed by months of rehabilitation. The tendon is named after Achilles, a Greek warrior who was shot in the ankle with an arrow by his enemy Paris, and bled to death. Legend has it that when Achilles was a baby, his goddess mother dipped him in the River Styx – the principal river in the Greek underworld (also called Hades) - to make him immune from death. As she held him by the back of his ankles, that part was not dipped, and so that was his 'Achilles heel' which crafty Paris took advantage of with his arrow. The expression 'Achilles heel' is often used to describe a person's weakness.

Continuous, intense physical activity, such as running and jumping, can cause painful inflammation of the Achilles tendon - known as Achilles tendonitis (or tendinitis). Achilles bursitis is another painful condition that can affect this area. The retro-calcaneal bursa sits between the calcaneus and the Achilles tendon. This small sac of fluid helps the tendon move smoothly over the bone, but repeated trauma through overuse can sometimes cause the bursa to become inflamed. This leads to pain at the back of the heel that tends to get worse during activity. Haglund's deformity is a bony enlargement on the back of the heel. The soft tissue near the Achilles tendon becomes irritated when the bony enlargement rubs against shoes and this can lead to painful bursitis. Haglund's deformity is sometimes called 'pump bump' because the rigid backs of pump-style shoes can create pressure that aggravates the enlargement when walking. It can be hereditary or due to a high-arched foot, a tight Achilles tendon, or a tendency to walk on the outside of the heel. The tibialis posterior, flexor digitorum longus and flexor hallucis longus muscles lie deeper within the back of the lower leg. The tibialis posterior pulls the foot inwards, the flexor digitorum longus flexes four of the toes and the flexor hallucis longus flexes just the big toe. All three of these muscles aid in plantarflexion of the feet.

Achilles Tendon Injuries

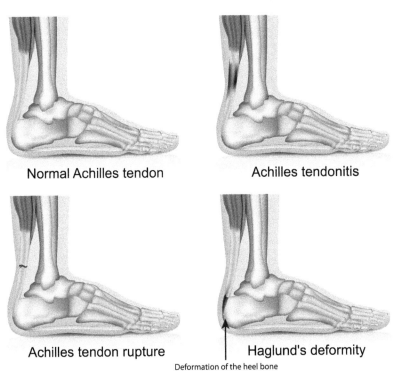

Normal Achilles tendon

Achilles tendonitis

Achilles tendon rupture

Haglund's deformity
Deformation of the heel bone

9.8 Achilles tendon injuries

Plantar fasciitis is a common foot problem where the plantar fascia is pulling on the heel bone, causing inflammation and pain. The plantar fascia is connective tissue that acts as a stabiliser and maintains the integrity of the arch of the foot. It originates at the bottom of the heel bone, is attached to the ball of the foot, and continues forward to insert at the toes. Those affected by plantar fasciitis usually complain of severe pain in the bottom of the heel area, particularly when they take their first few steps of the day, or after they have been off their feet for a prolonged period of time. The pain will often subside after walking for a short while and then return when they sit down for a period of time, but in some cases, the pain is constant.

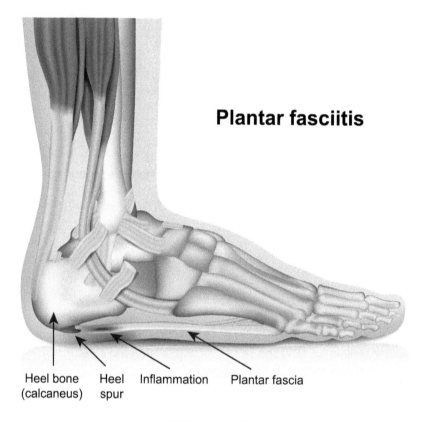

Plantar fasciitis

Heel bone   Heel   Inflammation   Plantar fascia
(calcaneus)   spur

9.9 Plantar fasciitis

Plantar fasciitis has many causes, including an unusual walk or foot position, being flat-footed, having a high foot arch, being obese, spending extended time standing on hard surfaces, or wearing high-heeled shoes. Treatments may include applying ice to the area, remedial exercises, massage therapy, rest, supportive shoes or inserts, or anti-inflammatory medication e.g. cortisone. If other treatments are not working, therapists and body workers with a knowledge of fascia would also consider the 'myofascial lines' – specifically the 'superficial back line' - to see if the problem is being referred from another area of the body. This is a line of muscle and fascia that starts at the plantar surface of each foot and travels up the entire back of the body, moving over the head and finishing at the brow bone. Because all fascia is thought to be connected, pain and/or treatment in one area of the body can have an affect in another area. Other not so common problems that can affect the plantar fascia include plantar fibromas - benign fibrous nodules in the arch of the foot, and plantar fibromatosis (also known as Ledderhose's disease) - a non-malignant thickening of the plantar fascia that can develop from the fibromas. It is thought that the thickened fascia might be a healing response to small tears, almost as if the fascia over-repairs itself following an injury, and there may also be a genetic link.

Cardiac muscle is a specialised type of muscle tissue found only in the heart. It pumps blood and helps regulate blood pressure. Although involuntary, its structure resembles skeletal muscle, but the fibres are shorter than skeletal muscle fibres and usually contain only one nucleus that is located in the central region of each cell. Specialised cardiac muscle cells called pacemaker cells control the contractions of the heart i.e. heartbeats. This specialised bundle of cells - also called the sinoatrial (SA) node or the pacemaker - is located in the upper part of the right atrium and behaves as both muscle and nervous tissue. When the nodal tissue contracts – just like muscle tissue - it generates nerve impulses – just like nervous tissue - that travel throughout the heart wall, causing both atria to contract. Although cardiac muscle cannot be consciously controlled, the pacemaker cells in the SA node respond to signals from the autonomic nervous system to speed up (sympathetic) or slow down (parasympathetic) the heart rate, depending on need. For example, heart rate is increased during exercise to keep up with the increased oxygen demand. A faster heart rate means that blood and oxygen are delivered to muscles at a more rapid rate. When a person stops exercising, heart rate is returned to a level appropriate for normal activity. The pacemaker cells can also respond to various hormones that modulate the heart rate to control blood pressure.

Smooth muscle - also called visceral or involuntary muscle - is found in the walls of all tubes and organs in the body e.g. blood vessels, digestive tract, urinary tract etc. and it contracts to move substances throughout the body as well as regulate organ volume. For example, the process of digestion is controlled by smooth muscle found in the gastrointestinal tract, and the smooth muscle in the urinary system contracts to assist with the process of urination. During pregnancy, the smooth muscle in the uterus grows and stretches as the foetus grows, and during labour it contracts and relaxes to help push the baby out through the vagina. Like cardiac muscle, most visceral muscle is regulated by the autonomic nervous system and is under involuntary control. Visceral muscle is called 'smooth' because it doesn't have the cross striations or stripes of actin and myosin like the other types of muscle tissue. It contracts slower than skeletal muscle, but the contractions can be sustained over a longer period of time.

Many muscular disorders are referred to as musculoskeletal disorders, as they also affect the skeletal system. An example is adhesive capsulitis or frozen shoulder that occurs when tissues in the shoulder tighten and swell. The swollen tissues cause pain and decrease shoulder movement, as if the shoulder were frozen – but no ice is involved! Signs and symptoms begin gradually, worsen over time and then resolve, usually within one to three years. Risk factors include recovering from a medical condition or procedure that prevents moving the arm e.g. a stroke or mastectomy. Treatment involves range-of-motion exercises and sometimes corticosteroids or numbing medications injected into the joint capsule. In a small percentage of cases, arthroscopic surgery may be needed to loosen the joint capsule so that it can move more freely. Some people can develop the condition in the opposite shoulder, but it's unusual for it to recur in the same shoulder.

Fibromyalgia is another common musculoskeletal condition that is often misdiagnosed and misunderstood. Doctors aren't sure what causes it, but some think it's a problem with how the brain and spinal cord process pain signals from the nerves. It is more common in females, and the classic symptoms are widespread muscle and joint pain with fatigue. Other symptoms include burning, twitching, tightness, low pain threshold, tender points, trouble concentrating and remembering, and insomnia or restless sleep. It often accompanies mood disorders like anxiety or depression, or another painful condition such as arthritis. There is no cure, but a combination of medication, exercise, stress management and healthy lifestyle habits may ease symptoms enough that sufferers can live a normal, active life.

All muscles are controlled by nerves, and neuromuscular disorders involving the nervous and muscular systems often affect the eyes or mouth, causing drooping eyelids, double vision, slurred speech, difficulty swallowing, or sometimes difficulty breathing. Neuromuscular disorders can cause problems with the nerves that control muscles, the muscles themselves, or the communication between nerves and muscles. These disorders generally cause muscles to become weak or to atrophy, as well as symptoms such as spasms, twitching and pain. Muscular dystrophy, which has already been covered in this chapter, is one such disorder. Another example is myasthenia gravis, an autoimmune disease that causes weakness in voluntary muscles e.g. the muscles for eye movement, facial expressions and swallowing, as well as other muscles.

Keeping the muscular system healthy so that it can function properly is extremely important for wellbeing, and the best ways to accomplish this is through regular appropriate exercise, a healthy, balanced diet, adequate water intake, and injury prevention measures. With any exercise programme, it is important to obtain professional advice, start slowly, increase intensity in small increments, and incorporate rest periods to allow muscles to repair. A special diet is not needed to ensure muscle health, and a well-balanced diet should provide sufficient nutrients. Drinking adequate amounts of water is vital for the health of muscles as well as overall health. Dehydration can lead to dizziness, headaches and muscle cramps. An easy way to ensure that you consume enough water daily is to carry a reusable water bottle and sip regularly.

Muscular injuries are extremely common but can be prevented by taking a few simple precautions. Warming up before exercise will help increase flexibility, and cooling down after exercise will help relax and loosen muscles that have been tightened during exercise. Wearing protective gear during competitive sports or activities that have a level of risk involved will help prevent injury to muscles and other body parts. When a muscle strain or injury does occur, be patient and give the body time to heal and repair the damage.

10. The Cardiovascular System

The cardiovascular system consists of the heart and blood vessels – arteries, capillaries and veins.

The main functions of the cardiovascular system are to carry oxygen from the air and nutrients from food to all body cells, and assist in removing waste products from the body. Blood is classified as a liquid connective tissue and has a pH of 7.4 (slightly alkaline). The function of blood is to transport oxygen, nutrients, hormones and other chemicals around the body, as well as transport waste materials to the organs of excretion. It also helps fight infection through the action of white blood cells and antibodies.

Plasma fluid makes up 55% of blood and consists of water (90%) and plasma proteins e.g. fibrinogen for blood clotting, albumin for osmotic pressure and antibodies for immunity. The remaining 45% of blood is made up of cells. The amount of blood in the human body is generally equivalent to 7% of body weight – around 5.5 litres for an average adult.

When blood is centrifuged it separates into red blood cells that sink to the bottom, white blood cells and platelets above that and plasma on top. All blood cells start out as hematopoietic stem cells and later differentiate into various blood cell types. The process of producing blood cells from hematopoietic stem cells is called hematopoiesis. Hematopoietic stem cells generate two lineages of blood cells known as myeloid lineage cells and lymphoid lineage cells and these will be covered in more detail in the next chapter on the lymphatic system and immunity.

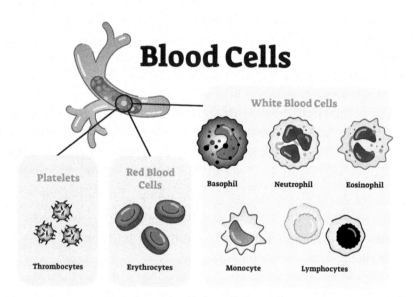

10.1 Blood cell types

Red blood cells make up around 40% of the blood. They produce haemoglobin that carries oxygen from the lungs to body tissues and carbon dioxide back to the lungs. Red blood cells are formed in bone marrow and both sides of the cell's surface curve inward like the interior of a sphere. This shape aids in a red blood cell's ability to manoeuvre through tiny blood vessels, delivering oxygen to organs and tissues. When oxygen levels in the blood begin to fall, the kidneys secrete a hormone called erythropoietin (EPO) that signals the bone marrow to increase production of red blood cells. Red blood cells live about 120 days and are broken down in the spleen and liver by phagocytes. Parts of the red blood cells are recycled into iron for new haemoglobin, amino acids to make proteins, bilirubin for bile pigment, and the final waste is excreted in faeces and urine.

Anaemia is defined as a low number of red blood cells and therefore low haemoglobin levels, so tissues and organs may not get enough oxygen. Symptoms of anaemia include dizziness, weakness, pale skin, cold hands and feet, headache and fast or unusual heartbeat. There are many types of anaemia and they're divided into three main groups: anaemia caused by blood loss, anaemia caused by decreased or faulty red blood cell production, and anaemia caused by destruction of red blood cells - also known as hemolytic anaemia. Thalassemia is an inherited form of anaemia characterised by reduced or absent amounts of haemoglobin, and usually affects people of Mediterranean, African, Middle Eastern and Southeast Asian descent. This condition can range from mild to life threatening. Sickle cell anaemia is an inherited disorder that mainly affects people of African ancestry. The red blood cells that are usually round become crescent-shaped and break down quickly, so oxygen doesn't get to the organs. The crescent-shaped red blood cells can also get stuck in tiny blood vessels and cause pain.

Iron-deficiency anaemia is due to a lack of iron in the body. Iron is needed for the bone marrow to make haemoglobin that carries oxygen. Vitamin-deficiency anaemia can happen due to a lack of vitamin B12 and folate (B9), both of which are needed to make red blood cells. Those who eat little or no meat may not get enough vitamin B12, and those who overcook or don't eat enough vegetables might not get enough folate. Pernicious anaemia can occur when the body doesn't absorb enough vitamin B12, usually due to lack of a protein called intrinsic factor (IF) needed to absorb vitamin B12. IF is a protein produced by cells in the stomach and it binds with B12, enabling it to be absorbed in the small intestine. In most cases of pernicious anaemia, the body's immune system attacks and destroys the cells that produce IF in the stomach. If these cells are destroyed, the body can't make IF and can't absorb vitamin B12 found in foods. The disease is usually treated with B12 injections or supplements. Without enough vitamin B12, the body may produce abnormally large red blood cells called macrocytes that may have difficulty leaving the bone marrow and entering the bloodstream. This decreases the amount of oxygen-carrying red blood cells in the bloodstream and can lead to fatigue and weakness.

White blood cells (WBC) - also called leucocytes - are larger and fewer than red blood cells. White blood cells have a nucleus and irregular shape. They protect the body and can reproduce by mitosis in cases of infection. A WBC count is a test that measures the number of white blood cells in the body, and is often included with a complete blood count (CBC). There are several types of white blood cells, and blood usually contains a percentage of each type. Sometimes the white blood cell count can fall or rise out of the healthy range, and this may indicate an underlying medical condition. A WBC count can detect hidden infections within the body and alert doctors to undiagnosed conditions such as autoimmune diseases, immune deficiencies and blood disorders. This test also helps doctors monitor the effectiveness of chemotherapy or radiation treatment in people with cancer.

There are about 500 to 1000 red blood cells for each white cell circulating in the blood, but this number fluctuates depending on the need to defend against infections and whether the cells are moving in and out of the circulation to reach inflamed tissues. There are two main types of white blood cells - granulocytes with small granules in their cytoplasm and non-granular leucocytes (agranulocytes) with no granules.

Granules are tiny sacs containing various enzymes and other components that are used to defend against pathogens, reduce inflammation and destroy certain cells. What the granules are filled with or used for depends on the specific type of granular leucocyte. There are three types of granulocytes defending the body against bacteria, viruses and other pathogens, and forming about 75% of the body's white blood cells. The specific types of granulocytes are neutrophils, eosinophils and basophils. Their numbers increase when there is a serious infection in the body and they can move through capillary walls into tissues.

Neutrophils account for 60-70% of granulocytes and help prevent infections by blocking, disabling, digesting or warding off invading particles and microorganisms. Eosinophils account for 2-4% of granulocytes and are mainly responsible for helping to break down blood clots and releasing chemicals that can kill parasites - especially parasitic worms. Their granules also contain histamine that is released in response to a pathogen entering the system. Basophils make up less than 1% of white blood cells at any given time. They contain heparin, a naturally occurring blood-thinning substance that prevents blood clotting. Basophils also release histamine from mast cells during allergic reactions. Histamine plays a major role in many allergic reactions, dilating blood vessels and making the vessel walls abnormally permeable, which allows fluid and white blood cells from the bloodstream out into the tissues, causing swelling. Histamine is part of the body's allergic response to substances such as pollens. Antihistamines work by preventing the release of histamine and blocking the allergic reaction.

Monocytes and lymphocytes are two main types of non-granular leucocytes (agranulocytes). Monocytes make up 2-8% of all leucocytes in the blood. They're usually quite large, which helps with their main function of phagocytosis – the eating up of pathogens, old blood cells, cellular debris and dead cells. They also secrete chemicals that bring other types of leucocytes to an area that needs help e.g. an area of infection or a wound.

Lymphocytes make up 20-30% of total leucocytes. They originate from stem cells in bone marrow, but some travel to the thymus gland where they become T cells, and others remain in the bone marrow where they become B cells. The job of B cells is to make antibodies, which are proteins produced by the immune system to fight foreign substances known as antigens. Each B cell is programmed to make one specific antibody, and each antibody matches an antigen, like a key matching a lock. Antibodies have two ends - one end sticks to proteins on the outside of white blood cells and the other end sticks to the germ or damaged cell and helps to kill it. The end of the antibody that sticks to the white blood cell is always the same, and is called the constant end. The end of the antibody that recognises germs and damaged cells varies, depending on the cell it needs to recognise, so it is called the variable end. There are different types of B cells and each type makes antibodies with a different variable end from other B cells. Memory B cells are a B cell sub-type that are formed following primary infection. They can remain in the body for decades, remembering previously found antigens and helping the immune system by starting a fast antibody response when they find an antigen they have encountered before. Regulatory B cells make up around 0.5% of B cells in healthy people. They have protective anti-inflammatory effects in the body by stopping lymphocytes that cause inflammation e.g. in autoimmune conditions. They also interact with several other immune cells and promote the production of regulatory T cells that do a similar job.

The job of T cells is to help the body kill cancer cells and control the immune response to foreign substances. They do this by destroying cells in the body that have become cancerous or been taken over by viruses. Killer or cytotoxic T cells scan the surface of cells in the body to see if they have become infected with germs or if they have turned cancerous, and they kill these cells. Helper T cells assist other cells in the immune system to start and control the immune response against foreign substances. Regulatory/suppressor T cells control or suppress other cells in the immune system. They maintain tolerance to germs and help to prevent autoimmune diseases by suppressing the immune response so it does not destroy normal cells once its job is done. But sometimes they can also suppress the immune system from doing its job against certain antigens and tumours. Memory T cells – just like memory B cells - protect the body against previously found antigens. They live for a long time after an infection is over, helping the immune system to remember previous infections. If the same germ enters the body a second time, memory T cells remember it and quickly multiply, helping the body to fight it faster.

A third type of lymphocyte known as a natural killer (NK) cell, is best known for killing virally infected cells and detecting and controlling early signs of cancer. NK cells (both B & T) kill infected or cancerous cells by releasing two types of chemicals. Perforins create small pores on the cell's surface, then enzymes known as granzymes pass through the pores into the cell, stimulating the release of further enzymes that kill the cell by apoptosis - programmed cell death.

Platelets – also called thrombocytes - are small disc-shaped fragments with no nucleus. They break off from large cells called megakaryocytes that mature and remain in the bone marrow. As the platelets break off they enter the blood stream, and when an injury or bleeding occurs the platelets change shape and stick together to form a clot. Blood clot formation, also known as haemostasis, is the body's way of stopping blood loss from the vascular system. Damage that is unable to be stopped by clot formation is referred to as a haemorrhage.

Vascular spasm is the first stage in the sophisticated process of blood clotting. When a blood vessel is damaged or cut, vascular spasms of the smooth muscle within the vessel wall lead to vasoconstriction, which stops or reduces the flow of blood. Vasoconstriction can last for up to 30 minutes and only affects the area that is hurt. In the platelet stage, collagen fibres that usually lie under the endothelial cells lining the blood vessel are exposed, and platelets stick to them. The platelets clump together and release various chemicals that attract more platelets to the site forming a platelet plug that seals the injury. The coagulation stage is the third and final stage of blood clotting, whereby other substances reinforce platelets in order to ensure the damaged area does not allow blood to ooze out of the damaged vessel. These substances are called clotting or coagulation factors, and they work together in a series of complex chemical reactions - known as the coagulation cascade - to form a fibrin clot that acts like a mesh to stop the bleeding. After two to three days, the area will be completely sealed, making it almost impossible for further haemorrhage to take place.

There are 13 coagulation factors in all, and they are named after those who discovered them. They circulate in the blood in an inactive form, but when a blood vessel is injured and the coagulation cascade is initiated, each coagulation factor is activated in a specific order to lead to the formation of a blood clot.

Hemophilia is a rare genetic disorder in which the blood doesn't clot normally because it lacks sufficient blood clotting factors. Small cuts aren't usually a major problem, but a severe deficiency can cause deep internal bleeding that can damage organs and tissues, and may be life threatening. Treatment includes regular replacement of the specific clotting factor that is reduced. Thrombocytopenia is a condition in which the blood has a lower than normal number of platelets, leading to a risk of excessive bleeding. It can have various causes including bone marrow cancer that destroys megakaryocytes, chemotherapy, excessive alcohol intake, or genetic causes. Blood clots are healthy and lifesaving when they stop bleeding, but they can also form when they aren't needed and cause a heart attack, stroke, or other serious medical problems. In cases like this, anticoagulant (blood thinning) drugs may be prescribed to prevent blood clot formation.

Anna Aksenova, a senior research associate at the Laboratory of Amyloid Biology at St Petersburg University, has advanced a hypothesis that the severe course of COVID-19 in some individuals may be associated with the von Willebrand coagulation factor (VWF).

186

As the researcher suggests, the replication of the virus stimulates the development of micro-damage on blood vessel walls. In its response to this, the body releases VWF into the blood, trying to 'patch' possible holes, but as a result, the risk of thrombosis increases. It is with this clotting process that a significant number of deaths from COVID-19 are associated, and Aksenova says: "Excessive production of VWF can lead to the development of thrombosis, including in the capillaries of the lungs." She also notes that this hypothesis explains why the drug chloroquine (which is usually used to treat malaria) used in preliminary trials has also shown efficacy in COVID-19 treatment. Chloroquine affects the process of autophagy in cells i.e. the cleaning out of any unnecessary or damaged components, and this process regulates the secretion of certain factors, including the secretion of VWF. The attention of researchers worldwide is now starting to focus on VWF, its role in COVID-19, and new treatment regimens that will take into account the individual characteristics of the human body associated with VWF. For example, ways to reduce the amount of VWF in blood plasma for the treatment of COVID-19 complications is now being discussed in scientific literature.

Infection can spread throughout the body in the bloodstream, leading to a serious condition called sepsis. The terms 'sepsis' and 'septicemia' are sometimes used interchangeably, but their definitions are different. Both come from the Greek word, 'sepsin', which means 'poison in putrid blood.' Sepsis is an extreme inflammatory response to infection, where the immune system is responding to an infection by releasing chemical messengers that produce inflammation throughout the body. The infection can be due to bacteria in the bloodstream, but sepsis can also be produced by an infection in one part of the body - such as pneumonia in the lungs. The inflammation in sepsis can produce blood clots and leaking blood vessels. Without treatment, this can cause damage to body organs, and may progress to septic shock with a severe drop in blood pressure and body systems starting to shut down. Signs and symptoms of sepsis include mental confusion, rapid breathing, fever, chills and warm skin. Sepsis is an emergency requiring prompt medical attention. Elderly people, babies, young children, people with weakened immune systems and those with long-term chronic illnesses are most at risk from sepsis. Septicemia - sometimes referred to as blood poisoning - is defined as having bacteria in the bloodstream that cause sepsis.

Experiments with blood transfusions - the transfer of blood or blood components into a person's blood stream - have been carried out for hundreds of years. In the past, many patients died in the process, and it was not until 1901 when Austrian-born biologist, Karl Landsteiner discovered human blood groups, that blood transfusions became safer. Landsteiner discovered that there are different types of human blood and he called these 'blood groups'. He found that there are substances in blood - antigens and antibodies - that induce clumping of red blood cells when red cells of one type are added to those of a second type. This blood clumping or 'agglutination' can cause the red blood cells to crack, releasing toxins that can lead to fatal consequences. Landsteiner carried out his experiments using samples of blood from colleagues, along with his own blood. He cross-tested the serum of blood with the red cells of the blood donors and observed that the red blood cells did not react with their own serum, but when the serum of one donor was combined with another donor's red blood cells, the red blood cells clumped together. Landsteiner discovered that this 'blood clumping' was an immunological reaction that occurs when the receiver of a blood transfusion has antibodies against the donor blood cells. In this way, he developed the ABO blood group system. If you have 'A' 'B' or 'O' blood group, you will have antibodies in your blood plasma that destroy some of the other blood groups. Those with blood group 'A' have 'A' antigens on the surface of red blood cells and 'B' antibodies in blood plasma, so they cannot receive blood that is group 'B' and vice versa. Those who belong to the blood group 'O' have neither 'A' or 'B' antigens on the surface of red blood cells but have both 'A' and 'B' antibodies in blood plasma, so will create antibodies to fight 'A' or 'B' blood. In 1902, the fourth blood type -'AB' - was discovered, and those with this blood group do not create antibodies for any of the other blood groups. For his discovery, Landsteiner was awarded a Nobel Prize in 1930.

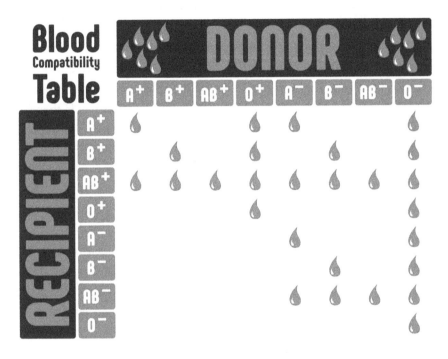

10.2 Blood donation chart

In 1940, Landsteiner and a colleague discovered another blood group - the 'Rh' system. 'Rh' stands for rhesus, which comes from the name of the monkey in which they discovered this blood group. Your Rh status will be listed as negative (-) or positive (+). If you have Rh- blood, your body may form antibodies against Rh+ blood and destroy it. In order for this to happen, you must first be exposed to Rh+ blood i.e. through a blood transfusion or carrying an Rh+ foetus. This can be a problem if you have antibodies against Rh+ blood and are pregnant with an Rh+ foetus. There is medication that can prevent this reaction from occurring if given immediately after you are exposed to Rh+ blood.

The immune system recognises its own blood group and knows not to wage war against it. When a blood antigen is present that your immune system does not recognize as 'self', it causes an immune response. This response can be extremely serious, causing internal blood clotting, kidney failure and even death. Type O negative blood is considered the universal blood type. People with type O negative blood are called universal donors, because type O negative blood is compatible to any blood recipient's type. People with type AB positive blood are considered universal blood recipients. The reason is that AB positive blood types do not make antibodies against the ABO blood groups. Those with AB negative blood type can receive red blood cells from all negative blood types. Blood group AB is very rare and although AB blood types are able to receive any type of blood, they are only able to donate blood to those that are blood group AB.

As well as donating blood, a person can also donate plasma. In this process the blood is collected by a machine, which further separates the blood components – plasma, red cells and platelets, to return the red cells and platelets back to the donor later. If a person wants to become a blood or blood plasma donor, they have to undergo a safety check, which includes testing for diseases that can be transmitted by a blood transfusion, such as HIV virus or viral hepatitis.

People who have recovered from COVID-19 have antibodies in their blood that may help treat people who have contracted the virus, and many patients have received plasma treatment for COVID-19. Some of the elements in plasma, including the antibodies and chemicals that help blood to clot, can help in medical emergencies like burns and trauma, and plasma products are also used to treat some cancer patients. Platelets can also be donated, and in this case the platelets are collected and the remaining blood components are returned to the donor. Platelets help blood to clot, and the donated platelets can be given to patients with leukemia, people receiving chemotherapy and babies with severe infections.

Blood vessels widen (dilate) and narrow (constrict) due to body temperature conditions. For example, when body temperature rises, blood vessels in the skin dilate to release heat - this is why the face can get red when working out. Sweat is also released from sweat glands onto the skin where it evaporates and cools the skin. When the body gets too cold, blood vessels in the skin constrict, sending blood inside the body to keep the vital organs warm, and so the face becomes paler. Shivering warms up the muscles and this in turn warms up the blood flowing through the muscles, which then travels to the rest of the body.

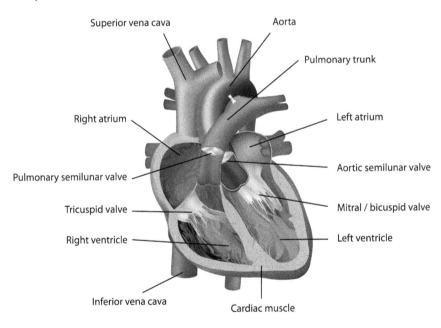

10.3 Anatomy of the heart

The heart pumps blood around the body in arteries and veins, making a complete circuit in about one minute. The heart lies between the lungs in the thoracic cavity - in an area called the mediastinum - and is under the control of the autonomic nervous system (involuntary). The heart wall has 3 layers: the inner endocardium is similar to the endothelial lining of blood vessels. The myocardium is the thicker, middle layer, composed of cardiac muscle tissue that contracts to pump blood. The outer pericardium is a two-layered membrane with fluid between the layers. The outer layer anchors the heart to the mediastinum and the inner layer of the pericardium is attached to and covers the heart. The heart is divided into four chambers - the two upper chambers that receive blood are called atria (s=atrium) and the two lower chambers are the ventricles that pump blood out of the heart. The left and right sides of the heart are divided by a septum (wall) that prevents mixing of blood between the two sides. Some babies are born with a hole in their heart septum, which can be in the upper walls between the atria – an atrial septal defect (ASD) - or in the lower walls between the ventricles – a ventricular septal defect (VSD). Depending on the size of the hole, symptoms can be trivial and may not cause problems, or it may be serious and require immediate medical attention.

There are valves that separate the ventricles from the atria to prevent the backflow of blood – the tricuspid valve between the right atrium and right ventricle and the bicuspid or mitral valve between the left atrium and left ventricle. There are also aortic and pulmonary semi-lunar valves that separate the ventricles from the aorta (on the left) and pulmonary trunk (on the right) to prevent backflow of blood. Problems with the heart valves can sometimes occur e.g. insufficiency is when a valve fails to close completely and permits a blood backflow.

Stenosis is thickened tissue that narrows the valve opening and limits the amount of blood that can pass through. Aortic stenosis can develop later in life and mostly affects older people. A mitral valve prolapse (MVP) is a condition in which the flaps of the mitral valve stretch, causing part of the valve to slips backwards loosely into the left atrium when the heart contracts. This can lead to a leakage of blood backwards through the mitral valve into the left atrium and may cause pressure and fluid volume to build, increasing pressure in the pulmonary veins leading from the lungs to the heart. However, many people with mitral valve prolapse have no symptoms.

Cardiomyopathy is a general term for diseases of the heart muscle. Depending on the type of cardiomyopathy, the condition may cause the heart muscle to become enlarged, rigid, thick or thin. In rare cases, the normal muscle tissue of the heart is replaced with scar tissue. Endocarditis is an infection of the endocardium – i.e. the inner lining of the heart chambers and heart valves. Endocarditis generally occurs when bacteria, fungi or germs from another part of the body spread through the bloodstream and attach to damaged areas in the heart. If not treated quickly, endocarditis can damage or destroy the heart valves and may lead to life-threatening complications. Treatments for endocarditis include antibiotics, and in certain cases, surgery.

The pulmonary circulation refers to the flow of blood to and from the lungs, while the systemic circulation refers to the movement of blood to and from body tissues and organs. The flow of blood through the heart is as follows: deoxygenated blood from the body enters the heart via the superior and inferior vena cava into the right atrium. The blood flows through the tricuspid valve into the right ventricle and then through the pulmonary semi-lunar valve into the pulmonary trunk. The pulmonary trunk divides into the left and right pulmonary arteries carrying the blood on to the lungs for oxygenation - you can read more about this process in Chapter 12.

The oxygenated blood returns from the lungs in the pulmonary veins that enter the left atrium, and then flows through the bicuspid valve into the left ventricle. From the left ventricle, it flows through the aortic semi-lunar valve into the aorta, which carries the bright red, oxygenated blood around the body.

Human Circulatory System

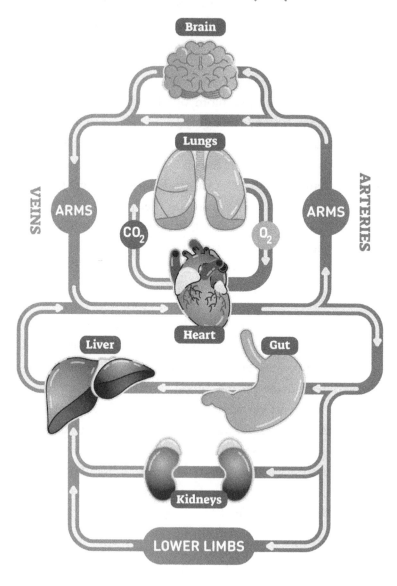

10.4 Blood circulation

After leaving the left ventricle of the heart, the aorta splits to form smaller arteries supplying all areas of the body. Arteries are tough on the outside, but contain a smooth interior layer of endothelial cells that allow blood to flow easily. Arteries also contain a strong, muscular middle layer (of smooth muscle) that helps pump blood through the body. The arteries branching from the aorta divide further to form smaller arterioles, and then branch out into capillaries with walls only one cell thick. Oxygen, nutrients and fluid (plasma) exit through the capillary walls and enter body cells, while the capillaries pick up waste products such as carbon dioxide and some excess fluid. Capillaries permeate all body organs and are so tiny that red blood cells have to flow through them in single file. If all the capillaries in the average human body were stretched out in a line, it would measure over 100,000 miles. Capillaries are most abundant in tissues and organs that are metabolically active e.g. muscle tissue and the kidneys have a greater amount of capillary networks than do connective tissues. After oxygen and nutrients have been delivered to the tissues and carbon dioxide and some waste has been picked up, this leads to a change in the colour of the blood, which now appears blue rather than bright red due to the loss of oxygen. The capillaries then unite to form small veins (venules) that eventually merge into larger veins.

Veins are similar to arteries but not as strong or as thick. Unlike arteries, veins contain valves that ensure blood flows in only one direction. Arteries don't require these valves because pressure from the heart is so strong that blood is only able to flow in one direction. The venous valves also help blood travel back to the heart against the force of gravity. Eventually all veins from the upper and lower body merge into the superior and inferior vena cava, two large veins entering the right atrium of the heart. From here the deoxygenated blood flows through the tricuspid valve into the right ventricle and out through the pulmonary semi-lunar valve to the pulmonary trunk, which splits into the right and left pulmonary arteries carrying the deoxygenated blood to the lungs. Carbon dioxide is exchanged for oxygen in the lungs and the oxygenated blood returns to the left side of the heart in the left and right pulmonary veins. The pulmonary arteries are the only arteries in the body carrying deoxygenated blood, and the pulmonary veins are the only veins carrying oxygenated blood.

Arteries and veins are usually named according to the region of the body in which they flow and their names change as they travel along. For example, the brachial, radial and ulnar arteries and veins are in the upper and lower arms. The left and right common iliac arteries originate from the abdominal aorta - the main blood vessel in the abdominal area - and split into the internal and external iliac arteries near the ilium bone of the pelvis. The internal iliac arteries provide blood to the pelvic organs including the bladder, the prostate gland in males and the uterus and vagina in females. The external iliac arteries provide the main blood supply to the legs. They become the femoral arteries and branch off as the popliteal arteries around the knees, and further down as the anterior and posterior tibial arteries. The femoral arteries supply blood to the thighs, the popliteal arteries supply the knee areas, and the anterior and posterior tibial arteries supply the areas below the knees - including the feet and toes. There are also similarly named veins in the same regions, carrying blood back to the heart.

The subclavian arteries supply blood to the shoulders, arms, back, chest wall and central nervous system. Branching from the subclavian arteries are the vertebral arteries carrying blood to the brain and spinal cord. These arteries enter the skull through the 'foramen magnum', a large opening in the occipital bone through which the spinal cord passes. They join at the base of the brain to form the basilar artery. From there the basilar artery provides blood to the back of the brain, including the brainstem, cerebellum, and cerebrum.

The left and right carotid arteries that branch from the aorta pass close to the trachea (where a pulse can be felt), and then divide in the neck to form the left and right internal carotid arteries as well as the left and right external carotid arteries. At the point where they divide, they swell slightly to form a space called the 'carotid sinus'. Receptors that help control blood pressure are located here. The internal carotid arteries pass into the skull below the brain through the left and right carotid foramina (small holes in skull bone). At the base of the brain, the internal carotid arteries branch off and become the left and right anterior cerebral arteries and the left and right middle cerebral arteries that supply blood to the front and middle of the brain. The occipital artery arises from the internal carotid artery and supplies blood to the back of the scalp. The external carotid artery supplies many tissues of the head through numerous branches such as the superior thyroid artery and the facial artery.

Several arteries are involved in supplying blood to the brain, forming a circle called the 'circle of Willis' - named after Thomas Willis (1621–1675), an English physician. This circular formation helps to equalise blood pressure to various parts of the brain and provides alternative routes for blood to enter the brain, which is important if any of the arteries are damaged. Although the brain is only about 2% of the total body weight in humans, it receives 15-20% of the body's blood supply. Because the brain requires a constant supply of oxygen and glucose, the arteries carrying blood to the brain are among the most important in the body. Any interruption in blood flow to the brain quickly results in a decline of mental function, loss of consciousness, and eventually death if not corrected. Lack of oxygen to the brain can cause permanent brain damage in as little as four minutes. Another four to six minutes without the brain receiving blood can result in increased brain damage, coma and death. However there have been cases of cold-water immersions where people were under water for a very long time e.g. almost an hour, and they were revived with no long-term problems! In order to reduce the chances of permanent brain damage in a person who is unconscious, cardiopulmonary resuscitation (CPR) should be performed until their breathing and heartbeat return, or until qualified medical help arrives. This emergency procedure consists of external cardiac massage and artificial respiration, and is something that everyone should learn.

All the smaller veins of the head and neck region drain into three pairs of veins. These are the internal and external jugular veins and the vertebral veins. Many of the veins have the same names as arteries leading into the head and neck - although there are a few differences. The three pairs of veins collecting blood from the head and neck all lead to the brachiocephalic vein. The right and left brachiocephalic veins unite to form the superior vena cava carrying de-oxygenated blood to the right atrium of the heart.

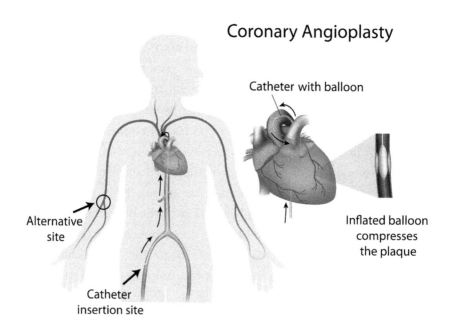

Coronary Angioplasty

Catheter with balloon

Alternative site

Catheter insertion site

Inflated balloon compresses the plaque

10.5 Coronary angioplasty

The coronary circulation refers to the collection of coronary arteries, capillaries and associated veins that circulate blood to and from the heart itself - especially the myocardium - the main pumping muscle mass of the heart. A coronary artery bypass graft (CABG) is a surgical procedure used to divert blood around narrow or clogged arteries due to coronary artery disease - a serious condition caused by a buildup of plaque in the arteries that can lead to ischaemic heart disease where less blood and oxygen is reaching the heart muscle. If cardiac ischaemia lasts too long, the starved heart tissue dies. This is a heart attack, otherwise known as a myocardial infarction - literally, 'death of heart muscle'. A new blood vessel (graft) is attached from the aorta to a point in the coronary artery beyond the blockage. The graft(s) can be created from blood vessels taken from the chest wall, leg or arm. The newly grafted vessel improves blood flow and oxygen supply to the heart.

A coronary angioplasty is a procedure using a tiny balloon catheter that is inserted in a blocked coronary artery to widen it and improve blood flow to the heart. Access for the catheter is usually made through the femoral or radial artery or femoral vein, from where it is guided up to the affected artery in the heart. Angioplasty is often combined with the placement of a small wire mesh tube called a stent. The stent helps prop the artery open, decreasing its chances of narrowing again.

The hepatic portal circulation - which is covered in more detail in the Chapter 13 - refers to the circulation of blood from the small intestine to the liver. Blood from the digestive organs passes through a second capillary bed at the liver before returning to the heart so that the liver can detoxify harmful substances, and nutrients can be stored or modified to maintain correct concentrations in the blood.

CARDIAC CYCLE

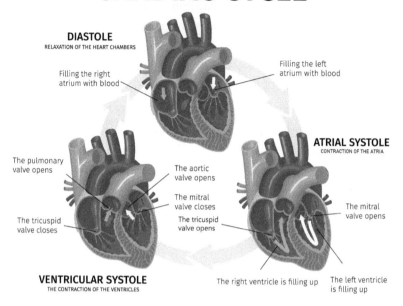

DIASTOLE
RELAXATION OF THE HEART CHAMBERS

Filling the right
atrium with blood

Filling the left
atrium with blood

ATRIAL SYSTOLE
CONTRACTION OF THE ATRIA

The pulmonary
valve opens

The aortic
valve opens

The mitral
valve closes

The mitral
valve opens

The tricuspid
valve closes

The tricuspid
valve opens

VENTRICULAR SYSTOLE
THE CONTRACTION OF THE VENTRICLES

The right ventricle is filling up

The left ventricle
is filling up

10.6 Cardiac cycle

The beating of the heart is due to the contraction and relaxation of the heart muscle (myocardium) and occurs an average of 70-72 times per minute in a healthy adult as follows: both atria contract, forcing blood into the ventricles; the atria then relax and the ventricles contract, forcing blood into the arteries. This process is started from the sino-atrial node (pacemaker) in the upper wall of the right atrium. The 'pulse' refers to how many times per minute the arteries expand and contract in response to the pumping action of the heart. The pulse rate is equal to the heartbeat, as the contractions of the heart cause the increases in blood pressure in the arteries that lead to a noticeable pulse. All arteries have a pulse that can be felt where they run close to the skin, and can easily be detected at points on the body such as the wrist, neck or groin. Place two fingertips gently on the area and when the position is right, you should feel the pulsation of your heartbeat.

When a person is seriously injured or ill, it may be hard to feel their pulse.

Blood pressure is the force that blood exerts on the blood vessels. Systolic blood pressure is when the pressure reaches its peak level as the heart muscle contracts and forces blood out into the aorta from the left ventricle. Diastolic blood pressure is when the heart is relaxing and filling with blood, and the pressure reaches its lowest level. A sphygmomanometer - also known as a blood pressure monitor or gauge - is a device used to measure blood pressure. It is composed of an inflatable cuff to collapse and then release the artery under the cuff in a controlled manner, and a mercury, mechanical or digital manometer to measure the pressure. The pressure in the cuff is increased until the brachial artery (a branch of the aorta) is constricted and no blood passes through. The pressure is then released slowly until the sound of the blood entering the artery is heard. This point is considered the systolic pressure. The pressure on the cuff continues to be released and the point when this sound disappears is considered the diastolic pressure – i.e. blood flow has now returned to normal. The blood pressure monitor shows measurements in millimetres of mercury, appearing as 'mmHg'. A blood pressure reading of 120/80mmHg means that the systolic pressure is 120 and the diastolic pressure is 80. This is regarded as normal for an average healthy adult. Anything below the 90/60mmHg mark constitutes low blood pressure (hypotension), while anything above 140/90mmHg indicates high blood pressure (hypertension), and this is the threshold where a medical professional would actively monitor blood pressure.

Causes of hypertension include stress, medication, narrowing or hardening of the arteries, smoking, alcohol, diet or hereditary factors. High blood pressure can put a strain on blood vessels in the heart, brain and kidneys, and if persistently high, may lead to serious health problems, including heart disease, kidney disease and strokes. Drugs called beta-blockers - also known as beta-adrenergic blocking agents -

are medications that reduce blood pressure. They work by blocking the effects of the hormone adrenaline, causing the heart to beat more slowly and with less force, thus lowering blood pressure. They also help open up veins and arteries to improve blood flow. Beta-blockers are not usually prescribed for high blood pressure unless other medications - such as diuretics - haven't worked effectively, and like most drugs, they can trigger unpleasant side effects. The best way to prevent high blood pressure is to make lifestyle modifications such as eating a healthier diet, maintaining a healthy weight, not smoking and getting more exercise.

In some people, low blood pressure can occur naturally and with no symptoms, and if blood pressure is naturally low, it is not usually something to worry about. However, it could be a cause for concern if symptoms like fainting, dizziness, blurred vision, heart palpitations or confusion are persistent. Drinking more water can reduce the risk of becoming dehydrated and also increases the circulating fluid volume in the body, and adding more salt to the diet can raise blood pressure, which in some cases may not be a bad thing.

Blood vessel problems and vascular diseases can inhibit the proper functioning of blood vessels, and are often due to high levels of lipids called cholesterol and triglycerides in the blood. Cholesterol and triglycerides are two forms of lipid (fat) that circulate in the bloodstream and both are necessary for life. Cholesterol is important for building and maintaining cell membranes, and for making several essential hormones and other compounds, including oestrogens, progesterone, steroids and vitamin D. Triglycerides - chains of high-energy fatty acids derived from dietary fats - provide much of the energy needed for organs to function. When blood levels of cholesterol or triglycerides become too high, the risk of developing heart attack, stroke and peripheral vascular disease is increased, so it is important to keep blood lipid levels in a healthy range. Cholesterol is derived from food e.g. eggs, fish, meat, dairy products, and it is also produced within the liver – about 75% of the body's cholesterol is produced here. Most fats such as natural oils - both polyunsaturated and monounsaturated - animal fats and trans fats, are triglycerides. While both healthy and unhealthy fats contribute to triglyceride levels, trans fats like margarine, and saturated fats like fatty red meats, lard, poultry skin and full-fat dairy products can elevate triglyceride levels more than leaner meat and unsaturated fats like olive oil, avocados, nuts and low-fat dairy products.

Dietary lipids are absorbed through the lymphatic vessels (lacteals) and blood capillaries in the digestive system and sent to the liver for processing. The liver places the cholesterol and triglycerides, along with special proteins, into tiny sphere-shaped packages called lipoproteins that are soluble in blood, and allow cholesterol and triglycerides to be moved with ease through the bloodstream. Cholesterol and triglycerides are removed from the lipoproteins and delivered to body cells when needed. Excess triglycerides that are not needed immediately for fuel are stored in fat cells for later use. Some of the fatty acids stored in our bodies actually originated as dietary carbohydrates. Because there is a limit to how many carbohydrates the body can store, any excess carbohydrates are converted to fatty acids, which are then packaged as triglycerides and stored as fat - this explains why a person can gain weight even on a low-fat diet. The stored fatty acids are split from the triglycerides and burned as fuel during periods of fasting.

There are two types of cholesterol - a 'good' type called high density lipoprotein (HDL) that transports excess cholesterol from the tissues - including the artery walls - to the liver for disposal, and a 'bad' type called low density lipoprotein (LDL) that transports cholesterol from the liver to the cells. The amount of cholesterol in blood is measured in units called millimoles per litre of blood - usually shortened to 'mmol/litre', 'mmol/L' or 'mM'. Current UK guidelines state that it is desirable to have a total cholesterol level under 5mmol/L, with an

LDL level under 3mmol/L and a HDL level of 1.2 mmol/L or more. However, it is advisable to have a total cholesterol level under 4mmol/L and an LDL level under 2mmol/L if a person is at high risk of heart disease. Having high triglyceride levels is also associated with increased risk of cardiovascular problems. High cholesterol levels can be due to diet as well as other factors including heredity, an underactive thyroid gland, obesity, drinking a lot of alcohol, and some rare kidney and liver disorders. As a rule, the higher the LDL cholesterol level, the greater the risk to health. A blood test only measuring total cholesterol may be misleading, and it is important to know the separate LDL cholesterol and HDL cholesterol levels. High total cholesterol may be caused by a high HDL cholesterol level, and is therefore healthy.

ATHEROSCLEROSIS

ILLUSTRATION OF
ATHEROSCLEROSIS STAGES

NORMAL FUNCTIONS

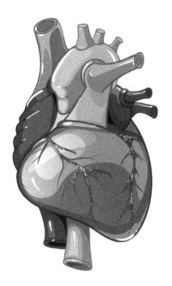

ENDOTHELIAL DISFUNCTION

PLAQUE FORMATION

PLAQUE RUPTURE THROMBOSIS

10.7 Atherosclerosis

One of the most common diseases of the arteries is atherosclerosis, in which cholesterol, triglycerides, and other substances circulating in the blood (e.g. calcium and cellular waste) accumulate inside arterial walls leading to the formation of sticky deposits called plaques or atheromas, and inhibiting blood flow to organs and tissues. The process begins when the inner layer of an artery (the endothelium) becomes damaged due to high blood pressure, toxins in tobacco smoke, or other causes. Having a high level of bad cholesterol and a low level of good cholesterol in the blood increases the risk of atherosclerosis as the cholesterol sticks to damaged areas of the artery and gradually builds up. Atherosclerosis can result in blood clots that may dislodge and block blood flow, or may cause a bulging called an aneurysm in a weakened area of an artery. An aneurysm can cause problems by pressing against organs, or it may rupture, causing internal bleeding and excessive blood loss.

When atherosclerosis narrows the arteries close to the heart, it can lead to coronary artery disease causing chest pain (angina), a heart attack or heart failure. When atherosclerosis narrows the arteries close to the brain, it can lead to carotid artery disease causing transient ischemic attack (TIA) or stroke, due to lack of oxygen to the area. Peripheral artery disease is narrowing of the arteries in the arms or legs leading to circulation problems. This can reduce sensitivity to heat and cold and increase the risk of burns or frostbite. In rare cases, poor circulation in the arms or legs can cause tissue death (gangrene).

Healthy arteries are flexible and elastic, but over time, the artery walls can harden, a condition commonly called hardening of the arteries or arteriosclerosis. This can result from atherosclerosis and generally affects small arteries and arterioles. It involves thickening of the vessel walls that narrows the lumen (space inside). Similar to atherosclerosis in the larger vessels, the process of arteriolosclerosis can lead to ischemia - insufficient blood flow to organs supplied by the blocked vessels. Arteriolosclerosis is most often seen in people who have diabetes mellitus or high blood pressure, though it is also considered to be a normal part of ageing.

Cor pulmonale is a condition that develops from high blood pressure in the pulmonary arteries that take deoxygenated blood from the right side of the heart to the lungs. It is also known as right-sided heart failure because it occurs within the right ventricle of the heart, causing it to enlarge and pump blood less effectively than it should. The ventricle is then pushed to its limit and ultimately fails. This condition can be prevented if high blood pressure is controlled.

A pulmonary embolism is a potentially life threatening condition that can occur due to a blockage of the pulmonary artery or one of its branches. The most common cause is when a deep vein thrombus - blood clot from a vein, usually in the legs - becomes dislodged from its site of formation and travels (embolises) to the arterial blood supply of one of the lungs. Symptoms vary depending on the extent of the blockage and include shortness of breath, rapid breathing and extreme anxiety.

Problems in veins are typically due to inflammation resulting from an injury, blockage, defect or infection. The formation of blood clots in superficial veins can cause superficial thrombophlebitis. Blood clots in deep veins can result in deep vein thrombosis (DVT). This can cause leg pain or swelling, but also can occur with no symptoms. Deep vein thrombosis can develop due to certain medical conditions that affect how the blood clots. It can also occur due to extended periods of immobility e.g. being confined to bed after surgery, an accident or illness. This condition can be very serious because blood clots in the veins can break loose and travel through the bloodstream to the lungs, blocking blood flow and causing a pulmonary embolism. It can also cause inflammation of the veins (phlebitis).

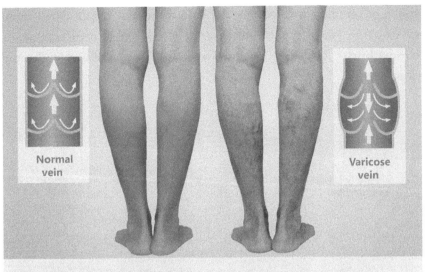

STRUCTURE OF NORMAL AND VARICOSE VEINS

10.8 Varicose veins

Damage to vein valves can cause an accumulation of blood in the veins. This may result in the development of varicose veins, which are twisted, enlarged veins. Any superficial vein may become varicosed, but the veins most commonly affected are those in the legs, because standing and walking upright increases pressure in the veins of the lower body. For many people, varicose veins and spider veins - a common, mild variation of varicose veins - are simply of cosmetic concern, but for others they can cause pain and discomfort and may lead to ulcers or blood clots. Varicose veins are more common in women, those with a family history, those who are overweight, and those who sit or stand for long periods. During pregnancy, the volume of blood in the body increases to support the growing foetus, and this can also lead to enlarged veins in the legs. The same measures to treat the discomfort from varicose veins can help prevent them and include exercise, maintaining a healthy weight, eating a healthy diet, avoiding high-heeled shoes and tight hosiery, elevating the legs, and changing sitting or standing positions regularly. In some cases medical treatment to strip the veins may be necessary e.g. laser treatment that sends strong bursts of light onto the vein, making it slowly fade and disappear.

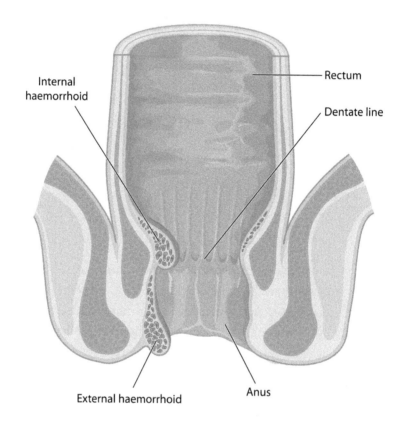

10.9 Hemorrhoids

Hemorrhoids - also called piles - are swollen veins in the anus and lower rectum - similar to varicose veins. Hemorrhoids can develop inside the rectum (internal hemorrhoids) or under the skin around the anus (external hemorrhoids). Hemorrhoids can be painful and cause itching and bleeding. They are common during pregnancy as the uterus enlarges and sometimes presses on veins near the lower end of the colon, causing them to bulge. Other risk factors for hemorrhoids include ageing, chronic diarrhoea, chronic constipation, sitting for too long, heavy lifting, anal intercourse, obesity and genetics i.e. some people inherit a tendency to develop hemorrhoids.

Eating high-fibre foods, drinking plenty of fluids, avoidance of straining when trying to pass stools, getting adequate exercise and avoiding long periods of sitting can all help alleviate this condition. In some cases medical intervention may be required.

Exercise is very beneficial for the cardiovascular system, and can also increase stamina and reduce fatigue as well as increasing heart and lung fitness and bone and muscle strength. The average heart rate for a healthy adult is around 72 beats per minute. During vigorous exercise the heart rate can increase dramatically, resulting in increased blood circulation as the heart pumps blood to the outer limbs. Exercise also helps to oxygenate the blood, bringing a good supply of oxygen to all organs in the body. It also helps strengthen the heart, which is largely muscle. The fitter a person is, the less the heart has to work because the blood vessels will work better as exercise helps keep the blood vessel linings more flexible. It also helps to keep blood pressure in check, as a stronger heart can beat slower but still pump large volumes of blood around the body, while a weak heart needs to work harder to do the same work. The resting heart rate is also lower if a person is fitter, because the heart doesn't need to pump so often - athletes often have a very low resting heart rate.

As well as exercise, other ways to maintain a healthy cardiovascular system include eating a healthy balanced diet, controlling blood cholesterol and blood pressure levels, not smoking, maintaining a healthy weight and body mass index and managing stress levels.

11. The Lymphatic System and Immunity

The lymphatic system is closely linked to the cardiovascular system, but its circulation is in a separate network. It consists of lymphatic capillaries, vessels, nodes, trunks and ducts, and provides channels through which excess fluid outside the cardiovascular system can be returned to the circulation.

When nutrients pass under pressure from blood capillaries to body tissues, they do so in what is known as interstitial fluid. Sometimes referred to as extracellular or tissue fluid, this is the fluid lying in small spaces around and between cells of the body. Nutrients and oxygen from blood capillaries pass into the interstitial fluid and are distributed to body cells, while cellular waste products enter the fluid to be removed. Some fluid returns to the capillaries to become plasma, but not all of it can get through due to their small pore size, and because the pressure inside the capillaries becomes too high as they fill up. The extra fluid passes through the walls of the lymphatic capillaries as they have lower pressure and larger pores, and the fluid is then referred to as lymph.

A study published in 2018 suggests that as well as the fluid that lies between individual cells, there are structured fluid-filled spaces within tissues, and the researchers are calling this network of fluid-filled spaces an organ - the 'interstitium'. The researchers think they may act as shock absorbers to protect tissues during daily functions, and that they have been missed for decades because they don't show up on the standard microscopic slides that researchers use to examine the cellular world.

Lymphatic capillaries are fine permeable tubes - like blood capillaries but blind ended - carrying fluid away from tissue spaces into larger lymphatic vessels. The lymphatic capillaries in the small intestine are called lacteals, and they absorb dietary fats and fat-soluble vitamins (A,

D, E & K), carrying them to larger lymphatic vessels that take them to the bloodstream. The fluid in the lacteals is a creamy white mixture called chyle. Lymphatic vessels have a structure very similar to veins and carry lymph from lymphatic capillaries into larger lymphatic vessels called trunks.

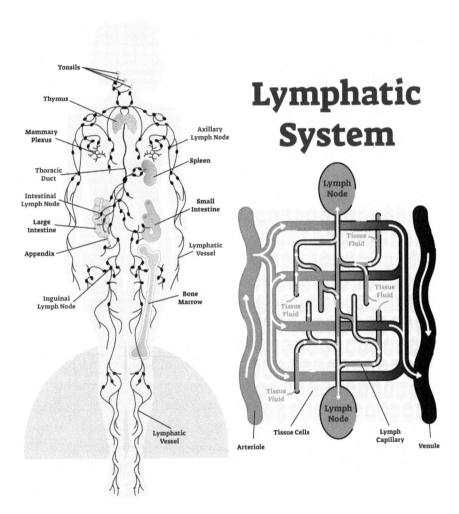

11.1 Lymphatic system

Located at various intervals along the lymphatic vessels are bean shaped structures called lymph nodes, covered by a capsule of connective tissue with an outer 'cortex' and inner 'medulla'. Humans have approximately 500–600 lymph nodes distributed throughout the body, with clusters found in the underarms, groin, neck, chest and abdomen. Lymph nodes vary in size from 1-25 millimetres and include anterior auricular (superficial parotid) - in front of the ears; posterior auricular (mastoid) - behind the ears; submandibular - under the mandible (lower jaw); submental - under the chin; occipital - at the base of the skull; deep and superficial cervical - in the neck; axillary - in the armpits; supratrochlear - in the elbow creases; ileocolic - in the abdomen (near the diaphragm); iliac - in the abdomen; inguinal - in the groin; and popliteal - behind the knees. Lymphadenitis is the medical term for enlargement of one or more lymph nodes - usually because an infection has started somewhere else in the body.

Lymph nodes contain lots of cells called lymphocytes, including T cells that engulf and destroy pathogens, and B cells that produce antibodies, enabling the body to 'remember' an antigen and properly respond if it is encountered again. A pathogen is an infectious agent that may cause disease - e.g. virus, bacteria, fungus, parasite - while antigens are molecules that are found on the surface of pathogens and are specific to that pathogen. Antigens are capable of causing the immune system to produce antibodies against it. Antibodies, which were also discussed in the previous chapter, are blood proteins produced in response to, and counteracting specific antigens. They combine chemically with substances the body recognises as alien. The nodes filter the lymph, trapping unwanted microorganisms, cell debris and harmful substances, so that the lymph is 'cleaned' before returning to the bloodstream. Afferent lymph vessels carry lymph to the nodes and efferent vessels carry it away.

Lymphatic vessels from various regions of the body merge to form larger vessels called lymphatic trunks. The major lymphatic trunks are the jugular, subclavian, bronchomediastinal, lumbar and intestinal trunks - named after the body region in which they drain lymph. The trunks take the lymph to two large lymphatic ducts in the neck – the thoracic duct on the left side and the right lymphatic duct. From here, the lymph is passed into the left and right subclavian veins where it becomes plasma again. And so the cycle continues – from plasma to tissue fluid to lymph to plasma. The thoracic lymph duct is the main collecting duct of the lymphatic system. It originates near lumbar vertebra 2 (L2) at a dilation called the cisterna chyli, a small, dilated sac in the lumbar region of the body's abdominal cavity that temporarily holds the lymph as it travels from the lower body upwards. The thoracic duct receives lymph from the left side of head, neck and chest, the left arm and the entire body below the ribs. The right lymphatic duct receives lymph from the upper right side of body only i.e. the right side of the head, neck and chest, and the right arm.

The lymphatic system has no pump like the heart to move it around the body, and depends on the contractions of smooth muscle in the lymph vessels and the 'milking' action of skeletal muscles as the body moves. Deep breathing also helps get lymph flowing properly so the body can work more efficiently. It rhythmically squeezes and releases the lymphatic system throughout all abdominal organs as well as helping to eliminate toxins, improve metabolism, and assist the intestinal lymph nodes to absorb fat. One-way valves in the lymphatic vessels prevent the backflow of lymph. When the lymphatic system slows down at night, fluid builds up in the tissues, sometimes leading to puffiness first thing in the morning, often on the face. Lack of physical exercise as well as poor diet, pollution and shallow breathing, all restrict lymphatic drainage and slow down the flow of lymph. This can manifest in the skin as spots, blackheads and dry patches. Massage can assist blood and lymph circulation and help with elimination of waste. Dry skin brushing also helps the lymphatic system to clean itself of toxins and improves surface circulation, helping the skin to look and feel healthier and more resilient. It is best done first thing in the morning for 5-10 minutes before showering. As well as livening the body up and stimulating better blood and lymph circulation, dry skin brushing removes dead skin cells, enabling the skin to produce more of its natural oils from unclogged pores. It is best to avoid brushing over open or inflamed skin areas, and use a natural bristle brush with a long handle. Start by brushing from the feet, up the legs and the back, then the stomach and chest area. Always brush in the direction of the heart as lymph flows upwards. On reaching the heart area, brush up the arms (front and back), the underarms, then the back of the neck, the top of the chest (avoiding the nipples), and finally very lightly on the sides of the neck in a downward motion.

As well as being present in the lymph nodes, lymphatic tissue is also found in other places within the body, assisting the lymphatic system. These areas include the tonsils, thymus, spleen, appendix, and some special areas in the gut. The tonsils are masses of lymphoid tissue found in the back of the throat and nasal cavity, helping to fight pathogens that may enter the body via the nose or mouth. The thymus gland, located behind the sternum, produces hormones to help the maturation of T cells of the immune system. The spleen is located in the upper-left part of the abdomen and it filters blood, removing old or damaged blood cells and platelets that are then phagocytised (eaten) by white blood cells called macrophages. The spleen also detects viruses and bacteria and triggers the release of lymphocytes. Infections and injuries can damage the spleen and cause it to enlarge or even rupture. If the damage is extensive, surgery may be needed to remove the spleen. It is possible to live a normal, healthy life without a spleen, but extra precautions will be needed to prevent infections. The appendix is a pouch of lymphatic tissue attached to the large intestine in the lower-right area of the abdomen. Although it's made of lymphatic tissue, the appendix doesn't appear to have much lymphatic function in humans, but it does release some mucus into the large intestine. Some lymphatic tissue similar to the tonsils is located in the digestive tract. Called gut associated lymphoid tissue (GALT); it includes areas of lymphoid tissue called Peyer's patches in the mucosa and submucosa of the small intestine - mainly in the ileum.

The cells located in lymphatic tissue include white blood cells that are found in lymph as well as blood, and include phagocytes (feeding cells) and lymphocytes. The phagocytes are the general cleaners of the body, eating up bacteria and other particles including old cells. They are often found in connective tissue and various organs such as the liver and spleen, as well as sites of injury. The lymphocytes include B and T cells, originating from bone marrow but migrating to lymphoid tissue (B cells) or the thymus (T cells) to specialise and mature.

The last chapter looked at some of the cells involved in protecting the body from pathogens. The organs and processes of the body that provide resistance to infection and toxins are commonly referred to as the immune system. In his book 'Epigenetic Principles of Evolution', Nelson R. Cabej states: "Immunity is a state of resistance of an organism to invading biotic or abiotic pathogens and their harmful effects, that prevents the development of infection and maintains the organism's integrity by counteracting, neutralising and clearing pathogens." In other words, it is a state of having sufficient biological defences to avoid infection and disease.

The immune system is immature at birth and develops throughout life as the body is exposed to different germs that can cause disease. Before birth, antibodies are passed from mother to baby through the placenta during the third trimester of pregnancy, and this gives some protection after birth, depending on the mother's own level of immunity. During birth, bacteria from the mother's vagina are passed on to the baby, and this helps build gut bacteria that contribute to immunity. Research has found that babies born via caesarean section may have an impaired immune system in later life due to the lack of exposure to maternal bacteria that would occur during the standard vaginal birthing process. After birth, more antibodies are passed on to the baby in colostrum and breast milk. Colostrum is the first secretion from the mammary glands after giving birth, and is rich in protein and antibodies. However a baby's immune system is not as strong as an adult's and premature babies have a higher risk of infection because their immune systems are even more immature, plus they haven't had as many antibodies passed on to them from their mothers. The passive immunity passed on from mother to baby at birth doesn't last long, and starts to decrease in the first few weeks and months after birth. Babies produce their own antibodies every time they are exposed to a virus or germ, but it takes time for this immunity to fully develop.

Immunity can be divided into two types of responses, innate (non-specific) and adaptive (specific) immunity that can adapt to a specific threat, or antigen. These are both very complex biological processes, and to make it easier to understand I will compare the two types and how they work together to protect the body.

The innate immune system is present from birth and does not have an immunological memory, whereas the adaptive immune system remembers specific pathogens when it comes across them again. Innate immunity is the body's first responder, and includes external barriers like the skin and mucous membranes of the throat and gut that provide the first line of defence against infection by microorganisms such as viruses, bacteria and parasites. These barriers help to stop pathogens from getting into the body in the first place e.g. cilia are tiny hairs in the respiratory system that sweep away bacteria and germs, and the skin and mucous membranes contain chemicals that inhibit viruses, bacteria and fungi. Blood and body fluids contain enzymes that can kill off germs e.g. tears contain enzymes that wash away bacteria and germs from the eyes.

If pathogens get past the skin and other external barriers (like a burglar!), the innate immune system sends out white blood cells that cause inflammation in the body e.g. a virus can cause a fever, which is part of the process of fighting the infection, and the swelling and redness due to injury is due in part to the immune system sending cells to repair the damage. Antibodies created by the adaptive immunity can also join in the battle because they 'remember' how the invader works. This is often the case when someone catches flu after having a flu vaccination. The body has already been exposed to inactivated flu viruses in the vaccine, and as a reaction to that exposure, the immune system produces antibodies so the person should get a much milder dose. This is sometimes referred to as active immunity, whereas passive immunity is when antibodies are introduced into the body rather than made by the body in response to a pathogen e.g. antibodies introduced from breast milk, or antiserum prepared from human or animal sources containing antibodies for combatting a specific disease e.g. the injection of snake antivenom following a snake bite.

Venom is a poisonous substance secreted by animals such as snakes, spiders and scorpions, and injected into prey or aggressors by biting or stinging. Antivenoms are produced by 'milking' the venom in a controlled setting and injecting it into donor animals such as horses or sheep. These animals have robust immune systems and produce powerful antibodies that are taken from their blood and used in creating antivenom that can be injected into a patient's body. Here they bind to the venom components, enabling the immune defences to eliminate these toxins. French scientist, Albert Calmette who worked in a branch of the Pasteur Institute in the late 1800s is credited with developing the very first snake antivenom.

As mentioned in the previous chapter, hematopoietic stem cells from which all blood cells are derived generate two types (lineages) of blood cells involved in immunity, and these are known as myeloid lineage cells and lymphoid lineage cells. 'Myeloid' cells refer to cells derived from bone marrow, while 'lymphoid' cells refer to those related to the lymphatic system.

There are several types of myeloid lineage cells and some lymphoid lineage cells that are regarded as part of the innate immune system, and this diagram will be helpful to refer to when reading about these.

CELLS OF THE IMMUNE SYSTEM

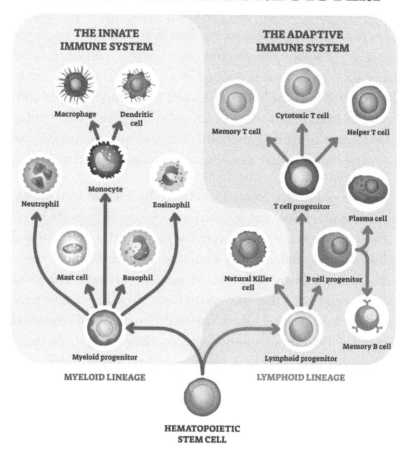

11.2 Cells of the immune system

Natural killer cells (NK) are aggressive lymphoid lineage cells of the innate immune system that play an important role in fighting cancer as well as attacking virally infected cells. While T cells are also important in fighting cancer, NK cells are the 'first responders' that are on the scene before the T cells are summoned. In this process, the NK cell penetrates the cell membrane, releasing toxic granules into the abnormal cell. These chemicals break down the membrane of the diseased cell, causing the cell to burst and initiating apoptosis (cell self-destruction). NK cells can also trigger the production of cytokines that stimulate other parts of the immune system to attack cancer cells or virally infected cells. Since NK cells are able to kill tumour cells by recognising the difference between cancer cells and normal cells, scientists are studying ways to increase the number or enhance the function of these cells in the body as a way to treat cancer more effectively.

Mast cell and basophils are two types of granular white blood cells (granulocytes), and are the major cells in the early phases of allergic reactions. The small granules in these cells are filled with the enzymes histamine and heparin that are released during inflammatory and allergic reactions. This produces local responses such as increased permeability of blood vessels leading to inflammation and swelling, contraction of smooth muscles (e.g. bronchial muscles) and increased mucus production. Heparin also prevents blood clotting. Mast cells are scattered throughout the connective tissues of the body, especially beneath the surface of the skin, near blood and lymphatic vessels, within nerves, throughout the respiratory system, and in the digestive and urinary tracts. Basophils are mostly found in the skin and mucous membranes that line body openings, and account for around 1% of the white blood cells in the body. Severe allergic reactions or having an overactive thyroid can reduce basophil levels in the body. In some cases, having too many basophils can result from certain blood cancers.

Neutrophils are the most common type of granulocytes found in the blood. They engulf bacteria through phagocytosis (eating it up) and migrate into sites of inflammation in the body. Eosinophils - also granulocytes - are involved in triggering inflammatory responses in allergic disorders and they also help combat parasites - so if there are parasites in the body, eosinophil numbers will increase. Monocytes are a type of non-granular leucocyte and are considered one of the most efficient types of phagocytes. They can invade tissues to become either macrophages or dendritic cells. A macrophage has the ability to locate and 'eat' particles such as bacteria, viruses, fungi and parasites. Dendritic cells initiate a primary immune response by activating the lymphocytes of the adaptive immune system, and secreting small, short-lived protein molecules called cytokines that act as chemical messengers between cells.

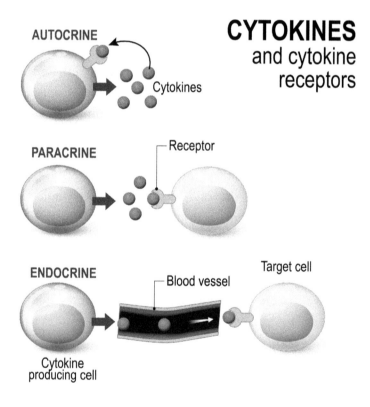

11.3 Cytokines

Cytokines include interferons, interleukins (secreted by some leucocytes and act on other leucocytes), lymphokines (produced by lymphocytes) and other molecules, and are produced by a broad range of cells, including macrophages, B lymphocytes, T lymphocytes and mast cells. They stimulate the movement of cells towards sites of inflammation, infection and trauma and based on the cells on which they act, the cytokines are said to have autocrine, paracrine or endocrine actions. Autocrine action means that cytokines act on the cell that secreted it i.e. itself. Paracrine action means that cytokines secreted by a cell act on other cells close by, while endocrine action means that the cytokines enter the circulation and affect other cells in distant parts of the body. Cytokines help to control the immune system and fight disease. Some act to promote inflammation (pro-inflammatory), whereas others reduce inflammation and promote healing (anti-inflammatory). Examples of cytokines are tumour necrosis factor (TNF) that helps the body fight off infections by increasing inflammation, and interleukin-1 (IL-1) that raises body temperature, stimulates growth of disease-fighting cells, and spurs the production of blood proteins called interferons that inhibit the replication of many viruses.

Interferons, so named because of their ability to interfere with virus reproduction, are produced by virally infected cells, and send signals to other body cells to heighten their anti-viral defences. When first discovered in 1957, interferon was thought to be a single substance, but since then several types have been discovered. Synthetic drug based interferons are now used to treat viral infections such as hepatitis and the herpes zoster virus. Viruses are small, non-living parasites, which cannot replicate outside a host cell. They infect the body by entering healthy cells and multiplying throughout the body. A virus consists of genetic information - either DNA or RNA - coated by a protein, and it injects its genetic information into a host cell, taking control of the cell's reproductive mechanism. This enables the virus to make copies of its DNA or RNA and make viral proteins inside the host cell. A virus can quickly make multiple copies of itself in one cell, release these copies to infect new host cells and make even more copies. The coronavirus (CoV-2) that causes COVID-19 has RNA as its genetic material. COVID-19 starts with droplets from an infected person's cough, sneeze or breath. These droplets can be in the air or on a surface that a person touches before touching their eyes, nose or mouth, giving the virus a passage to the mucous membranes in the throat. Within 14 days, the immune system may respond with early symptoms like a sore throat, fever or dry cough. Some viruses have an outer envelope made of lipids, which are fatty organic molecules. The coronavirus is one of these 'enveloped' viruses. Soap can dissolve this fatty envelope, leading to destruction of the whole virus particle, so that is one reason why hand washing with soap is so important. Studies around the world - including a study by the World Health Organisation (WHO) - are looking at different interferons to treat COVID-19 coronavirus as of April 2020.

Although inflammation can be a good thing as it can show that the immune system is doing its job, overproduction or inappropriate production of certain cytokines by the body can result in disease e.g. an overproduction of pro-inflammatory cytokines is found in autoimmune conditions like rheumatoid arthritis, where the body starts attacking itself. The term 'cytokine storm' is used when referring to an immune system gone awry, and an inflammatory response flaring out of control. Some doctors and researchers are increasingly convinced that an overzealous immune response may be contributing to the severe illness in some COVID-19 patients. Cytokines are part of what is called the complement system. The complement system - also known as the complement cascade - is a part of the innate immune system that enhances or complements the ability of antibodies and phagocytic cells to clear microbes and damaged cells from the body, promote inflammation, and attack a pathogen's cell membrane. It is a highly complex system of more than 30 proteins produced in the liver that circulate in the blood and interstitial fluid. The proteins circulate in an inactive form until needed to defend the body. When required, they become sequentially activated, and help cause the lysis (bursting) of foreign and infected cells, the phagocytosis (ingestion) of foreign particles and cell debris, and the inflammation of surrounding tissue. Although it is part of the innate immune system, the complement system can also be brought into action by antibodies generated by the adaptive immune system.

If the innate immune system is unsuccessful in destroying pathogens in the body, the adaptive immune response sets in after about four to seven days. If there is new contact with an antigen that is already known, the defence response can be quicker as antibodies will be ready to mount an attack. The adaptive immune system has a great memory e.g. childhood illnesses like chicken pox, measles and mumps will be remembered and we don't usually have to suffer through them again. Cells of the adaptive immune system come from the lymphoid lineage. Lymphoid lineage cells make up about 15% of the cells in healthy bone marrow. The lymphoid cell line begins with a lymphoid stem cell, also known as a lymphoblast or lymphoid progenitor cell. The lymphoid progenitor cell can subsequently differentiate further into the more specialised cells described here.

B lymphocytes (B cells) work to protect the body from infections by producing antibodies. In response to infection, B cells can differentiate into plasma cells that produce large proteins called immunoglobulins, or antibodies that attach to the surface of pathogens in the body. These antibodies act like flags over a battle site and attract other defensive molecules in the bloodstream to the site, working toward killing the infection-causing organism. They also signal other immune cells to wage war on the 'invader'. This part of immunity that is heavily dependent on antibodies is referred to as 'humoral immunity'. The term 'humoral' refers to the liquid, noncellular components of the blood and other tissues - such as plasma and lymphatic fluid - in which the antibodies circulate. Some of the activated B cells become memory B cells that have very long lives in the bone marrow, lymph nodes and spleen. They remember the antigen they are specific for and are ready to respond quickly if they encounter it again. These are the cells that give long-lasting immunity to different pathogens.

Immunisation is injection/vaccination with a weakened form of a disease, triggering the body's immune response to either produce antibodies to that particular disease or induce other processes that enhance immunity. Because B cells have long memories, they can produce antibodies that can last for months, or in some cases, years e.g. the tetanus vaccine provides immunity for about 10 years, after which a booster shot is advised. If exposed again to the actual disease-causing organism, the immune system is prepared to fight the infection. A vaccine will usually prevent the onset of a disease, or else reduce its severity. The words vaccine and vaccination come from the name for the cowpox virus 'vaccinia'. English surgeon Edward Jenner (1749-1832) is regarded as the founder of vaccinology in the West, after he inoculated a 13-year-old boy with vaccinia virus. Six weeks later, Jenner exposed the boy to smallpox, but he did not develop the infection then, or on 20 subsequent exposures to the disease. Since then, vaccines have been developed to combat many serious diseases such as polio, yellow fever, cholera and tetanus.

Progenitor T cells are T cells of the adaptive immune system that are capable of developing into mature T cells that find, kill and wage a war against foreign matter such as bacteria and viruses, and they play a key role in fighting cancer. After they are produced in the bone marrow, T cells spend some time maturing and developing in the thymus gland - hence the name T cells for 'thymus-derived' cells. After maturation, T cells migrate to the blood and lymph nodes. T cells are part of the body's cell-mediated immunity i.e. the part of the immune system that directly kills bacteria, viruses and cancer cells as opposed to humoral immunity that protects the body from pathogens by making antibodies. There are several types of T cells. Cytotoxic T cells find and directly attack pathogens such as bacteria, viruses and cancer cells. Helper T cells recruit other immune cells and organise an immune response. There are various types of helper T cells including CD4 T cells that are targeted for destruction by the HIV virus, and CD8 T cells that respond by producing substances to help fight off viruses and other pathogens. Memory T cells remember antigens they have encountered previously and can respond quickly following another exposure to the same antigen. Regulatory T cells are thought to suppress the immune system so that it doesn't overreact as it can do in autoimmune diseases. Natural killer T cells (NKT) are not the same as the natural killer cells that are part of the innate immune system, but they share properties of both T cells and natural killer cells, and both types can rapidly respond in the presence of tumour cells and participate in anti-tumour immune responses.

Although the function of the lymphatic system is to protect from disease, it can be responsible for spreading disease e.g. the metastasis of cancer from its origin to other sites occurs via the bloodstream and lymphatic system. Cancer can spread to any part of the body, although different types of cancer are more likely to spread to certain areas than others. The most common sites where cancer spreads are bone, liver and lungs. Immunotherapy is a newly emerging research therapy that involves re-engineering a patient's T cells so that they can recognise and kill cancer cells. This type of therapy has shown promising preliminary results in the treatment of lymphomas. Other types of immunotherapy include monoclonal antibodies (MABs) that recognise and attack certain proteins on the surface of cancer cells, vaccines to help the immune system recognise and attack cancer, cytokines to help boost the immune system, and adoptive cell transfer to change the genes in a person's white blood cells.

Lymphomas are cancers of the lymphatic system that can be confined to the lymph nodes or spread to other areas, and there are two main types. Hodgkin's lymphoma (Hodgkin's disease) is malignant lymphoma characterised by painless enlargement of one or more groups of lymph nodes. There may also be weight loss, fever, profuse sweating at night and itching. It slowly spreads to adjacent lymph nodes but rarely metastasises to distant sites. The cause is unknown but great progress has been made in the treatment of this disease, and it is now thought to be curable in many cases.

Under a microscope, Hodgkin's lymphoma shows a particular type of cell called a Reed-Sternberg cell that is not found in other lymphomas, so these other lymphomas are called non- Hodgkin's lymphomas (NHLs). There are at least 20 different types of NHL representing a broad category of cancers that arise from the lymph nodes or spleen. The prognosis and classification of the various NHLs is a very complex subject, and this type of cancer doesn't always respond to chemotherapy or radiation therapy as well as Hodgkin's disease. NHL is more common in elderly people and those with poor immune systems, and the main symptom is painless enlargement of lymph nodes in the neck, arms or groin. Other symptoms may include trouble breathing, chest pain, cough, feeling more tired than usual, fever, itchy skin, night sweats, unexplained weight loss, pain or swelling in the abdomen, and pain in the lower back or legs. Some types of NHL grow and spread slowly and are called indolent. Others grow and spread quickly and are called aggressive. Treatment depends on the type and how far it has spread in the body.

Chemotherapy is drug therapy used to treat cancer by killing tumour cells and is also used to shrink lymph nodes that contain cancer. Radiation therapy uses x-rays or gamma rays to kill cancer cells and may stop it from spreading. It may be given alone or with chemotherapy. A bone marrow transplant is a procedure to replace diseased bone marrow with healthy marrow. The bone marrow may come from a donor, or the patient's own bone marrow may be used if it is collected when the cancer is in remission (not active).

Cancer can weaken the immune system by spreading into the bone marrow that makes blood cells to fight infection. This happens most often in leukemia or lymphoma, but it can happen with other cancers too. Leukemia is a malignant progressive disease in which the bone marrow and other blood-forming organs produce increased numbers of immature or abnormal leucocytes. These suppress the production of normal blood cells, leading to anaemia and other symptoms. Many types of leukemia exist, and it can be acute or chronic. Some forms of leukemia are more common in children, while other forms occur mostly in adults.

Glandular fever (infectious mononucleosis) is an infectious disease caused by the 'Epstein Barr' virus and affects lymph nodes in the neck, armpits and groin. It mainly affects adolescents and is often called the 'kissing disease' as it can be spread through saliva. Symptoms include swelling and tenderness of lymph nodes, fever, sore throat, lethargy and loss of appetite. It is diagnosed by the presence of a large number of monocytes in the blood. There is no cure, and glandular fever usually passes without treatment, but the fatigue can last for some time. Rest and drinking plenty of fluids is advised.

Kawasaki disease - sometimes called mucocutaneous lymph node syndrome - causes swelling in the lymph nodes of the neck as well as swelling in the walls of medium-sized arteries throughout the body. Children under 5 years old are most at risk of Kawasaki disease, and it tends to affect boys more than girls. It also causes a red blotchy rash on the body and in the genital area, red, dry, cracked lips, swollen tongue, red eyes, and a fever that is often is higher than 39 degrees C and lasts more than three days. It can progress to peeling of the skin on the hands and feet - especially the tips of the fingers and toes - joint pain, diarrhoea, vomiting and abdominal pain. The causes of Kawasaki disease are unknown. A number of theories link the disease to bacteria, viruses or other environmental factors, but none has been proven. World Health Organization officials are investigating whether the coronavirus, SARS-CoV-2 causes a Kawasaki-type disease in children after several cases cropped up in Europe during the 2020 coronavirus pandemic. The disease gets its name from Japanese paediatrician, Tomisaku Kawasaki who first described its symptoms in 1967.

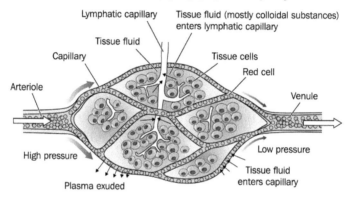

Capillary bed drainage by lymphatic capillary

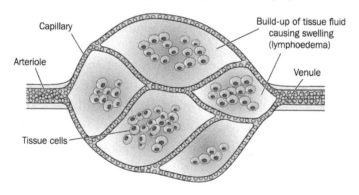

Capillary bed following loss/disruption of local lymphatics

11.4 Lymphoedema

Lymphoedema - also known as lymphedema or lymphatic edema - is a condition of localised swelling caused by a compromised lymphatic system and a buildup of lymph fluid. This happens when lymph nodes do not drain properly, often in the legs. It can be due to a congenital defect in which there is a lack of lymph nodes and vessels, or to surgical removal or damage to these. Parasites, tumours or injuries to the vessels can also cause lymphoedema. Treatments include compression therapy, good skin care, exercise, and manual lymphatic drainage (MLD) therapies, including massage and reflexology lymph drainage.

People with lymphoedema can be susceptible to infections like cellulitis, because the lymphatic system does not function adequately to fight infection. Cellulitis is a sudden, non-contagious infection of the skin characterised by redness, swelling and heat, and accompanied by pain, tenderness and often flu-like symptoms. The infection can enter through a break in the skin, such as an insect bite, a scratch, pre-existing wound or through an area of inflamed skin e.g. athlete's foot, eczema or dermatitis. However, it is not always possible to identify the cause, and prompt medical attention should be sought to prevent further damage to lymph drainage routes.

Not all swelling is lymphoedema - some is simply fluid retention (oedema/edema) due to an underlying medical condition, or most commonly localised, inflammatory oedema as a reaction to trauma or injury to tissues e.g. sprained muscles, torn ligaments, insect bites, cuts and abrasions. It can also be caused by venous thrombosis or sudden vascular blockages. Joint swelling caused by arthritis is another common type of localised oedema. Oedema may be due to prolonged immobility e.g. spending a long time sitting or being bedridden. Varicose veins and pregnancy are also common causes of oedema. It can also be caused by serious medical conditions such as heart failure, liver disease or kidney disease, and any cases of lymphoedema should be medically investigated if the cause is not clear.

HIV (Human Immunodeficiency Virus) is a virus that may lead to AIDS (Acquired Immune Deficiency Syndrome). AIDS - or stage 3 HIV - develops when the virus has caused serious damage to the immune system by destroying the CD4 helper T cells. It is a complex condition, with symptoms that vary from person to person. Symptoms of stage 3 HIV are related to infections like tuberculosis or pneumonia that a person may develop as a result of having a damaged immune system that can't fight these infections efficiently. The virus is spread by contact with bodily fluids of a person with HIV, most commonly during unprotected sex or through sharing drug injection equipment. It can also be spread by contact with infected blood, or from mother to child during pregnancy, childbirth or breast-feeding. There is no cure for HIV but it can be controlled, and nowadays people with HIV often have a near-normal lifespan with proper treatment. Although there is currently no cure for AIDS, treatment can increase a person's CD4 count to the point where they're considered to no longer have AIDS. Treatment can also help to manage the opportunistic infections that could otherwise be fatal to a person with AIDS.

Normally, the immune system can tell the difference between foreign cells and the body's own cells, and mount an appropriate response. In an autoimmune disease, the immune system mistakes part of the body - e.g. the joints or skin - as foreign, and releases proteins called autoantibodies that attack healthy cells. Some autoimmune diseases target only one organ e.g. type 1 diabetes damages the pancreas, while other diseases like systemic lupus erythematosus (SLE) can affect the whole body. Systemic lupus erythematosus (commonly called lupus) is a chronic autoimmune connective tissue disease that can affect any part of the body. Symptoms vary, but can include inflammation, painful joints, weight loss, fatigue, hair loss, dry eyes, enlarged spleen and a butterfly shaped rash across the cheeks. In some people, it can affect other internal organs like the kidneys, limiting their ability to filter the blood efficiently. This can lead to excess tissue fluid causing swelling of the legs, ankles, feet, face or hands. SLE mainly affects young women and the cause is unknown, though it may have a genetic link. Triggers may include viral infections, strong medication, sunlight, smoking and trauma. There is presently no cure and SLE affects each person individually. However, most of those affected experience 'flares' when the condition is particularly active and 'remission' when it is inactive. Although it is a serious illness that needs to be monitored, there is no reason why an affected person can't lead a full life with some adjustments. Discoid lupus generally affects areas of the skin exposed to sunlight, causing red scaly patches that leave pigmentation marks and scars. It can also affect the scalp, lips and inside the mouth. Unlike SLE, discoid lupus does not affect internal organs.

In rheumatoid arthritis (RA), the immune system attacks the joints causing redness, warmth, soreness and stiffness. Multiple sclerosis (MS) is an autoimmune disease that damages the myelin sheath - a protective coating that surrounds nerve cells in the central nervous system. Damage to the myelin sheath slows the transmission speed of messages between the brain and spinal cord to and from the rest of the body. This damage can lead to symptoms like numbness, weakness, balance issues and difficulty walking. The disease comes in several forms that progress at different rates. Hashimoto's thyroiditis - first described by the Japanese physician Hakaru Hashimoto in 1912 - is another autoimmune disease in which the immune system turns against the body's own tissues. In people with Hashimoto's, the immune system attacks the thyroid and this can lead to hypothyroidism, where the thyroid does not make enough hormones for the body's needs.

An allergy is a disorder of the immune system. Allergic reactions occur to normally harmless environmental substances known as allergens, and can only occur if the person has been previously exposed to the allergen and developed antibodies to it. Symptoms range from mild (runny nose, watery eyes), to severe (anaphylactic shock). Allergens can be inhaled, ingested or enter through the skin. Common allergic reactions such as hay fever, certain types of asthma, and hives are linked to an antibody produced by the body called immunoglobulin E (IgE). Each IgE antibody can be very specific, reacting against certain pollens and other allergens i.e. a person can be allergic to one type of pollen, but not another. When a susceptible person is exposed to an allergen, the body starts producing a large quantity of similar IgE antibodies. The next exposure to the same allergen may result in an allergic reaction. Allergies can affect anyone, but are generally more common in children. However, a first-time occurrence can happen at any age or recur after many years of remission. Hormones, stress, smoke, perfume, or environmental irritants may also play a role in the development or severity of allergies. Anaphylactic shock (anaphylaxis) is a severe, life-threatening reaction to certain allergens. Body tissues - including those in the throat - may swell, and there is usually a sudden drop in blood pressure as well as other symptoms including anxiety, difficulty breathing, light-headedness, nausea, headache, pain, cramps, abnormal heart rate or loss of consciousness. Some people who are aware of their allergic reactions or allergens carry an emergency anaphylaxis kit, containing injectable adrenaline that increases the rate and force of the heartbeat.

Psychoneuroimmunology (PNI) is a relatively new field of study that looks at the interactions between the central nervous system (CNS) and the immune system. There is plenty of existing research about the effects of stress on the immune system, and many of these studies focus on the release of cytokines in response to both physical and psychological stress. As already discussed, a cytokine is a small protein released by cells in the immune system. There are different types of cytokines, but the ones that are stimulated by stress are called pro-inflammatory cytokines. Under normal circumstances, the body releases pro-inflammatory cytokines in response to an infection or injury to help destroy germs or repair tissue. When a person is physically or emotionally stressed, the body releases certain hormones, including adrenaline, which can bind to receptors that signal the immune system to produce pro-inflammatory cytokines. This can lead to inflammation that has no beneficial purpose in the body and can trigger autoimmune conditions.

Psoriasis is an example of how the immune system, CNS, mental health and stress levels are all intertwined. The overgrowth of skin cells in psoriasis can sometimes be due to the release of cytokines from the immune system. Psychological stress can worsen or trigger episodes of psoriasis, and sufferers tend to have increased levels of the stress hormone, cortisol. The hypothalamus - part of the CNS and endocrine system - is involved in cortisol production. When it senses stressors, it signals the nearby pituitary gland to release the hormone ACTH that triggers the release of cortisol from the adrenal glands. This in turn can trigger the release of pro-inflammatory cytokines by the immune system, which can then trigger an overgrowth of skin cells. In addition, people with psoriasis often report having psychological conditions such as depression, which has also been linked with an increase in cytokine levels.

An interesting discussion related to immunity is the difference between germ theory and terrain theory. Germ theory - which was proven by Louis Pasteur and Robert Koch - states that many diseases are caused by the presence and actions of specific microorganisms within the body. Pasteur, (1822-1895) was a French chemist and microbiologist who originated the process of pasteurisation and developed vaccines against anthrax and rabies. German physician Koch (1843-1910) discovered the bacteria responsible for tuberculosis and cholera, and received a Nobel Prize in 1905 for his discoveries in relation to tuberculosis. Terrain theory, initiated by Claude Bernard (1813-1878) and later developed by French scientist Antoine Bechamp (1816-1908), states that the internal environment - known as the 'terrain' - is responsible for our state of health. In other words, the unhealthier the lifestyle and the more out of balance a person's body is, the more susceptible it will be to disease. Further, the disease will be much more severe in that person compared to a body that is physiologically stable and healthy. French born Bernard is known for his discoveries concerning the role of the pancreas in digestion, the glycogenic function of the liver, and the regulation of blood supply by the vasomotor nerves of the autonomic nervous system that control the diameter of blood vessels. His concept of the internal environment of the body led to our present understanding of homeostasis.

11.5 Boost your immune system

While it may seem a basic system with a singular task, the immune system is actually a complex and sophisticated set of biological processes working like a finely tuned orchestra to keep us healthy. In turn, we should do what we can to keep our immune system and internal terrain in tip-top condition by managing stress, and making healthy lifestyle choices to benefit body, mind and spirit.

12. The Respiratory System

The respiratory system enables the body to breathe. It moves oxygen and other gases from the air and enables them to be circulated in the blood for delivery to all body tissues. It also removes excess carbon dioxide from the body to the air.

Gaseous exchange is called respiration and consists of external respiration (pulmonary respiration) and internal respiration (tissue respiration). External respiration is the exchange of gases between the lungs and the blood – the blood gains oxygen and loses carbon dioxide. Internal respiration is the exchange of gases between the blood capillaries and body tissues/cells through diffusion across blood capillary walls – the blood distributes oxygen and nutrients and picks up carbon dioxide and other waste products. Cellular respiration is the set of metabolic reactions and processes that take place inside cells to convert chemical energy from oxygen and nutrients into adenosine triphosphate (ATP), and release waste products e.g. carbon dioxide.

Breathing is an automatic and rhythmic act produced by a network of neurons in the brainstem (the medulla and pons). The body has specialised nerve cells called chemoreceptors in the aorta and carotid arteries, and they constantly monitor levels of oxygen and carbon dioxide in the blood. The chemoreceptors send signals to the respiratory centre in the medulla, which then sends signals to the diaphragm (via the phrenic nerve), and to the intercostal muscles (via the intercostal nerves) to contract, causing inhalation. The pons antagonises the respiratory area of the medulla by limiting the actions of the phrenic and intercostal nerves in response to stretch receptors (nerve endings) in the lungs that detect when the lungs have stretched to capacity. This signal prevents the lungs from becoming overstretched and triggers exhalation. Air that comes into the body contains approximately 21% oxygen, 0.04% carbon dioxide, 78% nitrogen, and the remainder is water vapour and a small amount of trace gases such as argon. Air leaving the body contains approximately 16% oxygen, 4% carbon dioxide, 78% nitrogen, water vapour and trace gases.

The nose is the first passageway for air as it enters the body. It is made up of two openings called nares or nostrils, and two nasal bones plus cartilage. The nostrils lead to the two chambers of the nasal cavity that are divided by a septum composed of the vomer bone and septal cartilage. The nasal cavity has an internal mucous lining that is ciliated (with microscopic hairs) and olfactory receptors for the sense of smell – you can read more about olfaction in Chapter 15.

Anatomy of the Nose

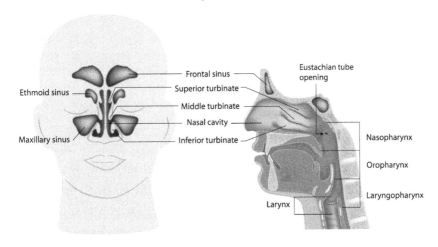

12.1 Anatomy of the nose

Tiny ducts called ostia open into hollow spaces called sinuses in the frontal, maxillae, ethmoid and sphenoid bones. These sinus cavities are also lined with a mucous membrane. The sinuses give clarity and tone to the voice, warm and moisten inhaled air, and lighten the weight of the skull. The maxillary sinuses are behind the cheeks, below the eyes and on either side of the nose. The frontal sinuses are at the very top of the nose - in the forehead, close to the eyebrows. The ethmoid sinuses are above the nose and between the eyes, and the sphenoid sinuses are in the sphenoid bone that forms the temples. If the sinuses become infected - e.g. during a cold - they fill with mucus and can become blocked, leading to pressure and pain around the nose and eyes, and sometimes sinusitis - inflammation of the sinuses.

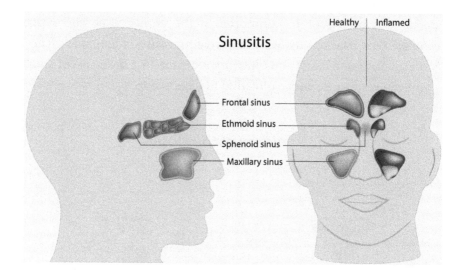

12.2 Paranasal sinuses

The nose helps to moisten and warm inhaled air, and also it filters dust, bacteria and other foreign particles from the air by trapping them in its mucous membrane. As well as sneezing, which is a powerful, involuntary expulsion of air to remove irritants, tiny hairs called cilia push the nasal mucus to the throat where it is swallowed and eventually subjected to the gastric acid of the stomach - this mechanism is sometimes referred to as the 'mucociliary escalator'. Mucus is important as it contains antibodies that help the body recognise pathogens like bacteria and viruses. It also contains scavenger cells called macrophages, enzymes that kill pathogens that it traps, and proteins to make the mucus gooey, stringy and inhospitable. The mucous 'blanket' is composed of two layers. The lower 'sol' layer is a thin fluid that allows the cilia to move easily. The upper 'gel' layer is a thick sheet of mucus that supplies an insertion point for the tips of the cilia. Even in a healthy person, the body makes 1 to 1.5 litres of mucus every day. Most of it trickles down the throat unnoticed, but a bad cold, allergy or contact with an irritant can throw the body's mucus production into overdrive. For instance, during an allergic response to an offending trigger such as pollen, mast cells in the body produce histamine that triggers sneezing, itching and nasal stuffiness. The mucous membranes start leaking fluid, and the nose becomes runny. Consuming dairy products or having allergies to certain foods can also make some people produce excess mucus. A cold can cause nasal mucus to change colour as the immune system sends white blood cells called neutrophils rushing to the area. These cells contain a greenish-coloured enzyme that in large amounts can turn the mucus green. Inflammation and an excess of thickened mucus can make the job of the cilia more difficult. Respiratory diseases, as well as dehydration, dry air and mouth breathing, can all lead to thickened mucus secretions and increased respiratory effort to clear them.

ANATOMY OF NASAL MUCOSA

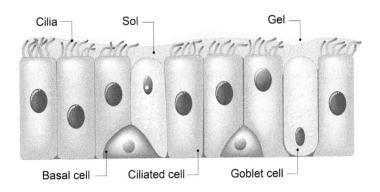

12.3 Nasal mucosa

Once air has passed through the nose (and mouth), it enters the pharynx (throat). The pharynx is a muscular and fibrous tube about 13 centimetres long, lined with a ciliated mucous membrane and divided into three sections - the nasopharynx, oropharynx and laryngopharynx. The pharynx contains small amounts of lymphatic tissue to filter bacteria. Adenoids are patches of lymphatic tissue high up in the throat, just behind the nose. They, along with the tonsils at the back of the throat, are part of the lymphatic system. The adenoids and tonsils work by trapping germs coming in through the mouth and nose. In adolescence, the adenoids start to shrink, and by adulthood, most people's adenoids have disappeared. Pharyngitis is a bacterial or viral inflammation of the pharynx and can accompany tonsillitis - inflammation of the tonsils. Symptoms include a sore throat, pain on swallowing, and sometimes earache if the infection travels up the Eustachian tube connecting the back of the throat with the middle ear. Sore throat is a feature of scarlet fever, a bacterial infection caused by group A streptococcus. Another classic symptom of this disease is a red rash that feels rough, like sandpaper. Although anyone can get scarlet fever, it is most common in children aged 5 to 15 years old. It is usually a mild illness, but people with scarlet fever generally need antibiotics to prevent rare but serious health problems.

From the pharynx, air travels to the larynx – also known as the voice box. This lies between the back of the tongue and the trachea, and consists of rings of hyaline cartilage and a leaf-shaped flap of elastic cartilage called the epiglottis at the base of the tongue that protects the opening of the larynx. The epiglottis stands open during breathing, allowing air into the larynx. During swallowing, it closes to prevent food entering the trachea, forcing the swallowed liquids or food into the oesophagus and towards the stomach instead. The thyroid cartilage is a hyaline cartilage structure that sits in front of the larynx and above the thyroid gland. It is composed of two halves that meet in the middle at a peak called the laryngeal prominence or Adam's apple. The size of an Adam's apple varies - with some being very prominent, while others are less pronounced - and they can be enlarged on some women as well as men. Its primary purpose is to protect the delicate vocal cords (vocal folds) in the larynx from injury. The last piece of cartilage in the larynx is a complete ring called the cricoid cartilage that connects the larynx to the trachea.

Sound is produced when air passing through the vocal cords causes them to vibrate and create sound waves in the pharynx, nose and mouth. These sound waves are converted into words by muscles of the pharynx, face, tongue and lips, while the pharynx, mouth, nasal cavity and paranasal sinuses help the voice to resonate. Males and females have different vocal cord sizes. As a male grows into sexual maturity, his voice becomes deeper as the larynx begins to grow and the vocal cords start thickening. The nasal, sinus and throat cavities also become larger, which allows the voice greater area through which to resonate. Laryngitis is inflammation of the larynx, causing a hoarse voice or the complete loss of the voice due to irritation of the vocal cords. It may include a sore throat, shortness of breath and a painful or tickly cough. It is usually due to a viral infection such as the common cold, but can be due to overuse of the voice, allergy or irritation from substances such as cigarette smoke.

The trachea – sometimes called the windpipe - is a tube about 10 centimetres long that divides into two bronchi. The anterior is composed of rings of hyaline cartilage, with connective tissue and smooth muscle at the back. It has a ciliated epithelium (inner lining) containing mucous-secreting goblet cells. The mucus traps inhaled matter and protects the lining of the trachea, and the waving cilia sweep the mucus along the respiratory tract, pushing it up into the pharynx where it can be swallowed or spat out. Tracheitis is inflammation of the trachea, usually caused by bacteria, and can sometimes develop after a common cold or flu.

The bronchi (singular: bronchus) are the two air passages that lead from the trachea to the lungs. Like the trachea, they are composed of hyaline cartilage (anterior), smooth (involuntary) muscle and connective tissue (posterior), with a ciliated epithelium (inner lining). Like the branches of a tree, the bronchi branch off further into secondary and then tertiary bronchi, and gradually become smaller as they travel inside the lung tissue until they become tiny branches called bronchioles. No gas exchange occurs in any of the bronchi.

When the bronchi become swollen due to irritants or infection, bronchitis results, and this can make breathing difficult. Bronchitis sufferers also tend to have more mucus and phlegm than someone without inflamed bronchi. Bronchiolitis is a viral infection of the bronchioles that commonly affects babies. Most make a full recovery but sometimes it becomes more serious and hospital care may be needed. Bronchiectasis is a lung condition that causes a persistent cough and excess phlegm, or sputum. It is a permanent condition that gets worse over time, and can affect those with tuberculosis and cystic fibrosis. The bronchi dilate - usually irreversibly - and phlegm builds up, leading to recurrent lung infections and lung damage.

As they branch out into the lungs, the bronchioles become smaller and smaller until they evolve into tiny air sacs called alveoli, which is the site of oxygen and carbon dioxide exchange in the respiratory system. In the alveoli, cells called macrophages replace the protective mechanism of the cilia. Macrophages are derived from white blood cells called monocytes that are produced by stem cells in bone marrow. When monocytes leave the blood, they mature into macrophages and can live for months, patrolling cells and organs and keeping them clean. The word 'macrophage' literally means 'big eater', and their job is to clean the body of microscopic debris and pathogens. A macrophage has the ability to locate and 'eat' particles such as bacteria, viruses, fungi and parasites.

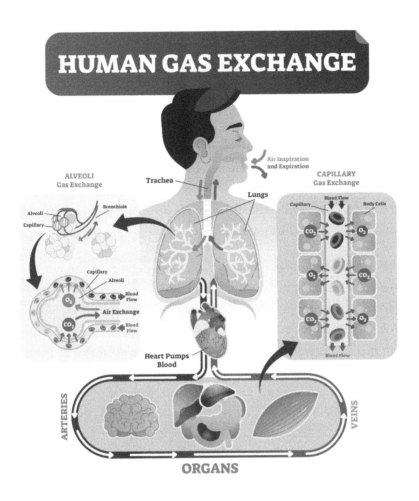

HUMAN GAS EXCHANGE

ALVEOLI
Gas Exchange

Trachea

Air Inspiration
and Expiration

CAPILLARY
Gas Exchange

Lungs

Bronchiole

Alveoli

Capillary

Capillary

Blood Flow

Body Cells

CO_2

O_2

Capillary

Alveoli

O_2

Blood
Flow

Air Exchange

O_2

CO_2

CO_2

Blood
Flow

CO_2

O_2

Heart Pumps
Blood

Blood Flow

ARTERIES

VEINS

ORGANS

12.4 Gas exchange in the respiratory system

A good way to think about the respiratory tract is like an upside-down tree. The trunk is the trachea that splits into smaller and smaller branches in the lungs. At the end of each branch are the tiny air sacs called alveoli, where the exchange of oxygen and carbon dioxide takes place. These tiny, balloon-shaped air sacs sit like little berries or bunches of grapes at the very end of the respiratory tree, and are arranged in clusters throughout the lungs. Alveoli contain collagen giving firmness, and elastin giving stretch. When air is inhaled into the lungs, elastin allows the alveoli to expand, and upon exhalation, spring back to their original size. The thin and permeable structure of the alveoli and the capillaries ensures that diffusion takes place rapidly between the alveoli and the blood. A large number of capillaries surround the alveoli with a very thin membrane separating them. The pulmonary arteries constantly deliver de-oxygenated blood from the right ventricle of the heart to this capillary network in the lungs. Oxygen from the alveoli attaches to haemoglobin molecules in the red blood cells, and the oxygenated blood then leaves the lungs in the pulmonary veins to the left side of the heart, from where it is pumped around the body in the systemic circulation.

While the total number can vary from one person to the next, there are literally millions of alveoli within the human lungs, spanning a surface area of roughly 70 square meters. Diffusion of oxygen from alveoli to capillaries occurs because the concentration of oxygen is lower in the capillaries. Similarly, carbon dioxide diffuses from the capillaries to the alveoli where the concentration of carbon dioxide is lower. During inhalation, alveoli expand like balloons as negative pressure in the chest is created by contraction of the diaphragm. During exhalation, the alveoli spring back as the diaphragm relaxes. Hiccups are involuntary contractions of the diaphragm that may result from a large meal, alcoholic or carbonated drinks, or sudden excitement.

The heart and the mediastinum - a wall of tissue extending from the sternum to the spine - separate the two lungs from one another. The left lung is smaller and divided into two lobes (superior and inferior), while the right lung has three lobes (superior, middle and inferior). Lung tissue is made up of the bronchioles, alveoli, blood vessels, nerves, connective tissue and elastic tissue with a two-layered membrane called the pleura covering them. One layer of the pleura covers the lungs themselves (visceral layer) and the other layer is attached to the chest wall (parietal pleura). The 'pleural cavity' between the two layers contains fluid that acts as a lubricant, allowing the lungs to glide smoothly as they expand and contract with each breath.

Things can sometimes go wrong with the lungs, affecting their efficiency to expand and contract and to do their job of taking in oxygen and getting rid of unwanted carbon dioxide. Pleurisy is inflammation of the pleura. When the pleural membranes are swollen and inflamed, they rub against each other in a sharp, stabbing, painful way when the lungs expand. Pleurisy can be caused by a virus such as the flu, or by a fungus. Bacterial infections such as pneumonia can also cause pleurisy. Pneumonia is an infection that inflames the alveoli and can result in the air sacs filling with pus, and in some cases becoming solid. The inflammation may affect both lungs (double pneumonia), one lung (single pneumonia) or only certain lobes (lobar pneumonia).

A pneumothorax is a collapsed lung that occurs when air leaks into the space between the lung and chest wall. This air pushes on the outside of the lung and makes it collapse (like a puncture in a tyre). Pneumothorax can be a complete lung collapse or a collapse of only a portion of the lung, and can be caused by a blunt or penetrating chest injury, certain medical procedures, or damage from underlying lung disease. Symptoms include sudden chest pain and shortness of breath, and it can be life threatening in some cases. Treatment usually involves inserting a needle or tube between the ribs to remove the excess air. However, a small pneumothorax may heal without treatment.

Pulmonary fibrosis is a scarring and thickening of the tissue around and between the alveoli, making it more difficult for oxygen to pass into the bloodstream. The damage can be caused by many different factors including long-term exposure to certain toxins e.g. asbestos, certain medical conditions, radiation therapy and some medications e.g. chemotherapy, heart medications. Sarcoidosis is a disease characterised by the growth of tiny collections of inflammatory cells called granulomas in any part of the body, but most commonly in the lungs and lymph nodes. The exact cause is unknown and many cases resolve spontaneously, although treatment may be required in some cases. The symptoms are similar to tuberculosis, and include persistent dry cough, shortness of breath, wheezing and chest pain.

Tuberculosis (TB) - once called consumption - is a highly infectious disease that primarily affects the lungs. The 'mycobacterium tuberculosis' bacteria cause TB and there are a variety of strains, some of which have become resistant to antibiotics. The bacteria are transmitted through inhalation of infected droplets in the air, and can be spread via sneezing, coughing, speaking or singing. Symptoms include coughing up blood or phlegm, a cough that lasts for over three weeks, and pain when coughing or with normal breathing. Other symptoms include unexplained fatigue, fever, night sweats, loss of appetite and weight loss. While TB usually affects the lungs, it can also affect other organs such as the kidneys, spine, bone marrow and brain. Symptoms will vary depending on which organ is affected e.g. tuberculosis affecting the kidneys can cause blood in the urine.

Influenza (flu) and the common cold are both common respiratory illnesses but they are caused by different viruses. Although they have similar symptoms, flu is generally worse than the common cold and symptoms are usually more intense. People with colds are more likely to have a runny or stuffy nose and generally do not experience serious health problems such as pneumonia, bacterial infections or hospitalisation that can sometimes result from flu. Cold symptoms appear more gradually than flu, which can have a sudden onset and bring on fever, chills and headaches that don't usually accompany the common cold. A flu vaccination can protect against the influenza viruses that research indicates will be most common during the upcoming season, and is generally recommended for people who are at high risk of developing serious flu complications. It takes about two weeks after vaccination for antibodies to develop in the body and provide protection against flu. There is no cure for a cold apart from getting lots of rest and drinking plenty of fluids. Most people recover in about 7-10 days, and over-the-counter medicines may help ease symptoms. Regular hand washing with soap and water, avoiding close contact with people who are ill, and not touching the face with unwashed hands can help reduce the risk of getting colds and flu.

Coronaviruses are a large family of viruses that may cause illness in animals or humans. The virus is so called because of the spiky crown ('corona' in Latin) that can be seen on its surface when observed under a microscope. Middle East Respiratory Syndrome (MERS) is a respiratory illness caused by the coronavirus MERS-CoV that was first reported in Saudi Arabia in 2012, and has since spread to several other countries. People infected with MERS-CoV developed severe symptoms including fever, cough and shortness of breath, and many of them died. Severe acute respiratory syndrome (SARS) is a viral respiratory illness caused by a coronavirus called SARS-associated coronavirus - SARS-CoV - that was first reported in Asia in February 2003. The illness spread to more than two dozen places in North America, South America, Europe and Asia, before the SARS global outbreak of 2003 was contained. Since 2004, there have been no known cases of SARS reported anywhere in the world.

SARS-CoV-2 (severe acute respiratory syndrome coronavirus 2), the virus that causes COVID-19 is part of the coronavirus family. COVID-19 was first identified in late 2019 as a cluster of pneumonia cases caused by a new coronavirus. Doctors have since learned that it can reach deep into the respiratory tract, including the lungs. COVID-19 can cause a range of breathing problems, from mild to critical. Older adults and people who have other health conditions like heart disease, cancer and diabetes may have more serious symptoms. When the virus gets into the body, it comes in contact with the mucous membranes that line the nose, mouth and eyes. The virus enters a healthy cell and multiplies, and the new viral cells infect nearby cells. The new coronavirus can infect the upper or lower respiratory tract, causing the lining to become irritated and inflamed. As the infection travels down the respiratory tract, the immune system fights back, and the lungs and airways swell and become inflamed. This may start in one part of the lung and spread. In some cases, the infection can reach all the way into the alveoli leading to pneumonia. Some people experience additional symptoms like muscle pain, sore throat and loss of taste or smell. Other reported symptoms include skin rashes e.g. hive-type rash (urticaria), 'prickly heat' or chickenpox-type rash, and 'COVID fingers and toes' i.e. red and purple bumps on fingers or toes - similar to chilblains - which may be sore but not usually itchy.

A 2020 French study that compared 150 patients with COVID-19 related respiratory failure who were treated in intensive care units, to 145 patients who had respiratory failure, but were not infected with the new coronavirus, found significantly higher rates of blood clotting in the COVID-19 patients. Why the blood congeals the way it does in some patients is still an open question – as mentioned in the previous chapter, one possibility is that it may be associated with certain clotting factors in the blood. About 80% of people who have COVID-19 get mild to moderate symptoms like a dry cough or a sore throat. However some people go on to develp long term symptoms including brain fog, anxiety, depression, joint or muscle pain, chest pains, palpitations, breathlessness and fatigue. 'Long COVID' is the term now used to describe effects of COVID-19 that continue for weeks or months beyond the initial illness.

The best modes of protection from COVID-19 or any virus is regular hand washing, keeping at least one metre away from anyone who is coughing or sneezing, not touching eyes, nose or mouth, covering mouth and nose with a bent elbow or tissue when coughing or sneezing and disposing of the used tissue immediately, and staying at home if unwell. Those with fever, cough or difficulty breathing should seek medical attention and follow local medical guidelines.

WEAR FACE MASK IN THE HEAVILY CROWDED AREAS

WHEN COUGHING OR SNEEZING, USE TISSUE TO COVER MOUTH AND NOSE

FREQUENTLY WASH HANDS WITH SOAP

AVOID DIRECT HAND CONTACT WITH EYES, NOSE AND MOUTH

AVOID SHAKING HANDS AND HUGGING

AVOID CLOSE CONTACT WITH SICK PEOPLE AND THEIR TOOLS

AVOID CONTACT WITH THE LIVE ANIMALS

AVOID UNDER COOKING MEATS, EGGS, RAW FRUITS

DO NOT SHARE EATING UTENSILS, CUPS, TOWELS

12.5 Prevention and treatment tips for COVID-19

Chronic obstructive airways disease (COAD)/ chronic obstructive pulmonary disorder (COPD) refers to a group of chronic diseases all having some degree of airway obstruction e.g. chronic bronchitis, asthma or emphysema. Symptoms include coughing (sudden explosive movements of air rushing upwards to clear air passages), wheezing (whistling sound when airways are partially blocked), dyspnoea (shortness of breath or laboured breathing) and sputum (material coughed up from respiratory tract). These diseases are typically caused by long-term exposure to irritating gases or particulate matter, most often from cigarette smoke. People with COPD have an increased risk of developing heart disease, lung cancer and a variety of other conditions. Emphysema and chronic bronchitis are the two most common conditions that contribute to COPD. These two conditions usually occur together, and can vary in severity among individuals with COPD.

Cystic fibrosis (CF) is a genetic disease in which thick mucus clogs the lungs and blocks the ducts of the pancreas, salivary glands and sweat glands. People with CF have a higher than normal level of salt in their sweat. Other symptoms include constipation, frequent and greasy stools, wheezing or shortness of breath, lung infections, infertility (especially in men), poor weight gain and stunted growth in childhood. Although CF is progressive and requires daily care, people with this condition can live a fairly normal and better quality of life than people with CF did in previous decades, due to improvements in screening and treatment for this condition.

Pertussis, also known as whooping cough, is a highly contagious respiratory disease caused by the bacterium 'bordetella pertussis'. It causes uncontrollable, violent coughing which often makes it hard to breathe, followed by a high-pitched intake of breath that sounds like a 'whoop.' Before a vaccine was developed, whooping cough was considered a childhood disease, but nowadays it mainly affects children too young to have completed the full course of vaccinations, or teenagers and adults whose immunity has faded.

Hay fever is a common condition affecting the upper respiratory system. This is an allergic disorder characterised by an exaggerated immune response to environmental triggers including pollen and animals – often cats. Also known as allergic rhinitis (inflammation of the inner lining of the nose), there are two types: seasonal - which occurs only during the time of year in which certain plants pollinate, and perennial - which occurs all year round. With hay fever the immune system views harmless inhaled pollen or other allergens as dangerous substances invading the body. The immune system overreacts, flooding the bloodstream with chemicals like histamine that inflame the lining of the nasal passages, sinuses and eyelids, and also cause other symptoms such as a runny nose and sneezing. Hay fever is often an inherited trait, and many people with hay fever have a family member who also has allergies. People with asthma or eczema (allergic dermatitis) are more likely than others to develop hay fever.

Asthma is a condition in which the airways narrow and swell - often in response to an allergen, cold air, exercise or emotional stress. Symptoms include wheezing, shortness of breath, difficulty exhaling, chest tightness, coughing and sneezing. For some people, asthma is a minor nuisance but for others, it can be a major problem that interferes with daily activities and may lead to a life-threatening asthma attack. There is no cure for asthma, but its symptoms can be controlled.

Cancer is the most serious disease of the lungs and typically starts in the cells lining the bronchi, or parts of the lung such as the bronchioles or alveoli. The majority of lung cancers are caused by exposure to cigarette smoke, but it can also occur in people who have never smoked or those who have not had prolonged exposure to second-hand smoke. There are different types of lung cancer, some of which are primary - starting in the lungs, and some of which are secondary - spreading from other body sites to the lungs.

Smoking has many negative effects on the respiratory system. The hot gases and other ingredients inhaled during cigarette smoking damage the tissue and mucous membranes in the mouth, larynx and pharynx. These areas suffer continual irritation from smoking, and tobacco users may develop symptoms such as hoarseness, coughing and wheezing due to inflammation. It decreases the flow of air in an out of the lungs, due to the constricting effects of nicotine on terminal bronchioles. Irritants present in cigarette smoke increase mucus secretions and cause swelling of mucous membranes. It reduces the amount of oxygen carried in the blood, as the carbon monoxide in cigarette smoke combines with haemoglobin on red blood cells more readily than oxygen does. Irritants in smoke decrease movement of cilia in the respiratory tract, and this hinders the removal of dust-laden mucus and other irritants. It can destroy the elastic fibres in the lungs, and can eventually lead to collapse of the small bronchioles.

The alveoli of the lungs suffer from cigarette smoking, eventually breaking down and losing their effectiveness in transferring oxygen to the blood, resulting in emphysema - a chronic condition in which inflammation in the lungs causes the dilation and destruction of alveoli. The walls of air sacs that remain begin to harden and lose their elasticity, and this makes it difficult to expel air from the lungs. This inability to expel air leads to further dilation of the alveoli and increased loss of function.

As well as emphysema, cigarette smoking has been medically linked to cardiovascular diseases such as atherosclerosis and strokes, as well as the early onset of osteoporosis. It is also known to cause cancer of the mouth, larynx, throat, blood and lungs. Adults and children can inhale airborne second-hand smoke, and pregnant women can transmit it to their developing babies. Toxic particles that cling to smokers' clothes and hair can contaminate indoor environments as dust.

Stress and anxiety can affect the respiratory system, and hyperventilation - overbreathing - is the primary cause of most anxiety-related respiratory problems. When a person breathes too quickly, the problem is not that they get too much oxygen, but too little carbon dioxide. This affects the pH balance of the blood, causing constriction of the small blood vessels that supply the brain. Reduced blood supply to the brain can cause a variety of symptoms including light-headedness and tingling of the fingertips, and severe hyperventilation can cause transient loss of consciousness. Hyperventilation can also cause chest pains and rapid heartbeat, and can lead to panic attacks. Anxiety can change breathing habits and activate the fight-or-flight system that pumps adrenaline into the bloodstream, causing breathing to speed up as a result.

Although every day we take thousands of breaths without even thinking about it, our breathing can sometimes be shallow and restricted, robbing us of oxygen and increasing tension in the body. Deep breathing is a mindfulness practice that provides numerous health benefits beyond the standard respiration required to live. The way we breathe affects the health of all our body functions. Deep, relaxed breathing can relieve stress throughout the entire body and is a component of yoga and other practices designed to improve the health of body, mind and spirit.

13. The Digestive System

Also known as the alimentary canal or gastrointestinal (GI) tract, the digestive system is composed of a set of organs that transforms what we ingest into substances the body can use for energy, growth and repair. Once useful substances are removed, the remainder is excreted as waste. There are six basic processes involved:

Ingestion (taking solid and liquid food into the body)

Secretion (secretions from digestive organs help to move and digest food)

Mixing and propulsion (mixing with digestive secretions and moving food along)

Digestion (mechanical and chemical transformation of solid and liquid food into microscopic particles)

Absorption (nutrients are absorbed into blood and lymph vessels and then into body cells)

Elimination (defecation of waste as faeces)

Organs of the digestive system include the mouth, pharynx, oesophagus, stomach, small intestine, large intestine, rectum and anus. The entire digestive tract from mouth to anus is about nine meters long, and the walls of most of the tract are composed of four layers.

The innermost layer is the mucosa, a three-layered mucous membrane that lines and protects the digestive tract wall, secretes substances, and absorbs the end products of digestion as it comes in direct contact with digested food (chyme).

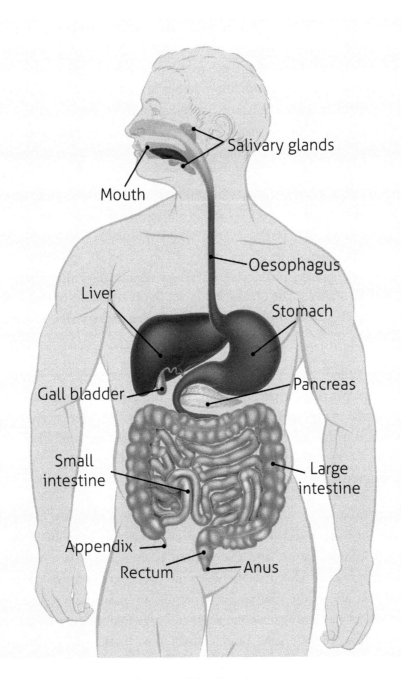

13.1 Organs of the digestive system

Specialised goblet cells secrete sticky the mucus throughout the GI tract. On the mucosa layer, small finger-like projections called villi and microvilli help to increase the surface area for nutrient absorption. The submucosa lies underneath the mucosa and consists of connective tissue with blood vessels, lymphatic vessels and nerves. The blood and lymph vessels of the submucosa pick up the absorbed elements that pass through the mucosa. The muscularis is the next layer, composed of skeletal muscle for swallowing in the mouth and pharynx, and smooth muscle for peristalsis (involuntary muscle movement) in the rest of the digestive tract. There are three muscularis layers in the stomach and two layers in the small and large intestines. The muscularis enlarges in some areas to form circular sphincters that control the opening and closing of various organs, allowing substances to pass through e.g. the cardiac sphincter between the oesophagus and the stomach, and the pyloric sphincter between the stomach and small intestine.

A layer called the serosa is the outermost covering of the digestive tube and provides a partition between the internal organs and the abdominal cavity. It is composed of two layers - a secretory epithelial layer and a thin connective tissue layer. Cells of the epithelial layer secrete a serous fluid that provides lubrication to reduce friction and the connective tissue layer provides blood vessels and nerves.

The peritoneum is a large membrane lining the abdominal cavity. It consists of two layers – the parietal peritoneum that lines the walls of the abdominal cavity, and the visceral peritoneum that covers the digestive organs. The space between the two layers contains a serous fluid that allows the viscera (large organs) to glide easily against the abdominal wall and against one another. Large folds in the peritoneum weave between the organs, binding them to each other and to the walls of the abdominal cavity. The folds contain nerves as well as blood and lymph vessels. Peritonitis is inflammation of the peritoneum, usually due to a bacterial or fungal infection. Peritonitis can result from any rupture (perforation) in the abdomen, or as a complication of other medical conditions. Peritonitis requires prompt medical attention to fight the infection and if necessary, to treat any underlying medical conditions. Treatment usually involves antibiotics, and surgery in some cases. Left untreated, peritonitis can lead to severe, potentially life-threatening infection throughout the body e.g. sepsis.

The mouth (oral cavity) is the first site of digestion as the mechanical action of the teeth and the chemical action of saliva work on ingested food. The mouth is a mucous membrane-lined cavity protected by the lips. The uvula, a fleshy piece of tissue hanging down over the tongue towards the back of the mouth, is part of the soft palate. The soft palate helps close the nasal passages when swallowing. The tongue is a muscular organ that moves food around between the teeth for chewing (mastication) until it is mixed into a soft ball called a 'bolus' ready for swallowing. The tongue also aids in swallowing by pushing the bolus towards the back of the mouth. The tongue is covered with moist, pink tissue called mucosa and tiny bumps called papillae, giving it a rough texture. Thousands of taste buds cover the surfaces of the papillae. Taste buds are collections of nerve-like cells that are connected to nerves running to the brain. The tongue also contains Ebner's glands (named after Victor von Ebner, an Austrian histologist) that secrete an acidic digestive enzyme called lingual lipase that begins the breakdown of fats.

There are three sets of salivary glands secreting saliva into the mouth - the parotid, submandibular and sublingual glands. Saliva is an alkaline liquid containing salivary amylase, an enzyme that begins the digestion of carbohydrates (starches), breaking them down into 'polysaccharides'. These are later broken down into single sugars called 'monosaccharides' in the small intestine, ready for absorption by the body. Saliva supplies a liquid to make the bolus, and it helps to maintain the correct pH in the mouth. Mouth pH can be affected by diet, and dentists generally recognise a healthy pH in saliva as falling between 5.6 -7.9. A pH level of less than 5.5 can put a person at risk of tooth enamel erosion that can cause decay. Saliva contains an antimicrobial enzyme called lysozyme that destroys some bacteria and prevents the decomposition of food. Aphthous ulcers - also known as canker sores and commonly referred to as mouth ulcers - are small painful sores that can occur in the mucus membranes lining the mouth. They typically last for around ten to fourteen days, and generally heal without leaving a scar. Aphthous ulcers can be caused by a vitamin or mineral deficiency (e.g. vitamin B or C, or iron), biting the tongue, or eating certain foods e.g. highly acidic foods.

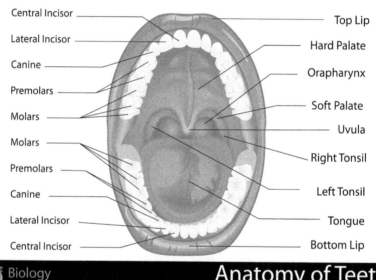

Biology — **Anatomy of Teeth**

13.2 Inside the mouth

Teeth play a key role in digestion by cutting, tearing and grinding food in preparation for swallowing. Chewing food properly is very important in the digestive process and should not be overlooked. It triggers the release of saliva to start the chemical breakdown of carbohydrates, and gives time for saliva to kill bacteria that naturally occur in some foods, yet may be harmful to the stomach. When food is thoroughly chewed, taste buds on the tongue send signals to the brain about the flavours being tasted. The brain then relays signals to the stomach, which secretes chemicals and enzymes that will help digest that particular food type. This means nutrients in the food are released and assimilated into the body faster. Well-chewed food prevents large particles from getting stuck in the oesophagus, and makes the work of the digestive system easier overall.

Teeth are composed of calcified connective tissue called dentin, with a pulp-filled cavity containing blood and lymph vessels and nerves. They are located in sockets in the mandible and maxilla. The sockets are covered with gums (gingivae) and lined with a periodontal ligament that anchors the teeth and acts as a shock absorber when chewing. Gingivitis is inflammation of the gums, usually caused by bacterial infection. If left untreated, it can become a more serious infection known as periodontitis. Each tooth has a crown covered with calcium enamel and 1-3 roots covered by cementum, attaching the root to the periodontal ligament. The junction between the crown and the root is called the 'neck'.

Humans get two sets of teeth in a lifetime. The primary or baby teeth - twenty in all - show at around six months and fall out between the ages of six and twelve years. Adults usually have thirty-two secondary or permanent teeth, four of which are the wisdom teeth. These four wisdom teeth might not develop at all or may need to be removed due to lack of space or for other reasons. There are different types of teeth, each with a particular function. Molars have a large surface with pits and grooves that make them suitable for grinding food between the opposing upper and lower molars. There are two molars and two premolars in each of the four arches of the mouth. There are potentially three molars on each side, with the third molar being the wisdom tooth. Incisors - front teeth - have sharp edges designed for cutting food. There are six upper and six lower incisors. At the corner of each set of incisors are the canines. These have long roots and are designed to tear food. The incisors and canines cut and tear the food and push it to the back teeth -molars and premolars - with the help of the tongue, where it is crushed, chewed and broken down.

The bolus of chewed food and saliva leaves the mouth and enters the oesophagus, a muscular tube about 25 centimetres long, leading from the pharynx to the stomach. The oesophagus lies behind the trachea and has a mucous lining to help the smooth passage of food. No digestion takes place in the oesophagus. Its function is simply to move food into the stomach by a process known as peristalsis - successive waves of involuntary contraction and relaxation of smooth muscle fibres in its wall that push the bolus forward.

The next 'pit stop' is the stomach - a J-shaped elastic organ that can expand and contract depending on its contents. The volume of the human stomach varies depending on the person. Generally, human stomachs have a volume of about one litre, but can distend to hold up to four litres. Gastric banding is a type of weight loss surgery (bariatric surgery) that involves placing a silicone band around the upper part of the stomach to decrease stomach size and volume and thus reduce food intake. This procedure constricts the stomach so that a person feels full after eating less food than usual.

Food enters the stomach from the oesophagus through the cardiac sphincter, a muscular valve that stops the back flow of food up into the oesophagus. A problem with the cardiac sphincter can lead to heartburn, which is an irritation caused by stomach acid flowing back up into the oesophagus, leading to a burning sensation and discomfort in the upper belly, below the breastbone. The presence of food in the stomach causes cells in its lining to secrete a hormone called gastrin, stimulating the production of gastric juice.

STOMACH ANATOMY

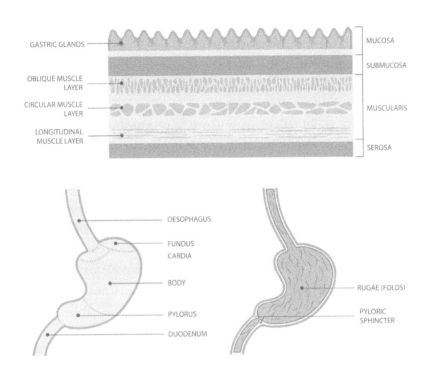

GASTRIC GLANDS

OBLIQUE MUSCLE LAYER

CIRCULAR MUSCLE LAYER

LONGITUDINAL MUSCLE LAYER

MUCOSA

SUBMUCOSA

MUSCULARIS

SEROSA

OESOPHAGUS

FUNDUS

CARDIA

BODY

PYLORUS

DUODENUM

RUGAE (FOLDS)

PYLORIC SPHINCTER

13.3 Anatomy of the stomach

Gastric juice contains water, which liquefies the bolus of food, as well as hydrochloric acid (HCL) that kills ingested microbes and begins the breakdown of proteins. HCL also stimulates hormones that promote the flow of bile and pancreatic juice, and it converts the inactive enzyme pepsinogen into the active enzyme pepsin, which is responsible for digesting proteins in the stomach. A substance called intrinsic factor needed for the absorption of vitamin B12 is also found in gastric juice. Lack of intrinsic factor, and hence lack of B12 in the blood, can result in a condition called pernicious anaemia that can cause permanent damage to nerves and other organs if it goes on for a long time without being treated. It also raises the risk of developing stomach cancer. Another ingredient in gastric juice is gastric lipase, an acidic enzyme that begins the breakdown of dietary fats (triglycerides) into smaller molecules called fatty acids and monoglycerides. The body makes two to three litres of gastric juice – also called stomach acid - every day. A thick mucous layer containing bicarbonate protects the stomach wall from damage by acid breakdown.

A peptic ulcer results if the digestive acid eats away at the tissues that line the stomach. Peptic ulcers can also be due to inflammation from bacterial infection, most commonly helicobacter pylori (H. pylori), a type of bacteria that grows in the digestive tract and has a tendency to attack the stomach lining in some people. Ulcers can also be due to long-term use of nonsteroidal anti-inflammatory drugs (NSAIDs) such as aspirin, ibuprofen or naproxen. Infants have gastric cells that produce an enzyme called rennin (chymosin) in order to curdle milk and promote better absorption, but this enzyme is not found in the stomach of adults.

The gastric folds (gastric rugae) are coiled sections of tissue in the lining of the stomach. They provide elasticity by allowing the stomach to expand when a bolus of food enters. The folds stretch out through the action of sensory nerve endings called mechanoreceptors that respond to the increase in pressure. Muscles in the stomach wall contract periodically, churning the food to enhance digestion. The length of time food remains inside the stomach differs from one person to another, and also depends on the type of food eaten. Starchy foods or those rich in carbohydrates and sugar can remain in the stomach for up to two hours, while protein-rich food like meat takes longer to digest, and may remain in the stomach for up to four hours.

After the stomach has done its work, the highly acidic mixture of gastric juices and food - known as chyme - leaves the stomach through the pyloric sphincter and enters the small intestine, where it spends the next three to five hours. The small intestine has three parts - the duodenum, about 25 centimetres long, is the first section, receiving chyme from the stomach. The entry of chyme triggers the release of a pancreas-stimulating hormone called secretin from glands in the duodenal wall. Ducts from the pancreas, gallbladder and liver enter the duodenum, bringing bicarbonate to neutralise the acid in the chyme, pancreatic enzymes to further aid digestion, and bile salts to emulsify fat. The mucous lining of the duodenum begins absorbing water and nutrients - in particular iron and calcium - before the food contents enter the next part of the small intestine - the jejunum. A duodenal ulcer is erosion of the mucosa in the duodenum. Duodenal ulcers are most likely to occur in the first section of the duodenum, which is exposed to the highly acidic chyme. The most common causes of duodenal ulcers are H. pylori infection and chronic NSAID therapy, both of which can also cause peptic ulcers in the stomach.

The jejunum is approximately one metre long and makes up about two-fifths of the small intestine. The main function of the jejunum is the absorption of important nutrients such as sugars (glucose) from carbohydrates, fatty acids from dietary fats, and amino acids from protein. It has a deep red colour due to its extensive blood supply, and its peristaltic movements are rapid and vigorous to move its contents along.

The ileum is the final and longest segment of the small intestine – about 3.5 metres - and is responsible for the absorption of vitamin B12, bile salts, and whatever products of digestion were not absorbed by the jejunum. It plays a crucial role in the breakdown of carbohydrates into simpler sugars, and lipids into fatty acids and glycerol. Various enzymes produced in the lining of the ileum assist with this process.

CELIAC DISEASE
DAMAGED SMALL INTESTINE LINING

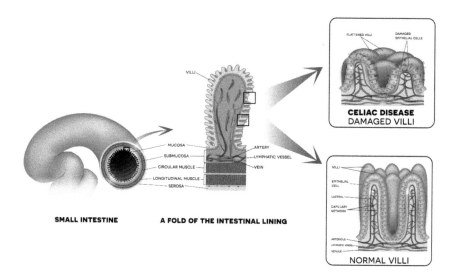

13.4 Celiac (coeliac) disease damages the villi in the small intestine

The walls of the small intestine are made up of folds, each of which has many tiny finger-like projections known as villi on the surface. The villi have several smaller projections called microvilli that play an important role in the absorption of vital nutrients and vitamins. Tiny lymphatic capillaries on the villi - called lacteals - absorb digested fats and fat-soluble vitamins. The lacteals merge to form larger lymphatic vessels that transport the mixture of lymph and emulsified fats - called chyle - to the thoracic duct of the lymphatic system, where it is emptied into the blood stream at the left subclavian vein.

In people with coeliac disease, exposure to gluten damages the villi of the small intestine, interfering with the absorption of nutrients from food. The intestinal damage often causes diarrhoea, fatigue, weight loss, bloating and anaemia, and can lead to serious complications unless a strict gluten-free diet is followed. In children, malabsorption can affect growth and development if not addressed.

The ileum meets the first part of the large intestine - the caecum - at the ileocaecal valve that prevents reflux of material back into the ileum. Attached to the caecum is the appendix that contains some lymphatic tissue. The large intestine - often called the bowel - deals with the waste products of digestion. It is wider and shorter than the small intestine - approximately 1.5 metres in length as compared with 7 metres in length for the small intestine - and has a smooth inner wall. Its internal mucosa contains cells that reabsorb water and any remaining nutrients, as well as goblet cells that secrete mucus for lubrication. After the caecum, which is approximately 6 centimetres long, the next part of the large intestine is the colon, which consists of ascending, transverse and descending sections. Muscles in the wall of the large intestine contract to gather the colon into pouches called haustra. These pouches relax and distend when filled, and contract to squeeze their contents along to the next pouch. Bacteria in the large intestine prepare the chyme for elimination by fermenting remaining carbohydrates, converting remaining proteins into amino acids, and breaking down amino acids into simpler substances. They also help in decomposing bilirubin - a pigment found in bile - as well as producing some B vitamins and vitamin K, which are absorbed via the colon.

The final result is faeces, consisting of indigestible roughage, dead blood cells, bacteria, fatty acids and mucus. The colour of faeces comes from the dead blood cells and bilirubin. The sigmoid colon is the lower section of the large intestine and connects the descending colon to the rectum. Faeces are stored in the sigmoid colon until ready to be eliminated from the body through the anal canal. The rectum - approximately 20 centimetres - lies in front of the sacrum and coccyx. The anal canal is the last 2-3 centimetres of the rectum with the anus - external opening - guarded by external and internal sphincter muscles that relax and open during defecation.

Several organs are regarded as accessory organs of the digestive system, as they assist with the digestive process. The gallbladder is a pear-shaped, green sac located behind the liver. It receives bile from the liver, which it concentrates and stores, and releases it into the duodenum via the bile duct. Bile - which is alkaline - helps to neutralise any excess stomach acid in the duodenum. It also digests fats, acting as a surfactant to emulsify fats in food in the same way that soap emulsifies fats, and it helps the body absorb fat-soluble vitamins and nutrients. In a healthy gallbladder, these processes occur painlessly. However, when a blockage occurs in the gallbladder, or it stops functioning correctly, it can cause considerable pain and discomfort - usually in the mid or upper-right section of the abdomen as well as in the chest, right shoulder blade and back.

Gallstones are solid masses of cholesterol or bile pigment that can be different sizes, and occur when high levels of fat and bile cause crystals to form. These crystals may combine over time and expand into stones that can be as small as a grain of sand or as large as a golf ball, and may or may not cause symptoms. Treatment options include surgically removing the gallbladder, medication to break up the gallstones, and antibiotics to treat infections. If the gallbladder is removed, a less concentrated version of bile is still delivered from the liver directly to the duodenum. Acute or sudden inflammation of the gallbladder (cholecystitis) occurs when bile can't leave the gallbladder. This commonly occurs when a gallstone obstructs the duct that carries bile out of the gallbladder.

The liver is a two-lobed organ in upper right side of abdomen, below the diaphragm. The lobes are composed of smaller lobes (lobules) made up of cells called hepatocytes arranged around a central vein. The human liver is thought to be responsible for up to 500 separate functions, usually in combination with other systems and organs. The liver receives oxygenated blood via the hepatic artery, and the hepatic portal system connects capillaries of the small intestine and other digestive organs to the hepatic portal vein that travels to the liver. As intestinal blood is nutrient-rich for a few hours after a meal, the liver collects nutrients that are not immediately needed before the blood is distributed to the rest of the body. It also helps in cleansing the blood of bacteria and toxins that are picked up from the intestines. The liver stores some vitamins as well as minerals such as copper and iron, releasing them into the bloodstream via the hepatic veins when the body needs them. The liver also helps to break down fats and either stores the fats or releases them as energy when needed. It also manufactures an estimated 800 to 1,000 ml. of bile daily.

Bile is a composition of water (85%), bile salts (10%), mucus and pigments (3%), fats (1%), inorganic salts (0.7%) and cholesterol (0.3%). The bile is stored in the gallbladder where it becomes more concentrated, and this increases its potency and intensifies its effect in digesting fats. The liver also breaks down proteins for easier absorption and the by-product of this process is called ammonia. Ammonia can be toxic to the body in large amounts, but the liver turns the toxic ammonia into a substance called urea that travels in the bloodstream to the kidneys and is excreted in the urine.

An enzyme called alanine aminotransferase (ALT) made by cells in the liver is involved in the breakdown of proteins. When the liver is damaged or inflamed, ALT can rise and be released into the bloodstream. Measuring the level of ALT in a person's blood can help doctors evaluate liver function or determine the cause of a liver problem, and an ALT test is usually part of an initial screening for liver disease. The liver also breaks down alcohol in the blood as well as medications. Long-term excessive alcohol use can lead to cirrhosis, a condition whereby scar tissue replaces healthy liver tissue.

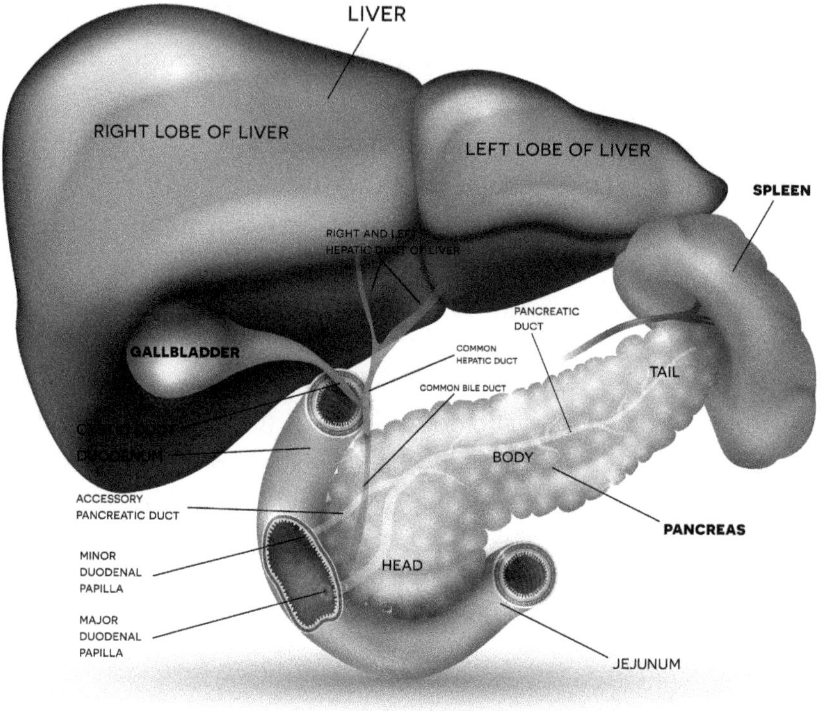
LIVER
RIGHT LOBE OF LIVER
LEFT LOBE OF LIVER
SPLEEN
GALLBLADDER
PANCREATIC DUCT
COMMON HEPATIC DUCT
COMMON BILE DUCT
TAIL
BODY
ACCESSORY PANCREATIC DUCT
PANCREAS
MINOR DUODENAL PAPILLA
HEAD
MAJOR DUODENAL PAPILLA
JEJUNUM

13.5 Liver, gallbladder and pancreas

A third accessory organ of digestion is the pancreas - a thin gland, 12-15 centimetres long, with a head, body and tail. It is located behind the stomach and connected to the duodenum by two ducts. Most pancreatic cells - approximately 99% - are exocrine cells, secreting pancreatic juice that is alkaline to buffer the acidic chyme from the stomach. The rest are endocrine cells, located in an area of the pancreas called the Islets of Langerhans that produces the hormones insulin and glucagon. A healthy, functioning pancreas secretes about eight cups of pancreatic juice into the duodenum daily. This fluid contains pancreatic enzymes as well as bicarbonate to neutralise stomach acid as it enters the small intestine. Pancreatic enzymes include an alkaline lipase that works with bile from the liver to break down fat molecules, proteases (trypsin and chymotrypsin) that break down proteins, and amylase that breaks down carbohydrates (starches) into sugars that are more easily absorbed by the body.

Disorders of the pancreas include pancreatitis - an inflammation of the pancreas that can be acute, chronic or hereditary - and pancreatic cancer. One of the major challenges associated with pancreatic cancer is that the condition often goes undetected for a long period of time because signs and symptoms seldom occur until advanced stages. By the time symptoms occur, cancer cells are likely to have spread to other parts of the body, often preventing surgical removal of tumours. Symptoms of pancreatic cancer include weight loss, pain, jaundice and bowel obstruction, and surgery depends on where the tumour is located. If the cancer is in the head of the pancreas, a pancreaticoduodenectomy – also called a Whipple procedure – may be carried out to remove the head of the pancreas, duodenum, gallbladder, part of the bile duct and nearby lymph nodes. In some situations, part of the stomach and colon may also be removed, and the remaining parts of the pancreas, stomach and intestines reconnected to allow digestion of food. Surgery to remove the left side (body and tail) of the pancreas is called a distal pancreatectomy, and the spleen may also need to be removed. In some people, the entire pancreas may need to be removed. This is called a total pancreatectomy, and lifelong insulin and enzyme replacement will be required. Chemotherapy and radiation therapy are often used alongside surgery for pancreatic cancer.

The energy required for all the processes and activities that take place in the body is derived from the foods that are ingested, and a healthy, well-functioning digestive system means a healthy body. Although it is remarkably resistant to abuse, the digestive system is still vulnerable and can break down. Some ailments are minor, but others are severe and life threatening, such as cancers that can target almost every part of the digestive system. Halitosis (bad breath) is a common problem that may be due to eating certain foods such as onions, garlic or some spices, or it can be due to poor dental hygiene. In some cases halitosis may indicate a more serious issue such as diabetes, liver or kidney disease, gastrointestinal problems or even cancer, and if persistent, it should be medically investigated. Some dogs can be trained to detect diseases like diabetes and cancer in humans, using their very sensitive sense of smell. Belching (burping) or passing gas (flatulence) is natural and common. Excessive belching or flatulence, accompanied by bloating, pain or swelling of the abdomen can sometimes interfere with daily activities or cause embarrassment. These signs and symptoms don't usually point to a serious underlying condition and are often reduced with simple dietary changes, but if they are severe or ongoing, medical investigation may be required.

Candida albicans is a species of yeast that is a normal part of the microbes living in the gastrointestinal tract. Small amounts of the yeast also live in various warm, moist areas throughout the body including the mouth, rectum, vagina and parts of the skin. Candida overgrowth syndrome (candidiasis) occurs when the balance between candida and the good bacteria in the body is being disturbed. In a healthy state, the good bacteria in the gut control the growth of candida. When this balance is disturbed, candida changes into a more aggressive fungal infection that spreads, and can cause a variety of symptoms including painful vaginal yeast infections (thrush), oral thrush, digestive issues, bloating, skin rashes, fungal infections, mood swings, depression and low energy levels. Causes of candida albicans overgrowth include antibiotics, food allergies, a high sugar diet and a weakened immune system.

Enteritis is inflammation of the small intestine. In some cases, the inflammation can also involve the stomach (gastritis) and large intestine (colitis). Enteritis can be due to viral or bacterial infection, parasites, or induced by radiation, medication, alcohol or drugs. It can also be related to inflammatory conditions such as Crohn's disease. Symptoms of enteritis may include fever, nausea, vomiting, diarrhoea and abdominal pain. Viral enteritis usually clears up without treatment in a few days. If it persists, medical attention should be sought. Gastroenteritis, sometimes called stomach flu, is an infection of the stomach and intestines and can be caused by bacteria, parasites or viruses - commonly the norovirus. It can be caused by close contact with an infected person or animal, food poisoning or drinking unclean water. Symptoms include diarrhoea, gas, nausea, vomiting, poor appetite, abdominal cramps, pain, fever, tiredness, weakness, headaches and muscle aches.

Helminths are parasitic worms that can infect the tissues and intestines. Symptoms of helminth infections include nausea, vomiting, abdominal pain, confusion and gastrointestinal bleeding. Helminths are found throughout the world, but are most commonly found in Central/South America, Africa and East Asia. The three main types are roundworms (nematodes), tapeworms (cestodes) and flukes or flatworms (trematodes). Schistosoma is a category of trematodes, commonly known as blood flukes that cause a disease known as schistosomiasis or bilharzia. The parasites that cause bilharzia live in certain types of freshwater snails and emerge from the snails into the water. A person can become infected when their skin comes in contact with the contaminated water. Parasitic worm infections in humans are usually treated with anthelmintic (anti-worm) medication prescribed by a medical professional.

Crohn's disease causes inflammation of the digestive tract that can lead to abdominal pain, severe diarrhoea, fatigue, weight loss and malnutrition. Inflammation caused by Crohn's disease can involve different areas of the digestive tract in different people, but it most commonly affects the ileum and the colon. Heredity and a malfunctioning immune system play a role in the development of

Crohn's disease. The disease is named after gastroenterologist Burrill Bernard Crohn, who in 1932, at Mount Sinai Hospital in New York, described a series of patients with inflammation of the terminal ileum - the area most commonly affected by this disease.

DIVERTICULOSIS and DIVERTICULITIS

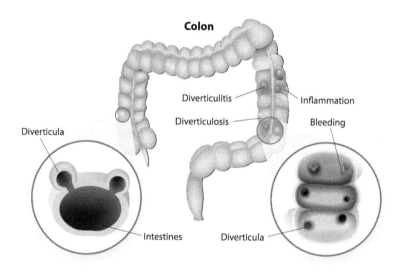

13.6 Diverticulosis and diverticulitis

Diverticulosis occurs when small, bulging pouches called diverticula develop in the large intestine. Diverticulosis is common, especially after the age of 40, and seldom causes problems. However, one or more of these pouches may become inflamed or infected, leading to diverticulitis. Diverticulitis can cause severe abdominal pain, fever, nausea and a marked change in bowel habits. Spastic colon - also called irritable bowel syndrome (IBS) - is the spontaneous contractions or loss of movement of the muscles in the small and large intestines, and is often due to stress. Patients with IBS have a range of symptoms, including abdominal pain and changes in bowel habits – either constipation with hard infrequent stools or diarrhoea with soft watery stools.

Ulcerative colitis is an inflammatory bowel disease (IBD) that causes long-lasting inflammation and ulcers in the innermost lining of the large intestine and rectum. Symptoms usually develop over time, rather than suddenly. Proctitis is inflammation of the lining of the rectum. It can cause rectal pain, diarrhoea, bleeding and discharge, as well as the continuous feeling of needing to have a bowel movement. Proctitis symptoms can be short-lived, or they can become chronic. Proctitis is common in people who have inflammatory bowel disease e.g. Crohn's disease or ulcerative colitis. Sexually transmitted infections are another cause, or it can be a side effect of radiation therapy for certain cancers. Colorectal cancer is cancer that occurs in the colon or in the lower colon near the rectum. Polyps are abnormal, benign growths of tissue on the inner lining of the colon or rectum. However, they can sometimes become cancerous and should be medically investigated.

Viral hepatitis refers to a viral infection that causes liver inflammation. There are different types including A, B and C, and each has different causes and severity. Hepatitis A is transmitted via contaminated food, drink, faeces or utensils. It causes loss of appetite, nausea, diarrhoea, fever and chills. Hepatitis A is more common in developing countries that lack clean drinking water and have poor sanitation systems. Most people recover from hepatitis A in 4-6 weeks without liver failure or long-term complications.

Hepatitis B is transmitted via sexual contact, contaminated syringes and transfusion equipment. This condition can cause serious complications, including liver failure and cancer. A vaccination is available to prevent Hepatitis B. Hepatitis C is usually transmitted via blood transfusions. It is a chronic disease that can cause inflammation leading to cirrhosis, liver failure or liver cancer.

Non-alcoholic fatty liver disease is an increasingly common condition where fat builds up in the liver, causing damage and inflammation. People who are obese and have conditions related to obesity - e.g. type 2 diabetes - are more likely to have this disease. A joint study by UK BioBank and Oxford-based diagnostic imaging company Perspectum, found that people with more than 10% fat in their liver were more than twice as likely to be hospitalised with COVID-19 than those who had healthy (less than 5%) levels of fat in their liver. This study was published in June 2020 and a link can be found in the references. Hemochromatosis causes an excess of iron to build up in the body and this can also damage the liver. The liver has the capacity to regenerate after injury or surgery to remove tissue, and starts growing back as the existing cells enlarge and multiply. Within a week after removing two-thirds of the liver, it can return to the same weight it was before surgery.

Eating disorders are conditions related to persistent eating behaviours that negatively impact a person's health and emotions. The most common eating disorders are anorexia nervosa, bulimia nervosa, binge eating and overeating. Anorexia and bulimia can have similar symptoms, such as an intense preoccupation with food and a distorted body image. However, anorexia sufferers severely reduce their food intake to lose weight, while bulimia sufferers eat an excessive amount of food in a short period of time, and then purge or use other methods to prevent weight gain. Those who have a binge-eating disorder regularly eat too much food (binge) and feel a lack of control over their eating. They may eat quickly or eat more food than intended, even when they are not hungry, and may continue eating long after they feel full. They may be normal weight, overweight or obese. The term 'obesity' means too much body fat, and is usually based on body mass index (BMI) that compares weight to height. To work out your BMI using metric measurements, divide your weight in kilograms by your height in centimetres squared and multiply your answer by

10,000. For example the BMI of a person who weighs 56kg and is 157cm tall is 23 (56 ÷ 157 ÷ 157 x 10,000 = 22.71 – the BMI is rounded up to 23). A BMI of less than 18.5 is regarded as underweight, a normal BMI is between 18.5 and 24.9, and a BMI of 25 to 29.9 is overweight but not obese, while a BMI of 30 or more is in the obese range. Although there are genetic, behavioural, medical, metabolic and hormonal influences on body weight, obesity occurs when a person takes in more calories than they burn through exercise and normal daily activities, and the body stores the excess calories as fat. A diet high in calories, lacking in fruits and vegetables, full of fast food and sugary beverages, oversized portions, and a sedentary lifestyle, all contribute to weight gain. Obesity is on the rise all over the world, even in children, and can lead to serious health conditions including heart disease and stroke, high blood pressure, diabetes, some cancers, osteoarthritis, and breathing problems such as asthma and sleep apnea (when a person stops breathing for short episodes during sleep).

The term 'metabolic syndrome' is often heard these days, and refers to a group of risk factors including high blood pressure, high blood sugar, unhealthy cholesterol levels and abdominal fat. Having any one of these risk factors is not good, but when combined, they can lead to serious health issues such as increasing the risk of blood vessel and heart disease that can lead to heart attacks and strokes, and greatly increasing the risk of diabetes. The good news is that metabolic syndrome can be controlled with healthy lifestyle changes. British researcher Professor Jimmy Bell coined the phrase TOFI meaning 'thin outside, fat inside', and this is now regarded as a fast-growing health concern. People who are TOFI have a lot of visceral fat, which is fat around the organs in the abdominal cavity i.e. liver, pancreas and intestines. Professor Bell and his colleagues studied visceral fat using MRI scans of the body and found that it is not always noticeable externally, but a person can have lots of it internally. They also found that it is directly linked to metabolic syndrome and type-2 diabetes -

so in other words, a TOFI is metabolically obese. An article written by Professor Bell and colleague in 2014 entitled "Body Fat, our own Janus" discusses adipose tissue and its importance in maintaining whole body homeostasis, and says that it is not about how much adipose tissue we carry, but also about its distribution. They also state: "Obesity is endemic in many parts of the world, with little signs of abating. If obesity continues to increase at the current rate, it is estimated that well over 1 billion people in the world will be overweight or obese by 2050."

One of the most cutting-edge areas of ongoing digestive research involves the 'gut-brain axis', which looks at the connection between the brain and the gut and its potentially huge influence over health. The gut and the brain are connected through the largest cranial nerve in the body - the vagus nerve - and they communicate both ways through this nerve connection. There are also a number of additional pathways that are involved in the complex functioning of the gut-brain axis, including communication through nerve endings, the endocrine system, gut hormones and nerve chemicals called neurotransmitters - many of which are made in the gut.

An extremely important neurotransmitter for digestive functioning is serotonin (5-HT) and it is thought that up to 95% of the serotonin in the human body is found in the digestive tract. Serotonin is considered to be a vital part of the communication system between the brain and the gut. It affects many aspects of gut function, including how fast food moves through the system, how much fluid - such as mucus - is secreted in the intestines, and how sensitive the intestines are to sensations like pain and fullness from eating. Studies have found that people with IBS who experience constipation often have lower levels of serotonin, the muscles in their rectums are less reactive to serotonin, and they're more likely to have hard or lumpy stools. Those with IBS who tend to have high levels of serotonin can have diarrhoea and their rectums are more reactive, with loose or watery stools.

Research on altering serotonin levels through medication to help IBS sufferers is ongoing.

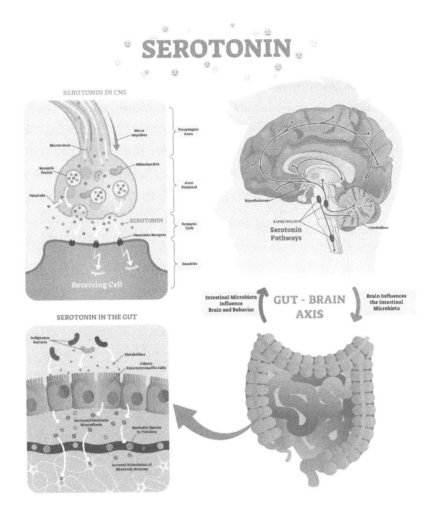

13.7 Serotonin and the gut-brain axis

What is happening in the digestive system may directly influence brain function and behaviour, and the gut is sometimes referred to as the 'second brain' or the enteric nervous system (ENS). The ENS is a web of sensory neurons, motor neurons and interneurons embedded in the wall of the gastrointestinal system, stretching from the lower third of the oesophagus - or some say from the taste buds of the tongue - right through to the rectum. The gut microbiome is thought to play an important role in the gut-brain axis, and in good health and disease prevention. The microbiome is made up of trillions of live microbes living within the human intestines - particularly the large intestine - and includes mainly bacteria and other microbial material. The development of the gut microbiome begins at birth, when a newborn baby's digestive tract is first exposed to microbes in the vaginal birth canal. However, evidence suggests that babies may come into contact with microbes even earlier while in the womb. With age, the gut microbiome continues to grow and develop, and is influenced by factors such as diet, lifestyle, medications and stress e.g. antibiotics can damage the good bacteria in the gut as well as kill pathogenic bacteria.

For a healthy gut microbiome, prebiotic and probiotic foods are recommended. Prebiotics are found in fibre-rich foods such as fruits, vegetables and whole grains, and they serve as fertiliser for the friendly bacteria in the digestive system. Probiotics are live bacteria that occur in many fermented foods, including yogurt and fermented vegetables. Both prebiotics and probiotics may support helpful bacteria and other organisms in the gut, and research into their benefits is ongoing. Anyone concerned about the risk of side effects should speak with a medical or nutritional professional before significantly increasing their intake of prebiotics or probiotics.

To prevent ill health, it is important that the gut maintains a natural balance of 'good' bacteria such as lactobacillus and bifidobacterium, as well as 'bad' bacteria like staphylococcus or clostridium that are naturally present and can cause problems if they get out of control. Leaky gut syndrome (LGS) is the term used for a digestive condition in which gaps in intestinal walls allow bacteria and other toxins to pass into the bloodstream. Many doctors and healthcare professionals do not recognise LGS as a diagnosable condition. However, current scientific evidence suggests that a leaky gut may contribute to a range of medical conditions e.g. a 2019 review shows evidence of leaky gut occurring before the onset of autoimmune type 1 diabetes, while a 2017 review suggests that leaky gut may contribute to mental health conditions such as anxiety and depression. However, scientists need to carry out further research to support these claims.

It probably goes without saying that what we eat has a significant impact on our health, but there is so much conflicting information available that it's often difficult to know what to do for the best. Some generally accepted ideas include avoiding sugar as well as processed and refined foods, eating a varied diet including fresh vegetables, fruits, legumes and whole grains, eating moderate portions, drinking plenty of water, eating more slowly and chewing food well, getting more fresh air and exercise - and enjoying our food. Once healthy eating habits are established, a person will generally have more energy, a happier digestive system, better health and can more easily maintain a healthy weight.

14. The Nervous System

The nervous system is the control and communication system of the body. It senses changes in the external environment and within the body, and responds to those changes through voluntary actions such as closing a window when we feel cold, and involuntary actions such as breathing.

The two divisions of the nervous system are the central nervous system incorporating the brain and spinal cord, and the peripheral nervous system incorporating twelve pairs of cranial nerves arising from the brain, and thirty-one pairs of spinal nerves emerging from the spinal cord. Some peripheral nerves are sensory, relaying information from receptors located all over the body (including every hair) to the central nervous system. Others are motor nerves carrying information from the central nervous system, leading to voluntary or involuntary actions by or within the body. There are also some mixed nerves containing both motor and sensory fibres e.g. nerves that enable the tongue to move as well as carry information to the brain about different tastes. Inter-neurons control complex networks between neurons, allowing them to send signals to one another in a harmonised way, and are also involved in reflex actions e.g. the sudden jerky withdrawal of a hand or leg when pricked by a pin, or sneezing because of irritants in the nasal passages.

The peripheral nervous system is divided into two branches – the voluntary (somatic) nervous system and the involuntary (autonomic) nervous system. The voluntary nervous system allows us to control some parts of the body - including the skeletal muscles - while the autonomic nervous system operates without our conscious control. This branch of the peripheral nervous system is further subdivided into the sympathetic and parasympathetic nervous systems, which have opposing functions in the body.

Sympathetic System

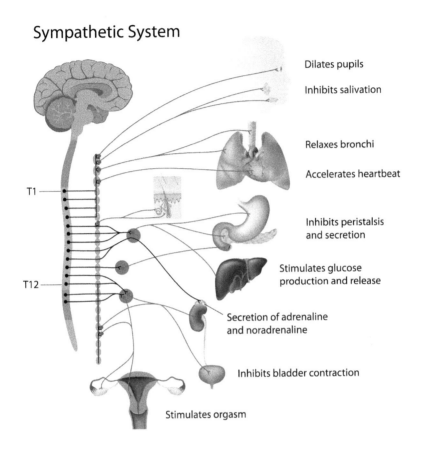

Dilates pupils

Inhibits salivation

Relaxes bronchi

Accelerates heartbeat

T1

Inhibits peristalsis and secretion

Stimulates glucose production and release

T12

Secretion of adrenaline and noradrenaline

Inhibits bladder contraction

Stimulates orgasm

14.1 Sympathetic nervous system

The sympathetic nervous system is activated in times of stress, preparing the body for 'fight or flight'. Some of its effects include stimulation of the adrenal and sweat glands, increased heart and breathing rate, release of stored glucose into the blood to fuel the musculoskeletal system for action, and decreased blood flow to the integumentary, digestive, urinary and reproductive systems. These bodily changes enable us to deal with dangerous or emergency situations quickly, but can be harmful if they occur too often. Austrian born endocrinologist Dr. Hans Seyle defined stress as 'the non-specific response of the body to any demands placed upon it'. Seyle, who coined the word 'stress' in the 1950's from the Latin word 'stringere' which means to 'draw tight', set up the International Institute of Stress in Montreal in 1976. He discovered that hormones released in response to stress participate in the development of many degenerative diseases. He also saw that when faced with demands, be they physical or emotional, people reacted in different ways and what was stressful for one person could be exciting and stimulating for another. Positive stress that motivates is defined as 'eustress' and we all need a certain amount of this in our lives in order to function well. Stress becomes harmful (distress) when it occurs too often or lasts too long. Fatigue is one of the first signs of distress and it is important to do something about it before it becomes exhaustion and leads to ill health.

The parasympathetic nervous system, which is associated with 'rest and digest', causes a lowering of heart and respiratory rates, and an increase in blood flow to the integumentary, digestive, urinary and reproductive systems. The vagus nerve - one of the cranial nerves - is an important parasympathetic nerve that helps the body return to a normal and healing mode after stressful situations. While there are actually two vagus nerves (left and right), they are usually referred to together as 'the vagus nerve.' It is the body's major parasympathetic nerve, supplying parasympathetic fibres to all the major organs of the head, neck, chest and abdomen. The vagus nerve is responsible for the gag reflex, slowing the heart rate, controlling sweating, regulating blood pressure, stimulating peristalsis of the gastrointestinal tract and controlling vascular tone.

Stimulation of the vagus nerve is a medical procedure that is used by doctors to treat a variety of conditions, and can be done either manually or through electrical pulses. Vagus nerve stimulation has been linked to treating epilepsy, improving digestive conditions, reducing inflammation, and managing anxiety disorders.

Parasympathetic System

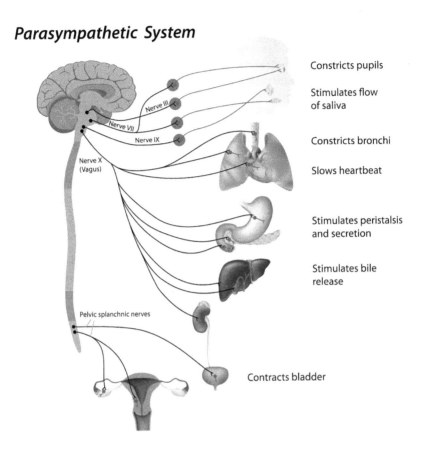

Constricts pupils

Stimulates flow of saliva

Constricts bronchi

Slows heartbeat

Stimulates peristalsis and secretion

Stimulates bile release

Contracts bladder

Nerve III

Nerve VII

Nerve IX

Nerve X (Vagus)

Pelvic splanchnic nerves

14.2 Parasympathetic nervous system

Factors that may stimulate the vagus nerve naturally include practices that bring about relaxation and help the mind switch off, and include yoga, meditation, deep breathing, singing, massage and reflexology, among other things. Nutrients and supplements that are being researched for boosting vagus nerve activity include probiotics, fibre, zinc and omega-3 fatty acids.

The nervous system is made up of nervous tissue consisting of several components. Neuroglia ('glia' is Latin for 'glue') is a special connective tissue that supports nerve cells and makes up 40% of the brain and spinal cord. Neuroglia cannot transmit impulses, but glial cells can divide by mitosis. Types of glial cells include oligodendrocytes – produce myelin that supports and protects nerves of the central nervous system; ependymal cells - form the epithelial lining of the ventricles (cavities) in the brain and the central canal of the spinal cord; star shaped cells called astrocytes - link nerve cells to blood vessels and wrap around brain capillaries, helping to form the blood–brain barrier; microglia - macrophage cells that act as the first and main form of active immune defence in the central nervous system, and Schwann cells - produce myelin in peripheral nerves and form the principal glia of the peripheral nervous system.

One of the most common types of primary brain tumour is a tumour of the glial cells called a glioma. Gliomas are classified according to the type of glial cell involved in the tumour e.g. astrocytomas, ependymomas, oligodendrogliomas. A glioma can affect brain function and may be life threatening, depending on its location and rate of growth. In general, glioma treatment options include surgery, radiation therapy, chemotherapy or targeted therapy such as 'CyberKnife' - a radiation therapy device that uses an approach called stereotactic radiosurgery or stereotactic body radiation therapy (SRS or SBRT) to deliver precise and targeted doses of radiation with extreme accuracy.

Neurons are nerve cells responsible for the sensory, motor and integrative functions of the nervous system. They are and long and narrow, are easily damaged, and cannot divide by mitosis. A nerve (e.g. the sciatic nerve that runs through the hip joint and down the lower limb) is composed of a bundle of nerve cells bound together by connective tissue. Endoneurium is the connective tissue that surrounds each nerve fibre, perineurium surrounds groups of nerve fibres (called fascicles) and epineurium is the outer covering of the nerve, binding the fascicles together. This connective tissue can be regarded as part of the body's fascia or fascial network.

NEURON

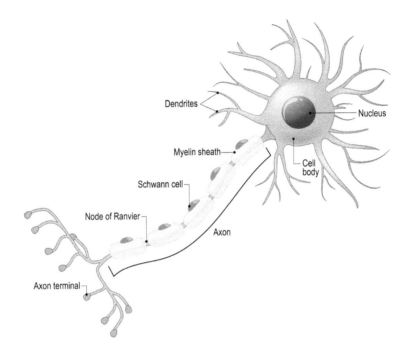

14.3 Structure of a neuron

Neurons are composed of several parts. The cell body contains the cytoplasm, nucleus and organelles - but no centrioles, as they do not divide by mitosis. Dendrites are the branching parts of a neuron that collect information from other neurons and send it to the cell body from where it is passed along to other nerve cells. The axon is a long, single nerve fibre transmitting signals away from the cell body. The axon has end feet (axon terminals) with sacs called synaptic vesicles that store nerve chemicals called neurotransmitters. Some axons like those in the sciatic nerve are quite long. The synapse (synaptic cleft) is a small gap where one neuron meets another. Neurotransmitters flow through this gap from the axon terminals of one neuron to the dendrites of the next. Myelin is a white fatty substance that insulates axons and speeds up nerve conduction. Like the rubber coating on an electrical flex, the myelin sheath coats the nerves of both the central and peripheral nervous systems. Schwann cells - so named after German physiologist Theodor Schwann, who discovered them in the 19th century - produce myelin for peripheral nerves, while oligodendrocytes produce myelin in the central nervous system.

Myelin contains proteins that can be targeted by the immune system. The destruction of myelin in the central nervous system is what triggers many of the symptoms of multiple sclerosis (MS), causing communication problems between the brain and the rest of the body, and eventually causing permanent damage or deterioration of nerves.

Signs and symptoms of MS vary widely, and depend on the amount of nerve damage and which nerves are affected. Some people with severe MS may lose the ability to walk independently or at all, while others may experience long periods of remission without any new symptoms. There is currently no cure for MS, but treatments can help speed recovery from attacks, modify the course of the disease, and manage symptoms.

Nodes of Ranvier are microscopic gaps found within myelinated axons. Their function is to speed up nerve signals along the axon, as the signal can jump from one node to the next rather than travelling down the length of the axon. The neurilemma is an extra membrane made by Schwann cells and surrounding myelinated axons in peripheral nerves, protecting the peripheral nerve fibres. Damaged nerve fibres may regenerate if the cell body is not damaged and the neurilemma remains intact.

Neuron communication

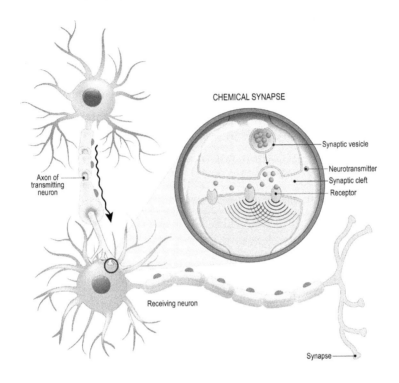

CHEMICAL SYNAPSE

Synaptic vesicle

Neurotransmitter

Synaptic cleft

Receptor

Axon of transmitting neuron

Receiving neuron

Synapse

14.4 Neuron communication

Neurons communicate or send impulses through an explosion of electrical activity called an 'action potential' that takes place from the dendrite all the way to the axon ends. Chemicals in the human body that are 'electrically charged' are called ions. Important ions in the nervous system are sodium and potassium, both of which have 1 positive charge, +, calcium, which has 2 positive charges, ++ and chloride, which helps to move fluid in and out of cells and has a negative charge, -. There are also some negatively charged protein molecules involved. When a neuron is not sending a signal, it is 'at rest.' When a nerve impulse comes by, the voltage changes and the negative state inside the axon turns positive due to the action of the sodium-potassium pump that uses active transport to move molecules from a high concentration to a low concentration (remember active transport from Chapter 4). Positively charged sodium surrounds the axon, while there is a high concentration of negatively charged chloride ions as well as some positively charged potassium inside. As a nerve impulse enters the axon, the sodium-potassium pump pushes sodium into the axon while it takes potassium out - this is called depolarisation. As more sodium enters, the potential of the impulse changes from -70 mV to +30 mV, (a difference of 100 mV) and this change is called an 'action potential'. The sodium-potassium pump works quickly to pass the impulse along the axon - when one segment becomes depolarised it causes the segment next to it to be depolarised, and so a wave of electricity is passed down the length of the axon. As the electrical impulse leaves the axon, the axon reverts to a normal state called the 'resting potential' – in other words, it has a break. At the end of the axon, the axon terminals release neurotransmitters that carry the nerve impulse across the gap (synapse) to the dendrites of the next neuron where the process is repeated - and in this way, a nerve impulse is carried along a nerve from one cell to the next. Used up neurotransmitters are removed by diffusion, broken down by enzymes or recycled.

Neurotransmitters play a role in nearly every function in the human body, and more than 100 neurotransmitters with different types of action have been identified in the body to date. Acetylcholine is a neurotransmitter that triggers muscle contractions, stimulates some hormones, and helps to control the heartbeat. It also plays an important role in brain function and memory. Low levels of acetylcholine are linked with memory and thinking problems, such as those that affect people with Alzheimer's disease. Alzheimer's disease is an irreversible, progressive brain disorder that slowly destroys memory and thinking skills, and can eventually affect the ability to carry out simple, everyday tasks. Alzheimer's is the most common cause of dementia among older adults. Dementia is the loss of cognitive functioning such as thinking, remembering and reasoning, as well as behavioural abilities, to such an extent that it interferes with a person's daily life and activities. There are different types of dementia and it ranges in severity from mild, when it is just beginning to affect a person's functioning, to severe, when the person must depend completely on others for basic activities of daily living. Alzheimer's disease is named after Dr. Alois Alzheimer, who in 1906 noticed changes in the brain tissue of a woman who had died of an unusual mental illness. Her symptoms included memory loss, language problems and unpredictable behaviour. After she died, he examined her brain and found many abnormal clumps (called amyloid plaques) and tangled bundles of fibres (neurofibrillary, or tau tangles). These plaques and tangles in the brain are still considered some of the main features of Alzheimer's disease. Another feature is the loss of connections between nerve cells in the brain. Some Alzheimer's medications help slow the breakdown of acetylcholine in the body, and this can help control some symptoms such as memory loss. High levels of acetylcholine can cause excessive muscle contractions that can lead to seizures, spasms and other health issues. The nutrient choline, which is present in many foods, is a building block of acetylcholine. Choline is found in meat, liver, fish, eggs, beans, nuts, peas, spinach and some other foods. Another disease that can affect the brain is Creutzfeldt-Jakob disease (CJD), a degenerative brain disease that leads to dementia and ultimately, death. Malformed 'prion' protein in the brain usually causes CJD. Prion protein is a normal part of the brain, but sometimes it can fold the wrong way as it forms and this 'misfolded' prion infects the brain and destroys brain cells. A small number of CJD cases have a genetic link.

Dopamine is an important neurotransmitter for memory, learning, behaviour and movement coordination, as well as being a pleasure or reward neurotransmitter that the brain releases during pleasurable activities. Dopamine is also involved in muscle movement, and a deficiency can cause Parkinson's disease that often starts with a slight tremor in one hand and a feeling of stiffness in the body. Over time, other signs and symptoms such as a shuffling gait, voice tremor, sleep problems, loss of sense of smell and poor coordination can develop, and some people develop dementia. Some research has shown that regular exercise improves dopamine signaling in people who have early stage Parkinson's disease.

Endorphins are neurotransmitters that inhibit pain signals and create an energised, euphoric feeling. One of the best-known ways to boost levels of feel-good endorphins is through aerobic exercise. A 'runner's high' for example, is a release of endorphins, and research indicates that laughter also releases endorphins. The word endorphin means 'endogenous morphine' which is a natural painkiller produced within the body.

Adrenaline - also known as epinephrine - which is involved in the body's 'fight or flight' response, is both a hormone released by the adrenal glands and a neurotransmitter released by the brain, and both have the same effects. When a person is stressed or scared, their body releases adrenaline, increasing heart rate and breathing, giving the muscles a jolt of energy, and helping the brain make quick decisions in the face of danger. While this is useful if a person is threatened, chronic stress can cause the body to release too much adrenaline leading to health problems such as decreased immunity, high blood pressure, diabetes and heart disease.

Gamma-aminobutyric acid (GABA) is a mood regulating neurotransmitter that stops neurons from becoming overexcited. This is why low levels of GABA can cause anxiety, irritability and restlessness. Benzodiazepines - drugs used to treat anxiety - work by increasing the action of GABA and this has a calming effect on anxiety attacks. These can have side effects such as drowsiness, dizziness etc. and should not be used without medical advice. Foods that may help with GABA production in the brain include whole grains, broccoli, bananas, spinach, almonds, walnuts, green tea, fish (especially halibut) and some other foods.

Serotonin is a neurotransmitter that plays a role in depression and anxiety. It helps regulate mood, appetite, blood clotting, sleep and the body's circadian rhythm. Drugs called elective serotonin reuptake inhibitors (SSRIs) can relieve depression by increasing serotonin levels in the brain. Seasonal affective disorder (SAD) causes symptoms of depression in some people when daylight is less abundant. Research indicates that SAD is linked to low levels of serotonin. It is thought that exercise and being exposed to bright light - especially sunlight - can increase serotonin naturally. Serotonin is synthesized from the amino acid tryptophan, and increasing levels of tryptophan-containing foods may affect serotonin levels in the brain. Tryptophan is one of the 10 essential amino acids that the body uses to synthesise the proteins it needs. Tryptophan occurs naturally in most foods that contain protein, and the following foods contain tryptophan in significant quantities: red meat, dairy products, nuts, seeds, bananas, soybeans and soy products, tuna, shellfish and turkey meat.

Depression can be defined as a mental disorder causing depressed mood, loss of interest or pleasure, feelings of guilt or low self-worth, disturbed sleep or appetite, low energy and poor concentration. As well as SAD, there are different types of depression with varying causes, including illness, certain drugs, distressing events or genetics. Clinical depression is a severe form of depression - also known as major depressive disorder - and can affect people of any age, including children. Symptoms include depressed mood, lack of interest in activities, insomnia, fluctuations in weight, fatigue, and in some cases, suicidal thoughts. It can lead to problems in personal relationships or in day-to-day activities e.g. work, school or social activities.

Psychological counselling, antidepressant medications or a combination of the two, is usually prescribed. Bipolar affective disorder - formerly called manic depression - is a mental health condition that causes extreme mood swings including emotional highs and depressive lows. Postpartum or postnatal depression is a mood disorder associated with childbirth and can affect both sexes. Symptoms may include extreme sadness, anxiety, low energy, crying episodes, irritability and changes in sleeping or eating patterns. Many treatment options are available for depression, and qualified and experienced mental health care professionals can help sufferers regain control of their life.

Many symptoms of depression overlap with the symptoms of post-traumatic stress disorder (PTSD) - once called shell shock or battle fatigue syndrome. PTSD is a serious condition that can develop after experiencing or witnessing a terrifying event. Symptoms may include nightmares, flashbacks and severe anxiety, as well as uncontrollable thoughts about the event. Families of victims, emergency personnel and rescue workers can also develop PTSD. Symptoms usually start within 3 months of the event, but in some cases they don't begin until years later, and the severity and duration of the condition can vary from person to person. Symptoms include reliving the event through thoughts or flashbacks, avoiding places, thoughts, or situations that can be reminders of the trauma, excessive emotions e.g. outbursts of anger, and negative changes in thinking and mood. Young children with PTSD may have delayed development in areas such as language, motor skills and toilet training. Treatment includes psychotherapy, medication or a combination of both. Eye Movement Desensitization and Reprocessing (EMDR) is a trauma-focused psychotherapy that is one of the most studied treatments for PTSD.

We often hear about white and grey matter in relation to the nervous system. White matter consists of the white myelinated axons of neurons in the brain and spinal cord. Grey matter consists of unmyelinated structures such as neuroglia, cell bodies, axon terminals and unmyelinated axons and dendrites. The brain, which weighs about 1.3 kilograms and consists of around 100 billion neurons and 10,000 billion neuroglia, has grey matter on the outside and white matter inside. The cerebrum is the largest part of the brain and is divided into left and right halves (hemispheres), connected by a large bundle of transverse white matter fibres called the corpus callosum. The outer layer (cerebral cortex) is composed of folds of grey matter made up of cell bodies that need to be near blood cells. Inside this lies the white matter, composed of myelinated axons connecting parts of the brain together.

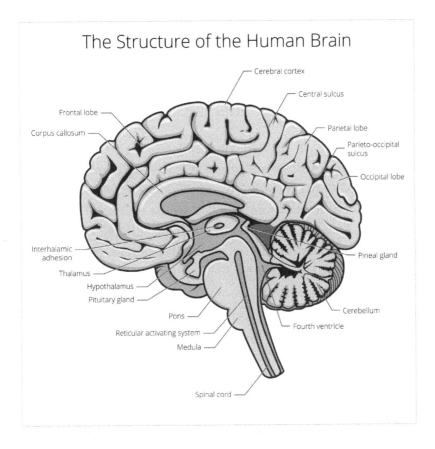

14.5 Anatomy of the brain

Each hemisphere of the brain is subdivided into four lobes, named after the bones that cover them - frontal, parietal, temporal and occipital. The frontal lobe is involved with speech production, concentration, higher-level cognition, expressive language, problem solving, decision making and voluntary muscle control. The occipital lobe is involved with vision, interpreting visual stimuli and information i.e. the ability to understand what you're seeing. The visual information is then sent to the parietal and temporal lobes for further processing. The parietal lobe is the interpretation area, understanding speech and processing tactile information like pressure and pain, as well as the body's senses. The temporal lobe is involved with visual and auditory memory, hearing and learning, and it contains the hippocampus, which is involved with the formation of memories. The olfactory cortex is an area of the temporal lobe that receives sensory information from the olfactory bulb (part of the olfactory nerve for the sense of smell), and is involved in the identification of odours - the olfactory system is described in detail in Chapter 15.

The diencephalon is an area located deep in centre of the brain, underneath the cerebrum and above the pituitary gland, and includes the epithalamus, thalamus and hypothalamus. Also located within the diencephalon is the third ventricle, one of the four brain ventricles or cavities filled with cerebrospinal fluid. The epithalamus – above the thalamus - contains the pineal gland that produces melatonin, a serotonin-derived hormone that modulates sleep and waking patterns. The thalamus (meaning 'storeroom' in Greek) is a large, dual lobed mass of grey matter located beneath the epithalamus and above the hypothalamus. Nerve fibres project out of the thalamus to the cerebral cortex in all directions, allowing hub-like exchanges of information between the spinal cord and the cerebrum. It is the part of the brain where sensory information from all over the body converges i.e. vision, sound, taste, touch (but not smell) and proprioception (the sense of where a person's body is in space), and the sensory signals are sent to the appropriate area of the cerebral cortex for interpretation. The thalamus is also thought to play a role in the regulation of sleep and wakefulness. During sleep, the thalamus suppresses the relay of sensory information to the cerebral cortex through a process known as GABA-mediated inhibition. GABA neurotransmitters bind to neurons in the thalamus and inhibit their action potential, with the end result being that less information is sent to the sensory-motor cortex, allowing a person to sleep. However, during REM (rapid eye movement) sleep, the thalamus is active, sending the cortex images, sounds and other sensations that fill our dreams. Damage to the thalamus can lead to sleep disorders and insomnia.

The hypothalamus - about the size of a pearl - directs many important functions in the body. It has a satiety center that regulates appetite via two counter-balancing chemicals that act like angel and devil! The satiety chemicals stimulate the hypothalamus to increase metabolism, reduce appetite and increase insulin to deliver energy to cells rather than be stored as fat, while the eating chemicals decrease metabolism and increase appetite, firing off signals that tell the body it is time to eat. The hypothalamus regulates body temperature by initiating the process of shivering and inhibiting the production of sweat. If the current body temperature is too high, heat is given off or sweat is produced to cool the body down. The hypothalamus is also responsible for helping to regulate the natural cycles of wakefulness and sleep. An area called the suprachiasmatic nucleus at the front of the hypothalamus receives information about light through the eyes, and directs the pineal gland to release the hormone melatonin at night, and stop its release in daylight, thus regulating the internal body clock. Sexual behavior is influenced by the hypothalamus as it stimulates the pituitary gland to release sex hormones, and when levels of those hormones fall, sexual desire follows suit. The hypothalamus is also an important emotional centre, controlling the molecules that generate feelings of exhilaration, anger or unhappiness. One of the most important functions of the hypothalamus is to link the nervous system to the endocrine system via the pituitary gland. There is more detailed information about the hormones that are produced and released by the hypothalamus in Chapter 16.

An area called the limbic system is located between the cerebrum and diencephalon, and is composed of various brain structures including the amygdala, cingulate gyrus, fornix, hippocampus, hypothalamus, thalamus and the olfactory cortex, which deals with the sense of smell. These limbic system structures are involved in many human instincts, emotions and motivations - particularly those related to survival such as fear and anger. The limbic system is also involved in feelings of pleasure that are related to survival - such as those experienced from eating and sex. The limbic system is regarded as being a primitive part of the brain, because these same structures were present in brains of the very first mammals. The parts of the limbic system directly involved with the sense of smell are sometimes collectively referred to as the rhinencephalon or 'smell brain'.

The amygdala is an almond-shaped mass of nerve cells involved in emotional responses, hormonal secretions and memory, and is responsible for fear conditioning - the process by which we learn to fear something. The amygdala is located in the medial temporal lobe, just in front of the hippocampus. Similar to the hippocampus, the amygdala is a paired structure, with one located in each hemisphere of the brain, and its activity increases during REM sleep. Non-REM sleep comes first and occurs in three stages, and each stage can last from 5-15 minutes. Stage one is the first 5-10 minutes of sleep, when the eyes are closed but it is easy to wake up. Stage two is light sleep, when the heart rate slows down and body temperature drops. Stage three is deep sleep, and during this stage the body rests and repairs. This is followed by REM sleep, which occurs about 90 minutes after falling asleep and can last from 10 minutes to an hour. The eyes move rapidly from side to side behind closed eyelids, and most dreaming occurs then, but the arm and leg muscles become temporarily paralysed to prevent dreams being acted out. Then the cycle starts over again – alternating between non-REM and REM sleep. With age, less time is spent in REM sleep e.g. babies can spend up to 50% of their sleep in the REM stage, compared to about 20% for adults. Memory consolidation most likely requires both non-REM and REM sleep.

The cingulate gyrus is a fold or bulge in the brain involved with sensory input concerning emotions, and the regulation of aggressive behavior. Damage to the cingulate gyrus may result in cognitive, emotional and behavioural disorders. The fornix (meaning 'arch' in Latin) is a c-shaped arch of white matter (axons) connecting different parts of the limbic system together e.g. hippocampus to hypothalamus. The hippocampus - shaped like a seahorse - is located in the inner region of the temporal lobe and is primarily associated with memory. It is thought to be mainly involved in storing long-term memories, and in making those memories resistant to forgetting. It is also thought to play an important role in spatial processing and navigation. The hippocampus is vulnerable to damage from chronic, heavy alcohol consumption.

The basal ganglia is a region made up of three clusters of neurons at the base of the brain, deep beneath the cerebral cortex, and is involved in controlling automatic movements of skeletal muscles and regulating muscle tone. It is responsible for involuntary movements like tremors, and is abnormal in a number of neurologic conditions, including Parkinson's disease and Huntington's disease. A person with basal ganglia dysfunction may have difficulty starting, stopping or sustaining movement.

The cerebellum ('little brain') is located at the back of the head, behind the brainstem. The cerebellum receives information from the sensory organs, spinal cord and other parts of the brain, and then regulates motor movements. It organises voluntary movements such as posture, balance, coordination and speech, resulting in smooth and balanced activity. It is involved in learning both motor and cognitive skills, and making them automatic when acquired. Although the cerebellum is a relatively small part of the brain (about 10% of the total weight), it contains roughly half of the brain's neurons. Evolutionarily speaking, the cerebellum is an older part of the brain, and is present in animals that scientists believe existed before humans. Damage to the cerebellum can result in a loss of ability to coordinate muscular movements - a condition called ataxia. Blindfolded people with ataxia cannot touch the tip of their nose with their finger, because they cannot coordinate movement with their sense of where a body part is located. Another sign of ataxia is a changed speech pattern, due to uncoordinated speech muscles. Cerebellar damage may also result in staggering or abnormal walking movements. People who consume too much alcohol show signs of ataxia because alcohol inhibits the activity of the cerebellum. Ataxia can also occur as a result of degenerative diseases like multiple sclerosis or Parkinson's disease, trauma, brain tumours, genetic factors, or as a side effect of medication prescribed for bipolar disorder.

The brainstem is continuous with the spinal cord and is divided into three areas - medulla, pons and midbrain - and each of these areas has a specific function. The lower part is the medulla (medulla oblongata), which is about 3 centimetres long and is the primary centre for respiration. In response to a decrease in blood pH, the respiratory centre in the medulla sends nerve signals to the diaphragm and the external intercostal muscles between the ribs, to increase the breathing rate and the volume of the lungs during inhalation. The medulla also controls the reflexes for non-respiratory air movements, such as coughing, sneezing, swallowing and vomiting. Cranial nerves VIII-XII originate in the medulla.

The pons (meaning 'bridge') is about 2.5 centimetres long and lies just above the medulla. One of its functions is to act as a bridge for the relay of signals to and from the cerebrum (thinking) and cerebellum (movement). It is the origin of various nerves in the body, including cranial nerves V-VIII. The vestibulocochlear nerve (cranial nerve VIII) attaches at the junction of the medulla and pons, and is the sensory nerve of hearing and balance. The pons is another respiratory centre, assisting the medulla in controlling the rate or speed of involuntary respiration. It triggers exhalation in response to stimulus from pulmonary stretch receptors in lung tissue that detect when the lungs have reached capacity. During sleep, the pons sends signals to relax muscles essential for body posture and limb movements, so that dreams are not 'acted out'.

Above the pons is the midbrain or mesencephalon - associated with vision, hearing, motor control, sleep and wakefulness, arousal (alertness) and temperature regulation. The midbrain is an important part of the central nervous system, and is the relay point that all signals from the peripheral nervous system in the body must pass through to reach the brain. It has reflex centres for vision, hearing and touch i.e. 'scary' experiences are processed here and reflex arcs are generated e.g. screaming, jumping, exclamations. Cranial nerves III-IV originate in the midbrain.

The spinal cord is about 42 centimetres long and 2 centimetres in diameter, extending from the medulla and ending above the second lumbar vertebra (L2). The lumbar, sacral and coccygeal nerves angle downwards, looking like wisps of hair coming off the end of the spinal cord, so this area is called the 'cauda equina' - meaning 'horse's tail' due to its appearance. The spinal cord transports nerve impulses from the periphery of the body to the brain and from the brain to the periphery of the body. It receives and integrates information and produces reflex actions i.e. predictable, automatic responses to specific changes in the environment. The spinal cord has grey matter in the centre to receive and integrate information, and white matter on the outside consisting of myelinated nerve fibres carrying impulses.

Spinal cord injury can result from direct trauma to the nerves themselves, or from damage to the bones, soft tissues or blood vessels surrounding the spinal cord. There are two kinds of spinal cord injury - complete and incomplete. In a complete injury, a person loses all ability to feel and voluntarily move below the level of the injury. In an incomplete injury, there is some functioning below the level of the injury. Spinal cord injuries can result from falls, diseases like polio or spina bifida, motor vehicle accidents, sports injuries, industrial accidents, physical assaults or other causes. If the spine is weak because of another condition such as arthritis, minor injuries can cause spinal cord trauma.

Polio (poliomyelitis) is a contagious, disabling and life-threatening disease caused by the poliovirus that can infect the spinal cord, causing paralysis. It can be transmitted through direct contact with someone infected with the virus, or less commonly, through contaminated food and water. Due to vaccination, polio is now a rare disease.

Spina bifida (split spine) is a birth defect that occurs when the spine and spinal cord don't form properly. The neural tube is the structure in a developing embryo that eventually becomes the baby's brain, spinal cord and the tissues that enclose them. It normally forms early in pregnancy and closes by the 28th day after conception. In babies with spina bifida, a portion of the neural tube doesn't close or develop properly, causing defects in the spinal cord and in the bones of the spine. The condition can range from mild to severe, depending on the type of defect, size, location and complications. When necessary, early treatment for spina bifida involves surgery - although this doesn't always completely resolve the problem.

Doctors aren't certain what causes spina bifida, though it may result from a combination of genetic, nutritional and environmental risk factors, such as a family history of neural tube defects and folate (vitamin B-9) deficiency.

The MeStructure

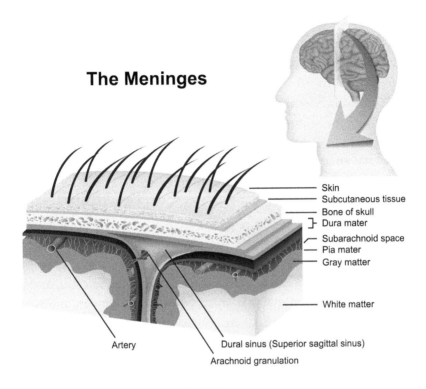

The Meninges

Skin
Subcutaneous tissue
Bone of skull
Dura mater
Subarachnoid space
Pia mater
Gray matter

White matter

Artery

Dural sinus (Superior sagittal sinus)

Arachnoid granulation

14.6 Meninges

Surrounding the brain and spinal cord is a three-layered membrane called the meninges. The outer dura mater is a double layered, tough, fibrous membrane attached to the inside of the skull. The arachnoid mater is the middle layer, and this delicate membrane under the dura is made up of a web-like connective tissue. The pia mater is the innermost vascular layer, and supplies blood to the brain and spinal cord. Cerebrospinal fluid (CSF) lies between the pia and arachnoid mater in the sub-arachnoid space. It circulates around the brain and spinal cord, supplying nutrients and carrying away waste. CSF is formed in ventricles of the brain called the 'choroid plexuses'. The pumping of the CSF between the cranium (skull) and sacrum (pelvis) is called the craniosacral rhythm (CSR). This rhythm is around 6-12 cycles per minute as compared to the respiratory rhythm 12-20 breaths per minute and the pulse rate of 60-80 beats per minute. CranioSacral

Therapy (CST) developed by osteopath Dr. John Upledger in the 1970's, is a gentle, hands-on method of evaluating and enhancing the functioning of the craniosacral system. CST is derived from cranial osteopathy and its effectiveness has been confirmed by research and clinical work for over 30 years. Treatments focus on encouraging the body to 'reset' by restoring a normal CSR.

Meningitis is an inflammation of the meninges usually caused by a viral or bacterial infection. Some cases of meningitis improve without treatment in a few weeks, but others - particularly bacterial meningitis - can be life threatening and require emergency antibiotic treatment. The swelling from meningitis typically triggers symptoms such as headache, fever and a stiff neck.

A meningioma is a tumour that arises from the meninges, and is the most common type of tumour that forms in the head. Although not technically a brain tumour, it is included in this category because it may compress the brain, nerves and blood vessels. Most meningiomas grow very slowly - often over many years - without causing symptoms, but sometimes their effects can cause serious disability. Meningiomas are more common in females than males and are often discovered later in life, but may occur at any age. Because most meningiomas grow slowly, often without any significant signs and symptoms, they do not always require immediate treatment, and may be monitored over time.

The nerves of the peripheral nervous system are the twelve pairs of cranial nerves from the brain and the thirty-one pairs of spinal nerves from the spinal cord. The cranial nerves and their functions are listed below. Each cranial nerve is paired and is present on both sides. The numbering of the cranial nerves is based on the order in which they emerge from the brain, front to back. Some are sensory nerves, some are motor nerves and some are mixed nerves with both motor and sensory functions.

The Cranial Nerves

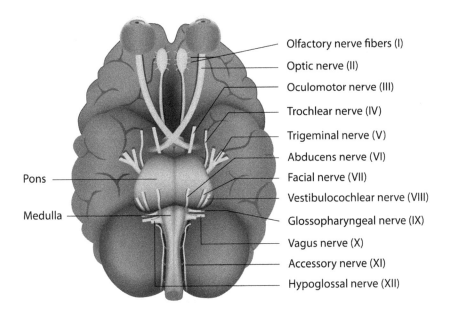

Olfactory nerve fibers (I)
Optic nerve (II)
Oculomotor nerve (III)
Trochlear nerve (IV)
Trigeminal nerve (V)
Abducens nerve (VI)
Facial nerve (VII)
Vestibulocochlear nerve (VIII)
Glossopharyngeal nerve (IX)
Vagus nerve (X)
Accessory nerve (XI)
Hypoglossal nerve (XII)

Pons
Medulla

14.7 Cranial nerves

The olfactory nerve (I) is instrumental for the sense of smell and is one of the few nerves that are capable of regeneration.

The optic nerve (II) carries visual information from the eye to the brain.

The oculomotor nerve (III) controls eye movements, the constriction of the pupil, and keeps the eyelid open.

The trochlear nerve (IV) innervates the muscles of the eye that control rotational movement.

The trigeminal nerve (V) is responsible for sensation and motor function in the face and mouth e.g. pain - trigeminal neuralgia (sensory) mastication (motor).

The abducens nerve (VI) innervates the muscles of the eye that control lateral movement.

The facial nerve (VII) controls the muscles of facial expression and carries taste sensations from the anterior two-thirds of the tongue and mouth. Bell's palsy, named after Scottish anatomist Charles Bell, is a condition that causes a temporary weakness or paralysis of the muscles in the face when the facial nerve becomes inflamed, swollen or compressed. The condition causes one side of the face to droop or become stiff, leading to difficulty smiling or closing the eye on the affected side. In most cases, Bell's palsy is temporary and symptoms usually disappear after a few weeks.

The vestibulocochlear nerve (VIII) is responsible for transmitting sound and balance information from the inner ear to the brain.

The glossopharyngeal nerve (IX) is involved with taste, salivation, swallowing, speech, the tonsils, and blood flow to the middle ear and brain.

The vagus nerve (X) is responsible for many tasks, including increasing gastrointestinal peristalsis, slowing down heart and breathing rate, sweating, controlling the muscles of speech and swallowing and keeping the larynx open for breathing. It is an important nerve of the parasympathetic nervous system. The word 'vagus' means 'wandering' in Latin, and this is a very appropriate name as the vagus nerve is the longest cranial nerve, running all the way from the brainstem to the colon.

The spinal accessory nerve (XI) controls specific muscles of the shoulder and neck.

The hypoglossal nerve (XII) controls tongue movements for speech, food manipulation in the mouth and swallowing.

Cranial nerves never cross, (except for the 4th cranial nerve that controls the eyes) and clinical findings are always on the same side as the cranial nerve involved.

The 31 pairs of spinal nerves originate in the spinal cord and emerge through openings called intervertebral foramina on each side of the vertebral column (spine). They form part of the peripheral nervous system and connect the central nervous system to receptors throughout the body. Spinal nerves are classified as 'mixed nerves' as they have motor and sensory functions. Each nerve has two roots - posterior (dorsal) roots with sensory axons, and anterior (ventral) roots with motor axons. Eight pairs of cervical nerves (C1-C8) innervate the skin and muscles of the head, neck and upper shoulders. Twelve pairs of thoracic nerves (T1-T12) innervate the shoulders and arms. Five pairs of lumbar nerves (L1-L5) innervate the abdominal wall, external genitals and part of the legs. Five pairs of sacral nerves (S1-S5) innervate the buttocks, perineum and legs, and one pair of coccygeal nerves (Co1) innervates the rectum and anus.

Some of the spinal nerves merge together to form a group called a 'plexus'. There are five main plexi formed by the spinal nerves:

The cervical plexus is composed of the merging of spinal nerves C1-C5. These divide into smaller nerves that carry sensory messages and provide motor control to muscles of the neck and shoulders.

The brachial plexus is formed by spinal nerves C5 -T1, and branches off into nerves carrying sensory messages and providing motor control to muscles of the arms and upper back.

The lumbar plexus is formed by spinal nerves L1-L4, and this plexus splits into nerves carrying sensory messages and providing motor control to muscles of the abdomen and legs.

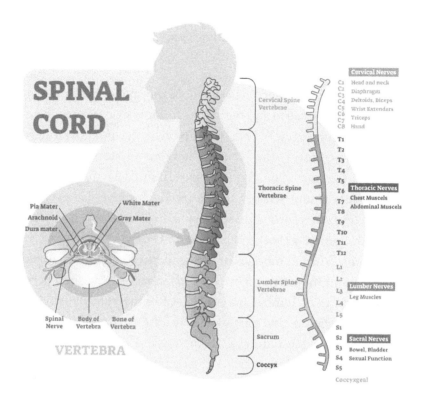

SPINAL CORD

Pia Mater
Arachnoid
Dura mater

White Mater
Gray Mater

Spinal Nerve | Body of Vertebra | Bone of Vertebra

VERTEBRA

Cervical Spine Vertebrae

Thoracic Spine Vertebrae

Lumber Spine Vertebrae

Sacrum

Coccyx

Cervical Nerves
C1 Head and neck
C2 Diaphragm
C3
C4 Deltoids, Biceps
C5 Wrist Extenders
C6
C7 Triceps
C8 Hand

T1
T2
T3
T4
T5
T6 **Thoracic Nerves**
T7 Chest Muscles
T8 Abdominal Muscels
T9
T10
T11
T12

L1
L2
L3 **Lumber Nerves**
L4 Leg Muscles
L5

S1
S2 **Sacral Nerves**
S3 Bowel, Bladder
S4 Sexual Function
S5

Coccyxgeal

14.8 Spinal nerves

The sacral plexus is formed by spinal nerves L4-S4, and then branches out into nerves carrying sensory messages and providing motor control to muscles of the legs. The coccygeal plexus is composed of the merging of nerves S4-Co1, and supplies motor and sensory control to the genitalia and the muscles that control defecation.

The lumbar nerves, sacral nerves and coccygeal nerve are often collectively referred to as the lumbosacral plexus.

Nerves T2 -T12 do not form a plexus; they are intercostal nerves that serve muscles between the ribs, as well as the skin and muscles of the anterior and lateral trunk.

The solar plexus - or what medics call the 'celiac plexus' - is a bundle of nerves located in the abdominal area. It includes the vagus nerve and the lesser splanchnic nerves of the autonomic nervous system that supply signals and information to and from the visceral organs and blood vessels. The visceral organs include the stomach, intestines, liver, gallbladder, spleen, pancreas, reproductive organs, kidneys, heart and lungs. Along with medical and anatomical importance, there is also a lot of mysticism and spirituality associated with this part of the body. Its vulnerability to physical blows is well known in martial arts, and the solar plexus chakra is a spiritual energy centre said to correspond with the feelings of fear, anxiety, introversion, personal power, opinion formation and spiritual growth.

Dermatomes and myotomes are areas of the body that are served by spinal nerves. A dermatome is a distinct area of the skin innervated by a particular spinal nerve root, and sends information to the central nervous system about body sensations such as heat, pain, itching, and the body's position. There are four major categories of dermatomes. The cervical dermatomes cover skin on the back of the head, neck, shoulders, arms and hands. The thoracic dermatomes cover skin on the inner arm, chest, abdomen and mid-back. The lumbar dermatomes cover skin on the lower back, front of the legs, outer thighs, outer calves and tops and bottoms of the feet. The sacral dermatomes cover skin on the genital and anal regions, back of the legs, central back of the thighs and calves, and the outer edges of the feet. Every muscle cell in the body needs input from a nerve in order to stay healthy and do its work. A myotome is a group of muscles innervated by a particular spinal nerve e.g. L3 (lumbar nerve 3) affects the quadriceps and adductor muscles that extend the knee. Both dermatomes and myotomes are 'mapped' and provide medical professionals and physical therapists with a reference for testing and determining the specific nerve root(s) that may be compromised or are causing symptoms. Medical professionals use their knowledge of the location of myotomes and dermatomes during physical examinations. To identify the specific spinal nerve(s) that may underlie muscle weakness, they perform isometric strength tests according to the myotome map.

Spinal nerves can be affected by a variety of medical problems, resulting in pain, weakness, or decreased sensation. A pinched nerve is due to pressure or compression of a spinal nerve and is the most common spinal nerve disorder. A herniated or slipped disc occurs when the structure of the spine is disrupted, allowing the vertebral structures to fall out of place and compressing the spinal cord and/or a spinal nerve. The first symptoms usually include neck pain or tingling down the arm or leg, depending on which area of the spine is affected. In some cases, a herniated disc can be a medical emergency as it could cause permanent damage to the spinal cord.

Motor neurone disease (MND) is the name given to a group of diseases in which the motor nerves fail to function normally. Muscles then gradually weaken and waste as neurons degenerate and die. MND is also known as Lou Gehrig's disease in the USA – so named after a famous baseball player who died of the disease. Myasthenia gravis is due to a breakdown in the normal communication between motor nerves and muscles, and is characterized by weakness and rapid fatigue of voluntary muscles. There is no cure for myasthenia gravis, but treatment can help relieve signs and symptoms, such as weakness of arm or leg muscles, double vision, drooping eyelids, and difficulties with speech, chewing, swallowing and breathing.

Charcot-Marie-Tooth disease (CMT) is a spectrum of nerve disorders named after the three physicians who first described this condition in 1886 - Jean-Martin Charcot and Pierre Marie of France and Howard Henry Tooth of the United Kingdom. It is a genetic disease that affects the peripheral nerves – particularly the myelin sheath - and progresses slowly, causing loss of normal function and sensation in the feet/legs and hands/arms. There is no cure for this condition and it can be severely disabling for some people. However physical/occupational therapy and moderate activity - but not overexertion - can help maintain muscle strength, endurance and flexibility.

When any part of the relay system such as the brain, nerves or spinal cord is damaged, the signals to move may not make it through to the muscles and paralysis may result. Complete paralysis is when a person cannot move, or has no control over their paralysed muscles, and they may also have no sensation in those muscles. Partial or incomplete paralysis (paresis) is when a person still has some feeling in, and possibly control over, their paralysed muscles. Localised paralysis affects just one specific area - like the face e.g. Bell's palsy, hands, feet or vocal cords. Generalised paralysis is more widespread and is grouped by how much of the body is affected, and usually depends on where the brain or spinal cord is injured. Monoplegia is a kind of generalised paralysis that affects just one limb, while diplegia affects the same area on both sides e.g. both arms and both legs. Hemiplegia affects just one side of the body and is usually caused by a stroke that damages one side of the brain. Quadriplegia (or tetraplegia) is when all four limbs are paralysed - sometimes along with certain organs - while paraplegia is paralysis from the waist down.

Locked-in syndrome is the most severe form of paralysis, where a person loses control of all their muscles except the ones that control their eye movements. Paralysis can be stiff and spastic - when muscles are tight and jerky e.g. cerebral palsy. It can also be floppy and flaccid - when muscles sag and eventually shrink. Paralysis can be caused by accidents that damage the spinal cord, strokes that block arteries to the brain, demyelinating diseases like multiple sclerosis, or motor neurone diseases that damage the motor nerve cells controlling the muscles used to walk, breathe, speak and move the limbs. Some people experience sleep paralysis on waking up or falling asleep. It is a feeling of being conscious but unable to move, and sufferers may also hallucinate. Sleep paralysis sometimes accompanies other sleep disorders such as narcolepsy, which is an overpowering need to sleep caused by a problem with the brain's ability to regulate sleep.

Neuritis is a general term used to describe various diseases involving the inflammation of a nerve or a group of nerves. It is often associated with pain, changes in sensations, weakness, numbness, paralysis or muscle wasting. Compression of a nerve or direct injury to a nerve can lead to inflammation. Administration of some medicines by injection can sometimes cause chemical injury and inflammation to the nerves lying in close proximity to the injection site e.g. neuritis may develop as a side effect of certain drugs used in chemotherapy. Neuritis and other diseases that damage peripheral nerves are collectively known as neuropathies.

Pain is a signal in the nervous system that something may be wrong. When a person feels pain, sensory receptors send messages via nerve fibres to the spinal cord and brainstem and then onto the brain where the sensation of pain is registered, the information is processed and the pain is perceived. The International Association for the Study of Pain defines pain as "an unpleasant sensory and emotional experience associated with actual or potential tissue damage, or described in terms of such damage". Acute pain is short-term pain, usually experienced after some sort of accident or injury. Once that injury has healed, the pain disappears and doesn't usually require further treatment. Chronic pain lasts longer and is a major source of suffering for many people. It interferes with daily functioning and is often accompanied by distress. In 2019, the World Health Organization (WHO) updated the International Classification of Diseases (ICD-11), and for the first time they included chronic pain and provided specific pain diagnoses. Under the new system, chronic pain is classified as either chronic primary pain (e.g. fibromyalgia, chronic migraine, non-specific back pain) or chronic secondary pain due to another disease in which the chronic pain becomes a problem in its own right e.g. pain related to surgery, cancer, injury, internal disease, disease in the muscles, bones or joints, headaches or nerve damage.

Pain is also typically divided into two types: nociceptive pain and neuropathic pain. Nociceptive pain includes pain from things like burns, bruises, muscle strains, ligament sprains, and inflammation from issues like arthritis and infections. The pain signals in these cases are caused by physical damage to body tissues, and act as a trigger to remove the cause of injury. Neuropathic pain involves trauma to the nerves, leading to abnormal or persistent pain sensations. Allodynia is an unusual symptom where a person feels pain from stimuli that don't normally cause pain e.g. lightly touching the skin or brushing the hair. There are many causes of nerve trauma, some involving direct damage to the nerves, and others where nerves are damaged as a result of damage to other tissues. Conditions that can lead to neuropathic pain include viral infections like herpes and shingles (i.e. post-herpetic neuralgia), cancer, limb amputation and carpal tunnel syndrome. Phantom pain occurs after the amputation of a limb and refers to painful sensations that feel as though they are coming from the missing limb. Doctors once believed this post-amputation phenomenon was a psychological problem, but experts now recognise that these real sensations originate in the spinal cord and brain.

Peripheral neuropathy is the term used when pain results from damage to the peripheral nerves outside the brain and spinal cord. Symptoms are numbness, weakness and pain, usually in the hands and feet, but it can also affect other areas of the body. One of the most common causes of peripheral neuropathy is diabetes, which damages the capillaries supplying oxygen and nutrients to the nerves, causing them to deteriorate. There are many others triggers for peripheral neuropathy, including chronic alcohol use/abuse, toxic exposure i.e. neuropathy may be a side effect of chemotherapy, and vitamin deficiencies (especially B vitamins). People with peripheral neuropathy generally describe the pain as stabbing, burning or tingling. In many cases, symptoms improve, especially if caused by a treatable condition. Medications can reduce the pain of peripheral neuropathy by blocking the pain messages sent to the brain for processing.

Neuralgia is defined as a sharp, shocking pain that follows the path of a nerve, and is due to irritation or damage to the nerve. Common neuralgias include post-herpetic neuralgia that continues after a bout of shingles, and trigeminal neuralgia, which is a stabbing or electric-shock-like pain along the course of the trigeminal nerve in the face. Sciatica refers to neuralgia or pain that radiates along the path of the sciatic nerve that runs from the lower back, through the hips and buttocks and down each leg. Sciatica usually affects only one side of the body, and most commonly occurs when a herniated disc, bone spur on the spine, or narrowing of the spine (spinal stenosis) compresses part of the nerve.

The sciatic nerve is composed of a number of nerves from the lumbosacral plexus i.e. from L4 - S3. Near the back of the knee, the sciatic nerve divides into 2 main branches: the tibial nerve that continues down the back of the leg to the heel and sole of the foot, and the common peroneal nerve that travels sideways along the outer part of the knee to the outer border of the leg and foot. Compression of the L4 nerve can result in pain radiating from the lower back down the leg to the knee, and compression of the S1 nerve can result in pain radiating down to the foot. Sciatica can sometimes be caused by pressure on the sciatic nerve from the piriformis muscle that that runs vertically over the nerve, and in some people, the nerve runs directly through the muscle.

As far back as the time of the Roman Empire, physician, writer and philosopher Claudius Galen (c.130 AD - c.210 AD) said: "Look to the nervous system as the key to maximum health."

The nervous system deserves as much attention as other more obvious body systems, and healthy habits can help treat or prevent nerve damage or deterioration, and keep the nervous system functioning smoothly. Learning new things is one of the best ways to exercise brain cells and improve brain health e.g. learning a foreign language, a new hobby that involves fine motor skills, or learning to dance - which is also good for physical fitness and social interaction. In a study done at the University of British Columbia, researchers found that regular aerobic exercise appears to boost the size of the hippocampus - the brain area involved in verbal memory and learning.

Nerves need glucose for energy, and regular meals will ensure that the body's glucose levels don't become depleted. A balanced diet that includes good levels of B12 and D vitamins, as well as healthy fats, can benefit the nervous system. Sleep helps strengthen circuits within the nervous system and maintains healthy levels of hormones and chemicals that regulate the body clock. Avoiding or limiting environmental factors that can cause nerve damage, such as repetitive motions, or exposure to toxic chemicals, can also contribute to a healthy nervous system.

15. The Senses

Humans have five basic senses: touch, smell, sight, hearing and taste. The organs associated with each sense send information to the brain to help us perceive, understand and enjoy the world around us.

Sense organs on the skin

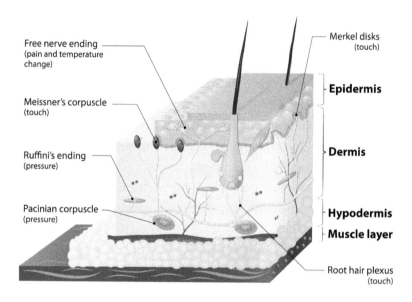

15.1 The sense of touch

Touch

The sense of touch is controlled by a network of nerve endings and touch receptors in the skin known as the somatosensory system. This system is responsible for all the sensations we feel – cold, hot, smooth, rough, pressure, itch, pain, vibrations and more. The somatosensory system is composed of four main types of nerve receptors: mechanoreceptors, thermoreceptors, pain receptors and proprioceptors. All four of these receptors are interspersed throughout the skin, and when activated, they generate impulses that are carried along nerves to the spinal cord and on to the brain.

Mechanoreceptors for touch detect sensations such as pressure, vibrations and texture. Some rapidly adapting touch receptors respond to a change in stimulus very quickly, while slowly adapting touch receptors are good at sensing the continuous pressure of an object touching or indenting the skin, but not very good at sensing when the stimulus started or ended. There are four types of mechanoreceptors that pick up touch sensations from the skin: Merkel's discs, Meissner's corpuscles, Ruffini's corpuscles and Pacinian corpuscles - all named after the people who discovered them. The most sensitive mechanoreceptors - Merkel's discs and Meissner's corpuscles - are located in the superficial skin layers (upper dermis and lower epidermis), and are most densely clustered on the finger pads - beneath the ridges of the highly sensitive fingertips. Merkel's discs are also found in hairy skin, in hair follicles and in oral and anal mucosa, while Meissner's corpuscles are most concentrated in thick hairless (glabrous) skin. The main difference between them is that the Merkel cells respond to the light touch, whereas the Meissner corpuscles respond to low-frequency vibrations. Merkel's discs are slowly adapting receptors and Meissner's corpuscles are rapidly adapting receptors, so the skin can perceive when we are touching something and for how long that object is touching the skin. Located deeper in the dermis and along joints, tendons and muscles are Ruffini's corpuscles and Pacinian corpuscles. These mechanoreceptors can feel sensations such as vibrations traveling down bones and tendons, rotational limb movements and the stretching of skin. Body organs also contain mechanoreceptors e.g. when the bladder is full of urine, stretch receptors in the bladder wall trigger the micturition (urination) reflex.

Thermoreceptors – including heat and cold receptors – are located in the dermis and detect sensations related to the temperature of objects felt by the skin. Heat receptors start to feel heat sensations when the surface of the skin rises above 86°F, and are most stimulated at 113°F. Beyond that, pain receptors take over to avoid damage to the skin and underlying tissues. Thermoreceptors are found all over the body, and cold receptors are more abundant than heat receptors. The highest concentration of thermoreceptors is in the face and ears, which always get cold faster than the rest of the body in cold temperatures. Cold receptors start to pick up sensations when the surface of the skin drops below 95°F. They are most stimulated when the surface of the skin is at 77°F and are no longer stimulated when the surface of the skin drops below 41°F. This is why feet or hands start to go numb when they are submerged in very cold water for a long period of time.

Pain receptors are called 'nociceptors' – 'noci' is Latin for 'injurious' or 'hurt' - and these nerve endings detect pain or stimuli that can cause damage to the skin and other tissues of the body, and they transmit pain signals to the spinal cord and brain. There are over three million pain receptors throughout the body e.g. in the skin, muscles, joints, bones, blood vessels and internal organs. There are different types of nociceptors, which are based on the type of stimuli they respond to e.g. mechanical nociceptors that respond to intense stretch or strain, like when you pull a muscle or tendon, chemical nociceptors that respond to chemicals released from tissue damage etc.

Joints, ligaments, muscles and tendons contain proprioceptors that detect the position and movement of the limbs. These specialised cells detect changes in muscle length and muscle tension. Without proprioceptors, fundamental things such as eating or getting dressed would be very difficult, if not impossible. They sense the position of different parts of the body in relation to each other and the surrounding environment. Proprioception is also referred to as kinesthesia - the sense of self-movement and body position - and is sometimes described as the body's 'sixth sense'.

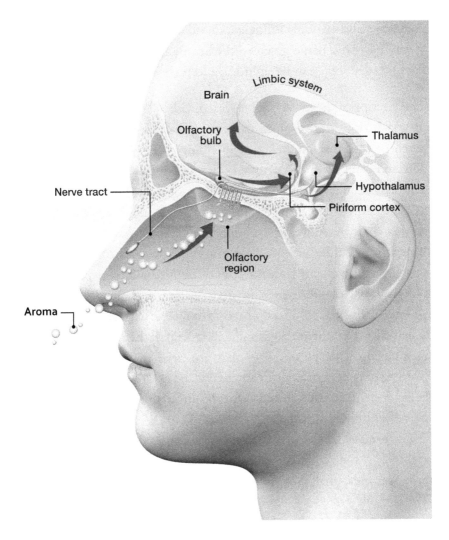

15.2 The olfactory system

Smell

The sense of smell is the most sensitive of human senses, and recognition of smell is instant. Other senses like touch and taste must travel through the body via neurons and the spinal cord before reaching the brain, whereas the olfactory response is immediate, extending directly via the olfactory nerve - the shortest cranial nerve in the body - to the brain. When activated, it can bring on a flood of memories and strongly influence mood e.g. the fresh, earthy scent of 'petrichor' - the name given to the aroma that arises when raindrops fall onto dry soil - can be uplifting and refreshing.

The interior of the nasal cavity is lined with a layer of epithelium, most of which does not respond to odours, but up at the top is a special patch of olfactory epithelium containing receptors where odours are detected. The lay and scientific literature typically claims that humans can discriminate up to 10,000 odours, but a 2014 study showed that humans are capable of discriminating at least 1 trillion olfactory stimuli. In connective tissue supporting the olfactory epithelium lie Bowman's glands that produce mucus, as well as olfactory binding proteins that facilitate transport of odorants to olfactory receptor cells. Odour molecules breathed in dissolve in the mucus and come in contact with olfactory receptor cells covered with microscopic hairs called cilia. The chemical stimulus dissolved in the mucus is converted into electrical nerve impulses that are fired through the cribriform plate – small perforations in an area of the skull's ethmoid bone - to a collection of cells in the olfactory bulb at the end of the olfactory nerve. The smell signal is transmitted along the olfactory nerve to the limbic system of the brain – an area composed of several structures including the olfactory cortex (piriform cortex), amygdala, hippocampus, thalamus, hypothalamus, cingulate gyrus and fornix. The limbic system is involved in motivation and the emotional association with memory, and for this reason smells are very powerful in triggering memories and emotions.

Anosmia is loss of the sense of smell - either total or partial - and may be caused by head injury, blockage of the nose or infection. Temporary anosmia is the main neurological symptom and one of the earliest and most commonly reported indicators of COVID-19. Taste and smell are closely linked, so people with anosmia are unable to taste food properly. When food is chewed, the odour is released and travels up the back of the throat to the nasal passages. If there is a blockage or swelling in the nasal passages, odour messages are not transmitted to the brain. Likewise, if the specialised olfactory neurons are damaged or destroyed, the brain cannot receive these sensory messages. Hyposmia - the reduced ability to smell - affects half of those over the age of 65 and 75% of those over the age of 80. As well as the ageing process, hyposmia can also be due to neurological problems such as a head injury, Alzheimer's or Parkinson's disease, certain drugs (e.g. antihistamines, analgesics, steroids), or the damaging effects of cigarette smoke. Smell training is a supportive technique for people who have suffered smell loss. It aims to stimulate the olfactory area of the brain by spending time each day sniffing essential oils or other scents. Smell training has been demonstrated in scientific studies to be of benefit for people who have lost their sense of smell after a virus or injury.

Hyperosmia is an enhanced sense of smell whereby a person can experience smells more strongly than others, and this may lead to feelings of discomfort or illness from certain odours. Hyperosmia may have a genetic link, or may be due to pregnancy, prescription medication, nutritional deficiencies (e.g. B12), or certain medical conditions such as autoimmune disorders, neurological conditions, diabetes or Lyme disease. Females usually have a keener sense of smell than males - especially at the time of ovulation - but with age the sense of smell deteriorates in both sexes.

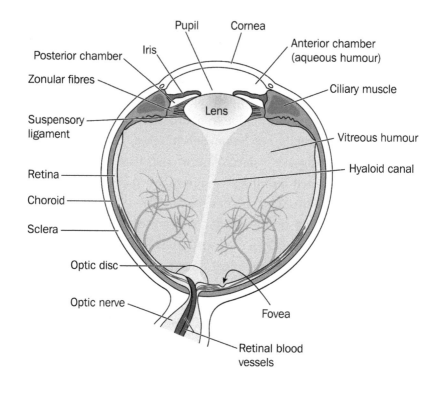

15.3 Anatomy of the eye

Sight

Although all of the senses are important, many people think that sight would be the most difficult one to live without. It helps us avoid danger, is vital for social interaction - the eyes play a role with regard to reading facial expressions, gestures and body language – and when the other senses are not effective for one reason or another, eyesight plays a crucial role in compensating for the loss. The eyes work much like a camera. Light bounces off images in front of us and comes into the eyes through the cornea, a clear, thin layer covering the front of each eye. The cornea directs the light towards the iris and pupil. The iris is the coloured, muscular ring with an opening (the pupil) in the centre, and these two parts work together to control the amount of light entering the eye. Stimulation of the autonomic nervous system's sympathetic branch that triggers 'fight or flight' responses when the body is under stress, induces pupil dilation, whereas stimulation of the parasympathetic system, known for 'rest and digest' functions, causes pupil constriction.

Once the light comes through the pupil, it travels through the lens that lies behind the pupil. Just like in a camera, the lens adjusts to focus on objects and directs light to the retina at the back of the eye. The retina has two types of cells that gather light: rods and cones. The rods are around the outer ring of the retina, and are active in dim light. A protein pigment called rhodopsin found in the cones is necessary for normal vision, particularly in low-light conditions. Vitamin A is needed for the production of rhodopsin. Cones are mostly in the centre of the retina and they help us see colour and fine detail. Colour blindness is an inherited inability to distinguish between certain colours. Most forms of colour blindness result from the absence or deficiency of one of the types of cones. The most common type is red-green colour blindness, in which red and green detecting cones are missing. As a result, the affected person cannot distinguish between red and green. Prolonged vitamin A deficiency and the resulting below-normal amount of rhodopsin may cause night blindness - nyctalopia - an inability to see well at low light levels. Once the cones and rods have been exposed to light, they translate the visual information into an electrical signal that is sent to the vision centre in the occipital lobe of the brain by the optic nerve. The vision centre decodes the nerve signal coming from the retina and interprets the image, creating a visual map of what is being looked at.

The fluid components of the eye include the vitreous humor, a gel-like substance found in the rear part of the eyeball between the lens and retina, keeping the eyeball in a circular shape, and the aqueous humor, a clear liquid found between the cornea and the lens of the eye. Aqueous humor is continuously generated and continuously drains from the front of the eye throughout a person's lifetime, whereas vitreous humor is produced only during the embryonic stage and stays for the entire lifetime. The macula is a small, sensitive part of the retina responsible for detailed central vision. The central part of the macula is called the fovea. The macula delivers images at a higher resolution than any camera and with damage to the macula, vision can resemble the screen of an ancient TV set, with a blurry picture and washed out colours. Macular degeneration, also known as age-related macular degeneration (AMD), is caused by deterioration of the retina and can severely impair vision. It has no cure, but can be treated with vitamins, laser therapy, medication and vision aids.

Other eye problems include cataracts, in which the lens of the eye becomes progressively opaque, resulting in blurred vision. Cataracts are common in elderly people, and can be due to disease or lens injury. A 2014 study offers an explanation for how years of chronic sunlight exposure can increase the risk of cataracts. Glaucoma is a condition of increased pressure within the eyeball, causing gradual loss of sight. It results from the inability of the eye to drain aqueous humor as quickly as it produces it. The fluid pressure compresses and damages the optic nerve causing vision loss. It can be hereditary or affect those with near - or farsightedness, diabetes or those with an eye injury. It can be controlled by medication in the form of eye drops or pills that reduce pressure by slowing the flow of fluid into the eye. Corneal ulcers are erosions or open sores in the outer layer of the cornea. They are usually caused by infection, most commonly with bacteria, viruses, fungi or a parasite. Symptoms include pain, a sense of something in the eye, and increased tear production. People who wear contact lenses are more likely to get corneal ulcers, and the risk is higher in those who use extended-wear (overnight) soft contacts.

Meibomian gland dysfunction (MGD) is a common eye condition that affects tiny glands in the eyelids called meibomian glands - named after Heinrich Meibom (1638–1700), a German physician, who first described them. These glands make an oily substance called meibum, which along with water (secreted by lacrimal glands) and mucus (produced mainly by goblet cells) forms the three layers of tear film, the fluid that keeps the eyes moist. The mucous layer is closest to the eye, the aqueous layer is in the middle, and the oil forms the outer layer and helps prevent the water from evaporating too quickly. Changes to the amount or quality of the oil, or to the glands themselves, can lead to MGD. The most common type, obstructive MGD, happens when the gland openings get clogged and less oil reaches the surface of the eye. It can be associated with prolonged contact lens wear, some medications e.g. retinoids, oestrogen replacement, as well as the ageing process. Medical treatment includes special eye drops and/or devices that send heat or pulsed light to open blocked meibomian glands and improve symptoms.

Less serious eye problems that usually clear up quickly include conjunctivitis and styes. Conjunctivitis (pink eye) causes redness and inflammation of the thin layer of tissue that covers the front of the eye (conjunctiva). Symptoms include redness, irritation, light sensitivity and a watery discharge from the eye. It can be viral, bacterial or due to chemical irritants. A stye (hordeolum) is an inflamed swelling on the edge of an eyelid, caused by bacterial infection of the sebaceous gland at the base of an eyelash. It usually lasts 2-4 days and is characterised by pain, tenderness and a pus filled cyst.

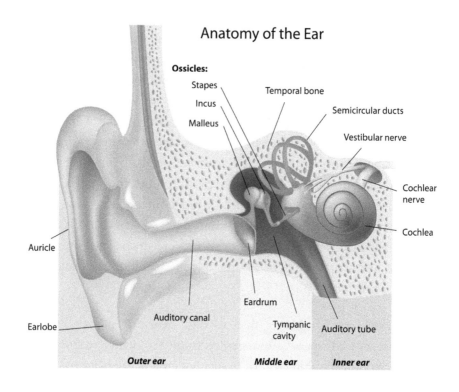

Anatomy of the Ear

Ossicles:
Stapes
Incus
Malleus
Temporal bone
Semicircular ducts
Vestibular nerve
Cochlear nerve
Cochlea
Auricle
Eardrum
Earlobe
Auditory canal
Tympanic cavity
Auditory tube
Outer ear
Middle ear
Inner ear

15.4 Anatomy of the ear

Hearing

The ears, which are located in the temporal bones, are the organs of both hearing and balance. We depend on our ears to help us interpret, communicate with, and understand the world around us. The human ear is fully developed at birth and responds to sounds that are very faint as well as sounds that are very loud. Even in the womb, babies can respond to sound. Sounds can evoke sweet memories, calm and soothe a troubled mind, or trigger the release of powerful hormones preparing the body for 'fight or flight'.

When we examine the ear in more detail we can see that it has three distinct sections - the outer ear, middle ear and inner ear. The outer ear consists of the pinna - a curvy flap of tissue on the side of the head

- and the ear canal, which is about 2.5 centimetres long. The pinna is like a sound-gathering trumpet, funnelling sound waves through the ear canal to reach the tympanic membrane – commonly known as the eardrum. The pinna is made of cartilage and soft tissue, so that it maintains its shape but is also pliable. The outer part of the ear canal contains lots of tiny hairs, as well as glands that produce cerumen - commonly called earwax. The hairs trap dust and other potential irritants, while the wax protects the skin that lines the ear canal, and contains fatty acids that slow the growth of certain bacteria. The wax also lubricates the eardrum, keeping it supple, and its bitter taste and smell are reputed to keep insects out! The eardrum is a tightly stretched membrane composed of three layers of tissue. When sound waves reach the eardrum, it vibrates like a stick beating a drum. Even faint vibrations from a whisper can push it inwards ever so slightly, causing it to vibrate.

The middle ear is an air-filled cavity about 1.3 centimetres across, connected to the nasopharynx (upper throat) by the Eustachian tube. Named after Bartolomeo Eustachio, a 16th century Italian anatomist, this tube is approximately 35 millimetres long with a diameter of 3 millimetres. It normally remains closed, but opens momentarily during swallowing, allowing air to move between the nasopharynx and middle ear to equalise pressure across the eardrum. When changes in air pressure occur outside the body - e.g. when flying or diving - the eardrum may stretch and bulge towards the area of lower pressure, and this can be painful. Chewing, swallowing or yawning can relieve this by opening the Eustachian tube to allow air into the middle ear, thus equalising pressure between the middle ear and the outside of the body. A popping sound may be heard as the Eustachian tube opens, and the eardrum returns to its original position. In children, the Eustachian tube is shorter and straighter due to the facial and skull structure, so infections can travel faster between the middle ear, nose and throat.

The middle ear is also connected to air cells in the mastoid process - a projection of the temporal bone that can be felt as a small bump behind the ear. The channel that connects them is called the 'antrum' and in some severe cases of middle ear infection, a mastoidectomy (removal of the mastoid process) may be necessary if the infection reaches this bony area. Hinged together in the middle ear are three tiny bones that conduct sound from the eardrum to the inner ear. These bones - collectively know as the ossicles - are the malleus, incus and stapes. Due to their shapes, they are also known as the hammer, anvil and stirrup. When sound enters the ears and makes the eardrums vibrate, the vibrations pass along the ossicles, triggering the stapes to push like a little piston against the oval window – a membrane separating the middle and inner ear - carrying the sound waves onwards.

The inner ear contains a maze of fluid-filled tubes. These bony tubes – called the labyrinth - are filled with a fluid called perilymph. Within this bony labyrinth is a second series of tubes (a tube within a tube) called the membranous labyrinth that is filled with a fluid called endolymph. The two parts of the labyrinth are the snail shaped cochlea that deals with hearing, and the semicircular canals that deal with balance. When the stapes pushes against the oval window, this sets the fluid inside the tubes of the cochlea sloshing back and forth.

The cochlea contains a small structure called the organ of Corti where the actual nerve endings for hearing are located. These nerve endings are called 'hair cells' because they have tiny hair-like structures called stereocilia that project into the cochlear fluid. The hair cells are connected to the cochlear nerve – sometimes referred to as the auditory nerve. This is a branch of the vestibulocochlear nerve (8th cranial nerve) that leads from the cochlea to the brain. When sound waves move the cochlear fluid, the stereocilia move, triggering an electrical impulse in the cochlear nerve. The nerve carries this electrical signal to the auditory cortex in the temporal lobe of the cerebrum, where it is translated into a sound that we recognise and understand.

The balance part of the inner ear is the vestibular system, consisting of three semi-circular canals and two tiny sac-like structures called the utricle and saccule, located in an area called the vestibule. While nerve endings in the semi-circular canals provide information about movements of the head, the sensory hair cells of the utricle and saccule provide information to the brain about head position when it is not moving. The functioning of the vestibular system depends on sensory information from different parts of the body - including the eyes, skin, muscles and joints - to work in harmony and maintain the body's coordination. As the body and head move, hair cells in the semicircular canals send nerve impulses to the brain by way of the vestibular portion of the 8th cranial nerve. These nerve impulses are processed in the brain stem and cerebellum. This gives the brain information about the position of the head, helping to maintain balance. For example, a sudden loss of balance creates fluid movement in the semicircular canals that triggers leg or arm reflex movements to restore balance.

Several disorders can affect the ears, impacting hearing or balance. Deafness is a partial or total loss of hearing that can affect one or both ears. Deafness can be due to mechanical problems that block the sound waves e.g. excess earwax or damage to the auditory nerve by infection or injury. It can also be due to age-related hearing loss - known as presbycusis - which is quite common. Otosclerosis is another common cause of hearing loss. It is caused by an abnormal overgrowth and scarring of the ossicles, limiting their ability to transmit sound vibrations from the middle to the inner ear. Only 3 mm x 2.5 mm in size, the stapes is the smallest ossicle, and the one mostly affected by otosclerosis. Sometimes only one ear is affected, but it can affect both ears. It is more common in females than in males, and can run in families. As the disease progresses, hearing aids can help. The most common medical procedure for otosclerosis is a stapedectomy, where the stapes is replaced with an artificial bone made of plastic or metal. In most cases, this operation is successful in restoring hearing.

Earache can be due to infection, or a blocked Eustachian tube that affects the equalising of pressure. It can also be referred pain from the nose, throat or sinuses. 'Otitis media' is the medical term for a middle ear infection – usually due to bacteria or virus. It is often a complication of colds or allergies, and symptoms include fever, pain and a red bulging eardrum. Glue ear (serous otitis media) is an accumulation of fluid in the middle ear due to a blocked Eustachian tube. Symptoms are a feeling of fullness in the ear, or a popping/crackling sound on swallowing, usually accompanied by temporary hearing loss. Glue ear is more common in children and can be very painful. To prevent the excess fluid from bursting the eardrum, tiny ventilation tubes called grommets are sometimes inserted into a small slit in the eardrum during minor surgery. Grommets allow excess fluid to drain out, and maintain normal middle ear pressure by allowing air into the middle ear from outside. They usually fall out naturally after 6 to 12 months.

Tinnitus is a ringing or buzzing in the ears in the absence of external sounds. It can have many causes, including age-related nerve cell loss, injury to the ear, stress, infection, high blood pressure, otosclerosis, a blocked ear canal or a blocked Eustachian tube. Vertigo is a sensation of whirling, giddiness and loss of balance, associated particularly with looking down from a great height, or caused by disease affecting the inner ear or vestibular nerve. It can also be a symptom of labyrinthitis, an inflammation of the inner ear, usually due to the spread of bacterial or viral infection from the head or respiratory tract into the inner ear.

Misophonia – also known as selective sound sensitivity syndrome - is a disorder in which certain sounds trigger emotional or physiological responses that some people might perceive as unreasonable. First named as a condition in 2001, 'misophonia' is the ancient Greek word for 'hatred of sound' and is an abnormality of the brain with both psychological and physiological symptoms. This hypersensitivity to sound can cause a fight-or-flight response that can interfere with daily life and cause feelings of anger, anxiety and panic upon hearing triggering sounds, often leading to isolation and depression. Research into misophonia is still relatively new and current studies are listed in the references section.

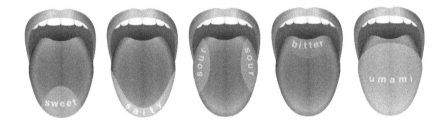

15.5 Sense of taste

Taste

Taste is one of our basic senses. It tells us what is edible and what is not, what is good for our body and what can be potentially dangerous. Taste is detected by taste (gustatory) receptor cells located in taste buds on the tongue. Taste buds are oval bodies with tiny receptor cells projecting through pores that enable molecules taken into the mouth to reach the receptor cells. They are found on projections called papillae that give the tongue its rough surface. The tongue contains five types of taste receptors that register sweetness, saltiness, bitterness, sourness and umami, which is a savoury or meaty taste. There are also some taste buds at the rear roof of the mouth (soft palate), inside the cheeks, and in the pharynx and larynx.

Food is dissolved by saliva in the mouth. Tiny hair cells of the taste receptors dip into this mixture and are stimulated by taste chemicals.

The taste receptors then send signals via nerves to the areas of the brain responsible for taste, appetite and saliva production. The facial nerve (cranial nerve V11) is responsible for taste in the anterior two-thirds of the tongue. The glossopharyngeal nerve (cranial nerve 1X) and the vagus nerve (cranial nerve X) are responsible for taste in the posterior one-third of the tongue and into the pharynx e.g. if you swallow a pill and it gets stuck in your throat, you can continue to taste its bitterness due to taste buds in the pharynx. With age, the number of taste receptors declines. By the age of 20, it is thought that we already have only half the number of taste receptors we had in childhood, and the decline continues with advanced age. As a result, many elderly people have a severely reduced sense of taste leading to a lack of interest in food, declining appetite, and loss of body weight - all of which can contribute to fragility and poor health.

Taste is not formed exclusively from information received via the taste buds. The smell of food - detected by the olfactory epithelium in the nose – is a contributing factor that works together with the taste perceived in the mouth. If the sense of smell is diminished, the sense of taste will be disturbed as well. Although taste and smell make up the majority of the flavour experience, the rest of the senses (vision, hearing, touch) are also involved e.g. the colour of food can affect the flavour we perceive, as does the sound food makes as we chew it.

The best way to keep our senses as sharp as possible as we age is to recognise any warning signs of deterioration - e.g. hearing loss or vision problems - and have regular check ups, eat well and manage medical conditions that may affect our senses.

16. The Endocrine System

The endocrine system is the body's communication system, regulating the activity of various organs, glands and tissues through the action of body chemicals called hormones. It provides the smooth running of body functions (homeostasis) by regulating activities such as the metabolism of proteins, fats and carbohydrates, and the concentration of chemicals in body fluids e.g. glucose, calcium etc. It works with the nervous system to help the body react to stress properly and is the major regulator of growth and development, including sexual and reproductive progression.

The body contains two types of glands - exocrine and endocrine. Exocrine glands secrete products into ducts, then into body cavities and the spaces inside various organs, or the outer surface of the body. These include sebaceous (sebum), salivary (saliva), lacrimal (tears), mammary (breast milk), eccrine and apocrine sweat glands (perspiration), as well as the gall bladder (bile) and pancreas (digestive juices and hormones – making this both an exocrine and an endocrine gland).

Endocrine glands secrete hormones into spaces between cells where they enter directly into the bloodstream and have their effects on distant parts of the body. From the Greek 'hormao' which means to 'arouse' or 'put in motion', hormones are the body's chemical messengers. At least 50 have been identified in the human body and more are being discovered e.g. a 2007 study by geneticist Gérard Karsenty of Columbia University discovered that a bone protein called osteocalcin acts as a hormone to keep blood sugar levels in check and burn fat. Later, his group showed that this hormone is important for maintaining brain function, physical fitness and memory. Some hormones are fat based (steroid hormones e.g. sex hormones) and others are protein based (e.g. insulin, oxytocin). Hormone release is stimulated or inhibited by signals from the nervous system, chemical changes in the blood, or levels of other hormones. Hormones bind to receptors on target cells where they initiate a cascade of events inside each target cell. Not all cells respond to all hormones, and certain hormones have very potent effects in some cells and no effects at all in other cells. Once hormones have been released, their levels are controlled by a negative feedback mechanism, in which rising levels of a hormone will inhibit further release of that hormone when it reaches its peak. Hormones can be produced synthetically in a laboratory setting, and are often prescribed by doctors to treat disease or hormone deficiencies. For example, if a person has their thyroid gland removed, they are usually prescribed synthetic thyroid hormones to replace those that the body can no longer produce. Hormones have potent effects at various stages of life, particularly during puberty, pregnancy, the menstrual cycle and menopause.

At the onset of puberty, the brain releases a hormone called gonadotropin-releasing hormone (GnRH) that kickstarts the changes associated with this stage of life. When GnRH reaches the pituitary gland, it releases luteinising hormone (LH) and follicle-stimulating hormone (FSH) into the bloodstream. These hormones give the male testes the signal to begin the production of testosterone and sperm. Testosterone is responsible for male bodily features like the growth of facial and pubic hair, muscle development, and possibly the aggressive and show-off behaviour of some boys. In females, FSH and LH target the ovaries that contain immature eggs (ova) that have been there since birth. The ovaries begin producing oestrogen, which along with FSH and LH cause the female body to mature and prepare for possible pregnancy.

At the onset of pregnancy, a hormone called human chorionic gonadotropin (hCG) produced by the developing placenta after implantation of a fertilised ovum stimulates the ovaries to produce high levels of progesterone. This halts the menstrual cycle and prevents degradation of the empty egg sac (called the 'corpus luteum' meaning 'yellow body' as it appears yellow), allowing it to continue secreting progesterone. Progesterone, which is formed in the ovaries and later in the placenta, affects every aspect of pregnancy, including relaxing muscles in the uterus to prevent contractions that could otherwise lead to miscarriage. Oestrogen, also normally formed in the ovaries but later in the placenta, strengthens and prepares the uterus for implantation of the fertilised ovum, prepares the breasts for lactation, and encourages milk production. Generally when we talk about oestrogen we are referring to oestradiol, as this is the most common type of oestrogen found in females during their reproductive years. As well as helping to develop and maintain the reproductive system and female characteristics, it regulates the sebaceous glands, helps bones absorb calcium, keeps the cardiovascular system healthy, and assists with other essential body processes. Males also produce small amounts of oestradiol.

There are different types of oestrogen, and oestrone is the form that is present in the body after menopause. It is a weaker form of oestrogen and one that the body can convert to other forms of oestrogen as necessary. A form of oestrogen called estriol is found in the female body during pregnancy, produced naturally by the placenta and foetus. It helps the uterus grow and prepares the body for delivery, with levels peaking just before giving birth.

A hormone called prolactin stimulates the production of breast milk, while oxytocin triggers contractions in labour as well as the sporadic uterine contractions that some women experience around sixteen weeks into a pregnancy. These 'Braxton Hicks' intermittent uterine contractions are named after John Braxton Hicks, an English doctor who first described them in 1872. Oxytocin also stimulates the mammary glands to release milk when a baby starts suckling. Endorphins - 'happy hormones'- are produced by the pituitary gland and central nervous system, and these help the mother to deal with stress and pain. A hormone called relaxin softens ligaments and tissues to increase flexibility in the lower back and pelvic joints in preparation for birth.

FEMALE SEXUAL CYCLE

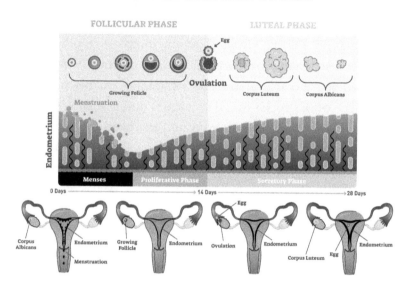

16.1 The female cycle

Hormones dictate the smooth running of the female menstrual cycle. At the beginning of the cycle, the pituitary gland produces FSH, kickstarting the development of several immature ova (female eggs) in ovarian follicles. One follicle becomes dominant around day six, and this is called the Graafian follicle - so named after Dutch physician and anatomist, Regnier de Graaf (1641- 1673). The Graafian follicle continues to enlarge until ovulation while the other follicles degenerate. The developing follicle produces oestrogen that inhibits FSH secretion, and repairs the lining of the uterus after the last menstruation. The pituitary then produces LH that triggers ovulation and stimulates the empty follicle (corpus luteum) to produce progesterone. The progesterone causes the lining of uterus to thicken, ready for a fertilised ovum. If the ovum is not fertilised, the production of oestrogen and progesterone stops, the lining of the uterus breaks down and menstruation occurs, before a new cycle starts again.

Menopause represents the end of menstruation. While technically it refers to the final menstrual period ('meno' means 'month' and 'pause' means 'stop'), it is not an abrupt event, but a gradual process. Menopause is not a disease that needs to be cured, but a natural life-stage transition. Many women have irregular periods and other problems that can begin several years beforehand in the 'peri-menopause' years. It is not easy to predict when menopause begins, although doctors agree it is complete when a woman has not had a menstrual period for twelve months, and the average age of menopause is fifty-one. During peri-menopause, female hormones fluctuate and become unpredictable. Oestrogen and progesterone are at lower than usual levels, and FSH and LH increase in an attempt to get the ovaries working as they once did. After menopause, the typical pattern of hormones is continually high levels of FSH and continually low levels of oestrogen and progesterone. Testosterone also declines during this period, but at a much slower rate than oestrogen and progesterone in many women. The ovaries continue to secrete some testosterone even after menopause.

Many women who are approaching menopause experience hot flashes (flushes) - sudden feelings of warmth that spread over the upper body, often with blushing and sweating. These flashes can range from mild in most women, to severe in others. Other symptoms include mood swings, sleeping problems, as well as dry skin and bone loss due to reduced levels of oestrogen. Menopause is a natural process and many symptoms disappear over time. If they're causing problems, treatments including hormone replacement therapy can help some women feel better, but professional medical advice should be sought before embarking on any protocol. Healthy lifestyle changes can help many women deal with uncomfortable menopause changes.

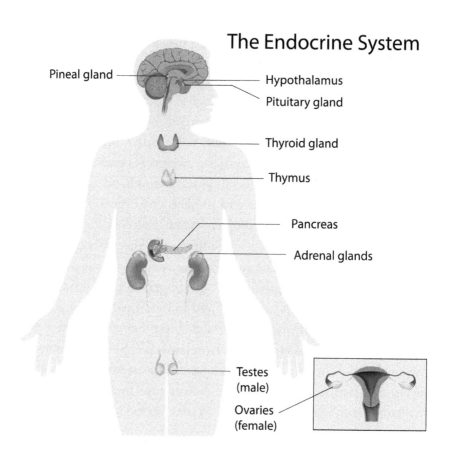

The Endocrine System

Pineal gland

Hypothalamus

Pituitary gland

Thyroid gland

Thymus

Pancreas

Adrenal glands

Testes
(male)

Ovaries
(female)

16.2 The endocrine system

The endocrine glands located in the head and neck region include the pituitary gland, often called the 'master gland' because it produces hormones that control other glands and many body functions. The pituitary is located directly below the hypothalamus (discussed in Chapter 14) and is divided into two parts - anterior and posterior pituitary. The main hormones secreted by the anterior pituitary include human growth hormone (HGH), adrenocorticotropic hormone (ACTH), luteinising hormone (LH/ICSH), follicle stimulating hormone (FSH), prolactin (PRL) and melanocyte stimulating hormone (MSH). The posterior pituitary secretes anti-diuretic hormone (ADH – also called vasopressin) and oxytocin. We will now examine each of these hormones in more detail and see what happens when there is too much (hypersecretion) or too little (hyposecretion) in the bloodstream.

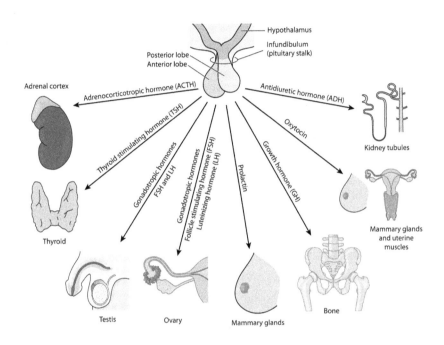

16.3 Hormones of the pituitary gland

Human growth hormone (HGH) regulates growth. If too much of this hormone is secreted during the years when the long bones are growing, it results in a condition called gigantism, characterised by excessive growth and height significantly above average. A pituitary gland tumour is usually the cause of this rare condition. Acromegaly is a hormonal disorder that develops when the pituitary gland produces too much growth hormone during adulthood. When this happens, bones of the hands, feet and face increase in size, and the soft tissues begin to swell. There are a range of other symptoms including coarse body hair, thickened ribs (creating a barrel chest), protruding jaw, enlarged lips, nose and tongue, joint pain, fatigue, increased perspiration accompanied with body odour and other symptoms. Too little growth hormone (hyposecretion) can cause a slow rate of growth in children and changes in muscle mass, cholesterol levels and bone strength in adults, and is often treated with HGH replacement therapy. In children, the earlier the condition is treated, the better the chance that a child will grow to be a near-normal adult height. However, HGH replacement therapy does not work for all children. Dwarfism is short stature, generally related to a genetic disorder or some medical conditions, but the cause is sometimes unknown. Dwarfism is generally defined as an adult height of 147 centimetres or less, and the average adult height among people with dwarfism is 122 centimetres. In disproportionate dwarfism, some parts of the body are small and others are of average or above-average size. Disorders causing disproportionate dwarfism inhibit the development of bones. In proportionate dwarfism, all parts of the body are small to the same degree and appear to be proportioned like a body of average stature. The terms 'short stature' or 'little people' are often preferred rather than 'dwarf' or 'dwarfism', and it is important to be sensitive to the preference of someone who has this disorder.

Thyroid stimulating hormone (TSH) controls the thyroid gland and the release of its hormones. Overproduction or underproduction of a pituitary hormone will affect the respective end organ, so insufficient production of TSH in the pituitary gland will cause hypothyroidism, while overproduction of TSH will cause hyperthyroidism.

Adrenocorticotropic hormone (ACTH) regulates levels of the steroid hormone cortisol that is released from the adrenal glands. If too much ACTH is produced, this can lead to high levels of cortisol in the body, also known as Cushing's syndrome. The most common cause of increased ACTH production is a benign pituitary tumour. When this is present, the disorder is called Cushing's disease. Signs and symptoms of Cushing's include weight gain in the upper body, a rounded face, extra fat on the upper back and above the collarbones, high blood sugar (usually leading to diabetes), high blood pressure (hypertension), thin bones (osteoporosis), muscle loss and weakness, thin, fragile skin that bruises easily, purple-red stretch marks (usually over the abdomen and under the arms), depression, difficulty thinking clearly, and excess facial hair in women. Growth failure associated with weight gain is a hallmark feature of Cushing's disease in children. The most common treatment for a pituitary tumour is to have it surgically removed. A low concentration of ACTH in the blood leads to a reduction in the secretion of adrenal hormones, resulting in adrenal insufficiency (hypoadrenalism), so the adrenal glands will not function efficiently.

Luteinising hormone (LH) stimulates ovulation and the secretion of oestrogen and progesterone in females. LH is also called interstitial cell-stimulating hormone (ICSH) in males, and stimulates the production of testosterone. In women, luteinising hormone levels that are too high are often connected with polycystic ovarian syndrome, which creates inappropriate testosterone levels. Low levels of luteinising hormone may cause infertility, because insufficient levels will limit the production of sperm and the ovulation process.

Follicle stimulating hormone (FSH) in females stimulates the growth of ovarian follicles in the ovary before the release of an egg from one follicle at ovulation. It also increases oestrogen production. In men, FSH acts on specialised Sertoli cells of the testes to stimulate sperm production. Low FSH levels may indicate that a female isn't producing ova and a male isn't producing sperm. High FSH levels in women may indicate a loss of ovarian function, menopause or polycystic ovarian syndrome.

Prolactin - also known as PRL or lactogenic hormone - is mainly used to help women produce milk after childbirth, and is important for both male and female reproductive health. The specific function of prolactin in men is not well known. However, prolactin levels have been used to measure sexual satisfaction in both men and women e.g. low prolactin may cause low libido.

Melanocyte-stimulating hormone (MSH) stimulates the production of cells called melanocytes in the basal layer of the epidermis. MSH is essential for the development of pigmentation and protecting the skin from ultraviolet rays. A deficiency of MSH results in a lack of skin pigmentation and subsequent loss of natural protection from the UV rays of the sun. In secondary adrenal insufficiency, damage to the pituitary gland prevents the release of ACTH and MSH, so there is reduced pigmentation of the skin. MSH deficiency can cause increased inflammation, pain and sleeping problems, as well as a reduction in the levels of anti-diuretic hormone, causing thirst and frequent urination. MSH deficiency may also result in increased food intake and obesity, as MSH can suppress appetite by acting on receptors in the hypothalamus. This process is enhanced by leptin - a hormone released from fat cells. The name 'leptin' is derived from the Greek word 'leptos' meaning 'thin', and this hormone is sometimes referred to as the 'fat controller'. MSH levels increase during pregnancy and in women using birth control pills, and this can cause hyperpigmentation of the skin. Abnormal darkening of the skin is also found in those with primary adrenal insufficiency – i.e. when the adrenal glands are damaged and cannot make certain hormones needed by the body. In Addison's disease, the adrenal glands do not produce enough of the hormones cortisol and aldosterone. As a consequence, the hypothalamus stimulates the pituitary gland to release more ACTH to try and stimulate the adrenal glands to produce these hormones. ACTH can be broken down to produce MSH, leading to hyperpigmentation of the skin, which is a feature of Addison's disease.

The posterior part of the pituitary gland secretes two hormones, anti-diuretic hormone (ADH) - also called vasopressin - and oxytocin. ADH helps to maintain blood pressure, blood volume and tissue water content by controlling the amount of water and concentration of urine excreted by the kidneys. ADH is made by specialised nerve cells in the hypothalamus and transported down nerve fibres to the posterior pituitary gland, where it is stored and released into the bloodstream. As the kidneys filter blood, ADH works by allowing water in the urine to be reabsorbed back into the body in a specific area of each kidney. As more water returns to the bloodstream, urine concentration rises and water loss is reduced. Higher concentrations of ADH cause blood vessels to constrict, and this increases blood pressure. Water intake is essential to prevent dehydration and restore body fluids. The release of ADH into the bloodstream is controlled by special osmotic sensors in the hypothalamus that react to the concentration of certain particles in the blood. These particles include molecules of sodium, potassium, chloride and carbon dioxide. When particle concentration isn't balanced, or blood pressure is too low, the osmotic sensors tell the kidneys to store or release water to maintain a healthy range of these substances. ADH is also released by thirst, nausea, vomiting and pain, and acts to keep up the volume of fluid in the bloodstream at times of stress or injury. Excess alcohol and excess caffeine can inhibit anti-diuretic hormone release, causing an increase in urine production and dehydration.

Hyposecretion of ADH will cause the kidneys to excrete too much water, leading to an increase in urine volume, dehydration, and a fall in blood pressure. Low levels of ADH may indicate damage to the hypothalamus or pituitary gland, or primary polydipsia (compulsive or excessive water intake). In primary polydipsia, the low level of ADH shows that the body is trying to get rid of excess water. Diabetes insipidus is a rare condition where a person either makes too little ADH (usually due to a tumour, trauma or inflammation of the pituitary or hypothalamus), or where the kidneys are insensitive to it. Symptoms include increased thirst and urine production. Excessively high levels of ADH cause the kidneys to retain water and can lead to a condition called syndrome of inappropriate anti-diuretic hormone secretion (SIADH) - where the blood is diluted, giving a low salt concentration and oedema. Excessive ADH release can have various causes including diseases of the lungs, hypothalamus or pituitary as well as some tumours - particularly lung cancer.

Like ADH, oxytocin is produced in the hypothalamus and secreted into the bloodstream by the posterior pituitary. The two main actions of oxytocin are contractions of the uterus during childbirth, and lactation i.e. the secretion of milk from the mammary glands when breastfeeding. Oxytocin stimulates the uterine muscles to contract and also increases production of prostaglandins that increase the contractions further. Prostaglandins are hormone-like substances that participate in a wide range of body functions such as the contraction and relaxation of smooth muscle, the dilation and constriction of blood vessels, control of blood pressure, and modulation of inflammation. They are produced in the body from a fatty acid called arachidonic acid that is found inside the body - particularly in muscles, liver and the brain. Pitocin - a synthetic oxytocin - is sometimes given to induce labour if it has not started naturally, or it can be used to strengthen contractions in childbirth. It is also given to speed up delivery of the placenta, and reduce the risk of heavy bleeding by contracting the uterus. During breastfeeding, oxytocin promotes the movement of milk into the breasts, allowing it to be excreted by the nipples. Oxytocin is also present in men, playing a role in sperm movement and production of testosterone by the testes.

Many research projects have looked at the role of oxytocin in addiction, brain injury, anorexia, stress and other topics. In the brain, oxytocin acts as a chemical messenger and has been shown to affect human behaviours including sexual arousal, recognition, trust, anxiety and mother–infant bonding. As a result, it is sometimes referred to as the 'love' or 'cuddle' hormone.

PINEAL GLAND

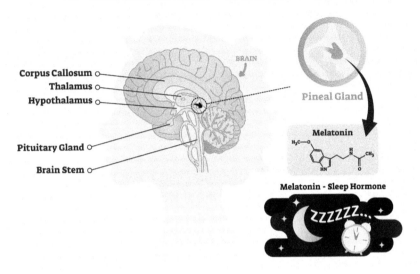

16.4 The pineal gland

The pineal gland is a small, cone-shaped organ in the brain that secretes the hormone melatonin, which regulates sleeping and waking cycles. Various tissues in the body produce melatonin, although the major source is the pineal gland. Melatonin is produced in the pineal from the amino acid tryptophan when reduced light is entering the eyes, sending the melatonin secretion signal from the optic nerve to the pineal once darkness has fallen. The pineal converts tryptophan into 5-hydroxytryptophan (5-HTP), which is turned into serotonin and then converted into melatonin. Melatonin is secreted into the blood stream and cerebrospinal fluid around the brain and spinal cord, and carried to all areas of the body. Having adequate tryptophan levels provides the body with the resources it needs to make serotonin, and this helps to ensure that melatonin can be produced. Tryptophan is found in foods like turkey, chicken, meat, cheese, yogurt, eggs and fish, and exercise helps trigger its release into the bloodstream. Serotonin can be described as the body's feel-good hormone that increases positivity and relaxation, as well as helping us feel more energised. This energy is particularly important to get us going in the morning, and wash away the lethargy that might otherwise keep us in bed. As well as being produced from tryptophan, serotonin levels can be boosted by getting outside in the open air and getting as much sunlight during the day as possible. Sunlight also helps with the production of Vitamin D3, which is important for healthy bones as well as keeping the mood uplifted.

The body's internal clock - also known as the circadian rhythm - influences how much melatonin the pineal gland makes. Melatonin production is also influenced by the amount of light that a person is exposed to each day. Melatonin levels typically start to rise in the mid-to-late evening, after the sun has set, and remain elevated during the hours of darkness. They drop in the early morning as the sun rises, and this helps the body to wake up. During the shorter, darker days of winter, the body may produce melatonin earlier or later in the day. This can upset the natural sleep cycle, and may lead to fatigue, low energy, mood changes or other symptoms of seasonal affective disorder (SAD). Nighttime melatonin secretion is suppressed by light when the eye pupils are dilated, and it has been suggested that the use of devices such as laptops and smartphones before bedtime can have a negative impact on melatonin secretion, circadian rhythms and sleep. For optimum melatonin production, it is best to sleep in complete darkness if possible e.g. using blackout blinds to make the bedroom very dark at night, or carrying a blackout sleep mask when travelling. Using nighttime lights or leaving a bathroom light on can suppress natural melatonin production.

As well as natural light, foods such as tomatoes, walnuts, olives, rice, barley, strawberries, bananas, cherries and cow's milk contain melatonin. When the body absorbs melatonin from these foods, a person may begin to feel calm and sleepy. Some spices can boost melatonin e.g. a teaspoon of mustard seeds or fenugreek has as much melatonin as a few tomatoes. The pineal gland begins to shrink and calcify with age, thereby reducing the amount of circulating melatonin - possibly one of the reasons we sleep less as we age. Melatonin can be taken in capsule form - under medical supervision - to help address age-associated insomnia, jet lag and shift work, and reset the body's circadian rhythms.

The thyroid gland produces hormones that regulate metabolic rate, controlling heart, muscle and digestive function, brain development and bone maintenance. Its correct functioning depends on a good supply of iodine from the diet as this is used to create thyroid hormones. The signal to produce and secrete thyroid hormones comes from thyroid-stimulating hormone (TSH) released by the pituitary. TSH levels in the blood rise and fall depending on the body's needs to produce more or less thyroid hormones. The hypothalamus is also involved, as it releases a hormone called thyrotropin-releasing hormone (TRH) that stimulates the release of TSH in the pituitary, which then sends signals to the thyroid gland – a wonderful orchestration!

The thyroid gland produces thyroxine (T4 – an inactive prohormone) and the more active triiodothyronine (T3), collectively referred to as thyroid hormone. T3 makes up 20% of thyroid hormone and T4 makes up the other 80%. Once secreted by the thyroid, enzymes in tissues like the liver or kidneys transform T4 into the active hormone T3 when needed.

THYROID HORMONES

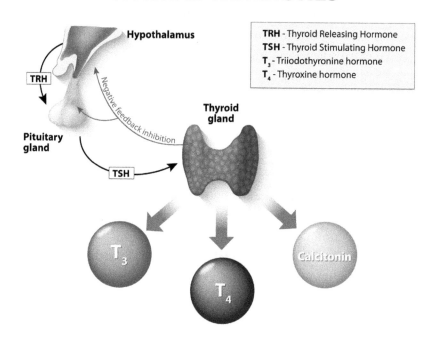

Hypothalamus

TRH

Pituitary
gland

Negative feedback inhibition

TSH

**Thyroid
gland**

T₃

T₄

Calcitonin

| **TRH** - Thyroid Releasing Hormone |
| **TSH** - Thyroid Stimulating Hormone |
| **T₃** - Triiodothyronine hormone |
| **T₄** - Thyroxine hormone |

16.5 Thyroid hormones

In some people, the thyroid gland produces too much hormone (hyperthyroidism) or does not produce enough (hypothyroidism), resulting in the body using energy faster or slower than it should. Because thyroid hormone plays such an important role in the body's metabolism, lack or excess of this hormone seriously upsets the balance of body processes. Symptoms of hyperthyroidism include weight loss, fast heart rate, irritability, nervousness, muscle weakness and tremors, infrequent menstrual periods, sleep problems, eye irritations and heat sensitivity. Graves' disease is a condition where the entire thyroid gland is overactive, producing toxic levels of thyroid hormone, and sometimes becoming enlarged. Thyroid surgery may be necessary to remove part of, or in some cases the entire thyroid, when structural changes occur e.g. growths that affect hormone production.

There are several different types of thyroid surgery including lobectomy, subtotal thyroidectomy and total thyroidectomy. A lobectomy is when a nodule, inflammation or swelling affects only half of the thyroid gland, and only one of the lobes is removed. The remaining lobe should retain some or all of its function, and thyroid hormone supplementation may not be needed. A subtotal thyroidectomy removes the thyroid gland but leaves behind a small amount of thyroid tissue, preserving some thyroid function. Those who undergo this type of surgery usually develop hypothyroidism, which is treated with daily hormone supplements. When nodules, swelling or inflammation affect the entire thyroid gland, or when cancer is present, a total thyroidectomy is performed to remove the entire thyroid gland. If this occurs, the body cannot make thyroid hormone, and without replacement a person will develop signs and symptoms of hypothyroidism. As a result, daily thyroid hormone replacement containing the synthetic thyroid hormone 'levothyroxine' will be needed. The amount of hormone replacement needed will be based on blood tests to monitor thyroid hormone levels.

Symptoms of hypothyroidism include weight gain, slow heart rate, fatigue, more frequent and stronger menstrual periods, forgetfulness, dry skin and hair, hoarse voice and intolerance to cold. An enlargement of the thyroid gland known as goitre, often accompanies hypothyroidism - although goitre can also develop in cases of severe hyperthyroidism. Myxoedema (myxedema) is a term used to describe severely advanced hypothyroidism. The term also applies to the effects that hypothyroidism can have on the skin, making it appear swollen and puffy. When thyroid hormone levels become extremely low, a person may experience symptoms such as drowsiness, confusion, hypothermia, or the life-threatening complication of myxoedema coma. People of all ages and races can get thyroid disease, but women are more likely than men to experience problems with their thyroid function. Undiagnosed hypothyroid children may experience slow growth rate. Additional symptoms include sluggishness, pallor, dry and itchy scalp, enlarged tongue, short and wide face, increased sensitivity to cold and constipation. Administration of thyroid hormone medication, which must be continued for life, can result in normal growth and mental development of these children. If untreated, the condition can have devastating effects, such as stunted physical growth, sterility and mental retardation. In the past this condition in children was referred to as 'cretinism'.

Thyroiditis is inflammation of the thyroid gland, leading to a reduction in thyroid hormone production. Hashimoto's thyroiditis - first described by the Japanese physician Hakaru Hashimoto in 1912 - is an autoimmune disease in which the thyroid gland is gradually destroyed. Inflammation from Hashimoto's disease - also known as chronic lymphocytic thyroiditis - often leads to hypothyroidism. In addition, thyroiditis can sometimes occur in women after giving birth, and this is referred to as postpartum thyroiditis. It is usually a temporary condition and is quite rare.

Nutrition also impacts thyroid function, particularly iodine deficiency, which can cause hypothyroidism. However, excessive iodine intake may have negative effects on the thyroid, causing it to produce either too much or too little hormone in some individuals. Anyone concerned about thyroid function or iodine levels should seek medical attention to have blood levels checked.

C-cells within the thyroid produce calcitonin that plays a role in regulating calcium and phosphorous levels in the blood for bone health and maintenance. Calcitonin acts to reduce calcium levels in the blood by inhibiting the activity of osteoclasts - the cells responsible for breaking down bone and releasing calcium into the bloodstream. It can also decrease the reabsorption of calcium in the kidneys, again leading to lower blood calcium levels. There does not appear to be any direct negative effect on the body as a result of having too much or too little calcitonin. However, inappropriate levels may indicate a thyroid disease and should be investigated.

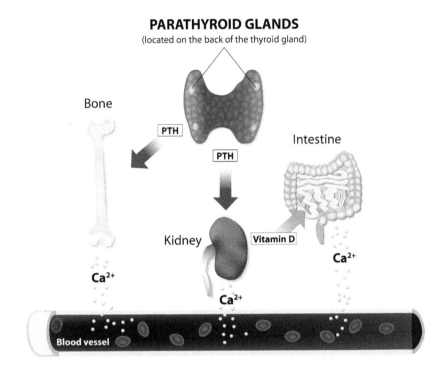

PARATHYROID GLANDS
(located on the back of the thyroid gland)

16.6 Thyroid and parathyroid glands

Located on the thyroid gland are four pea-sized parathyroid glands. The parathyroid hormone (PTH) made by these glands increases the level of calcium in the blood when it is too low – opposing the action of calcitonin. It does this through its actions on the kidneys, bones and intestines. PTH stimulates the release of calcium from large calcium stores in the bones, into the bloodstream. In the kidneys, it reduces the loss of calcium in urine by drawing it back into the blood during the reabsorption process following filtration. PTH also stimulates the production of active vitamin D (calcitriol) in the kidneys from its inactive form. Calcitriol helps increase blood calcium concentrations because it stimulates the absorption of calcium from the gastrointestinal tract.

PTH levels are controlled by the negative feedback of calcium levels in the blood to the parathyroid glands. Low calcium levels in the blood stimulate PTH secretion, whereas high calcium levels in the blood prevent the release of PTH. A deficiency of PTH can result in low levels of calcium (hypocalcemia) and high levels of phosphorous, leading to a variety of problems including muscle cramps, usually in the legs. Over time, hypocalcemia can affect the brain and cause symptoms such as confusion, memory loss, delirium, depression and hallucinations. These symptoms disappear if the calcium level is restored. Hypocalcemia is a common complication of thyroid surgery, because the parathyroid glands may get damaged or are sometimes removed entirely during surgery, and if they are left intact, they may not work properly for a while following surgery. This usually resolves in a couple of weeks but sometimes remains a problem, and supplemental calcium and/or vitamin D may be prescribed.

The main effects of excessive PTH (hyperparathyroidism) are a depletion of calcium from the bones and an elevation of blood calcium levels, called hypercalcemia. This can result in weak, brittle bones that fracture easily (osteoporosis). Excess calcium in the blood may lead to excess calcium in the urine that can cause kidney stones. Most parathyroid problems occur because one of the parathyroid glands develops a benign tumour. Secondary hyperparathyroidism can result from another condition that lowers calcium levels e.g. severe deficiency of calcium or vitamin D that is needed to absorb calcium. This can cause the parathyroid glands to overwork and compensate for the calcium loss.

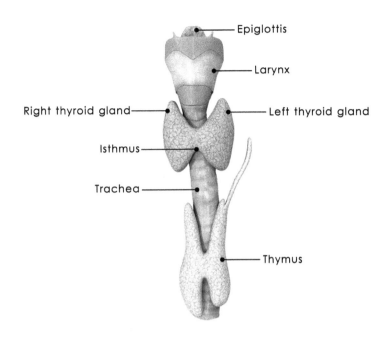

Epiglottis

Larynx

Right thyroid gland

Left thyroid gland

Isthmus

Trachea

Thymus

16.7 Thymus gland

The thymus is a bi-lobed organ in the thorax above and in front of heart. The thymus gland is large in infants and reaches its maximum size during puberty. It shrinks after puberty and is gradually replaced by fatty tissue. It produces several hormones including thymopoietin and thymulin that assist in the process whereby T cells of the immune system differentiate into various types. T cells - also known as T lymphocytes or thymus derived lymphocytes - begin in bone marrow and mature in the thymus gland. The immature T cells that leave the bone marrow migrate to the cortex (outer part) of the thymus, where they are taught to recognise antigens i.e. pathogens that induce an immune response in the body. Once T cells have learned to recognise specific pathogens in the cortex of the thymus gland, they travel to the medulla (centre) and here they are introduced to the body's own antigens. Since T cells that would react with the body's antigens could attack a person's own cells, these T cells are eliminated, and either die or are turned into regulatory cells. The surviving T cells are then exposed to hormones produced by the thymus gland to complete their maturation, before being released to do their job of circulating in the bloodstream or waiting in the lymph nodes for pathogens.

The three primary types of T cells are cytotoxic (killer) T cells - responsible for directly killing infected cells, helper T cells - responsible for both causing the production of antibodies by B cells and activating other types of T cells to attack pathogens, and regulatory T cells that function as 'police' and suppress both B cells and other T cells, helping to prevent autoimmune diseases. Memory T cells (and memory B cells) are immune cells that remain in the body after an initial infection and retain the memory of a pathogen, firing up a fast and powerful immune response when the same pathogen appears again.

Diseases and disorders that affect the thymus gland range from genetic disorders that are evident at birth, to cancers that are more common in older adults. These disorders can lead to problems with immunity and autoimmunity, such as myasthenia gravis (MG) and hypogammaglobulinemia. MG is an autoimmune, neuromuscular disease caused by problems in communication between nerves and muscles, and is characterised by profound weakness of muscles - both in the extremities and respiratory muscles. Hypogammaglobulinemia is a problem with the immune system that prevents it from making enough antibodies called immunoglobulins. People with this condition can more easily catch infections that a healthy immune system would normally protect against.

PANCREAS

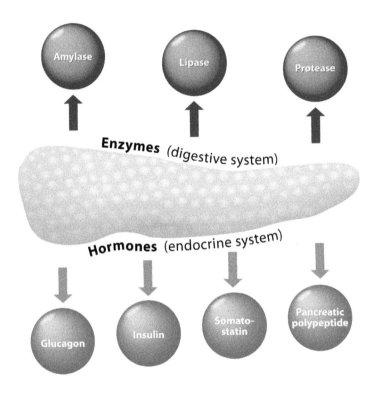

16.8 Pancreas

The pancreas is located behind the stomach and is surrounded by other organs, including the spleen, liver and small intestine. It is about 15 centimetres long, oblong and flat, and is divided into a head, body and tail. Its two important roles are to make digestive juices consisting of powerful enzymes, and to make hormones that control blood glucose levels. The region of the pancreas containing the hormone-producing cells is called the islets of Langerhans. Discovered in 1869 by 22-year-old German pathological anatomist Paul Langerhans, the islets of Langerhans constitute approximately 1-2% of the mass of the pancreas. The most important hormone produced by the pancreas is insulin, which is released by 'beta cells' in the islets of Langerhans in response to food. Insulin lowers blood glucose (sugar) levels by carrying glucose into the cells, and promotes the storage of excess glucose – in the form of glycogen - in fat, muscle, liver and other body tissues. 'Alpha cells' in the islets of Langerhans produce another important hormone called glucagon. This has the opposite effect of insulin, helping to release energy into the bloodstream from where it is stored, thus raising blood sugar levels. Other hormones produced by the pancreas include pancreatic polypeptide and somatostatin. They are believed to play a part in regulating and fine-tuning the insulin and glucagon producing cells.

When the insulin producing cells either stop working or become inefficient and don't make enough insulin, this causes a condition called diabetes mellitus. Type 1 diabetes mellitus is caused when the body's immune system attacks its own cells in the islets of Langerhans, so that these cells cannot produce insulin. Type 2 diabetes mellitus (previously called non-insulin-dependent diabetes mellitus) accounts for 90% of all cases of diabetes mellitus, and is a public health problem around the world. It is a metabolic disorder where the body is no longer able to produce insulin, or body cells become insulin resistant. Insulin resistance is when cells in muscles, fat and liver don't respond well to insulin, and cannot use glucose from the blood for energy. To make up for it, the pancreas makes more insulin and over time, blood sugar levels increase.

The connective tissue damage and chronic inflammation resulting from a diabetic's sustained high blood sugar can lead to debilitating conditions such as cataracts, Alzheimer's, vascular tightening, and diseases of the pancreas and liver. Symptoms of diabetes mellitus include frequent urination and severe thirst, as well as weight loss, blurred vision and loss of sensations in the extremities. It is an increasingly common disorder, and is linked to an increased risk of heart attacks, strokes, poor blood circulation to the legs, and damage to the eyes, feet and kidneys. Early diagnosis and strict control of blood sugar, blood pressure and cholesterol levels can help to prevent or delay these complications. Maintaining a healthy lifestyle with regular exercise, eating well and maintaining a healthy weight can all help to reduce the risk of developing type 2 diabetes and in some cases, may reverse damage already done.

Some women get gestational diabetes temporarily when they are pregnant. There are also more rare forms of diabetes, some of which are inherited. In addition, people will get diabetes if their pancreas is taken away surgically, or damaged by conditions like pancreatitis – a painful inflammation of the pancreas due to digestive enzymes leaking back into the pancreas and damaging the delicate tissues in and around it. Most pancreatic cancers begin in the cells that produce digestive enzymes, and as described in Chapter 13, malignant pancreatic cancers are often hard to detect as there are few symptoms until the cancer is advanced. In rare cases, tumours can develop in the cells that make up the islets of Langerhans. These are usually benign tumours, where a particular kind of cell multiplies and makes large quantities of its hormone whether it is needed or not. For example, if the tumour is made of insulin-producing cells, it is called an insulinoma. This can also happen with glucagon-producing cells, creating a glucagonoma that produces too much glucagon.

The adrenal glands are small structures weighing 4-5 grams and are attached to the top of each kidney. They are composed of two distinct parts: the outer adrenal cortex and the inner adrenal medulla. ACTH secreted by the anterior pituitary affects the release of adrenal cortex hormones. The three hormone groups from the adrenal cortex (adrenocortical hormones) are steroid compounds made from cholesterol and include mineralocorticoids, glucocorticoids and androgens.

ADRENAL GLAND
(hormones)

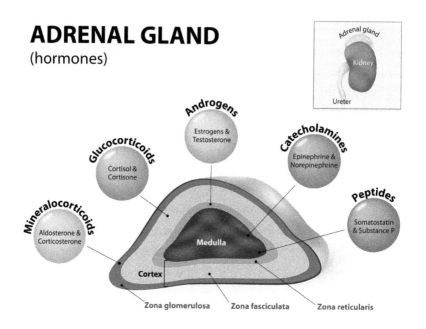

16.9 Adrenal glands

The most important of the mineralocorticoids group is aldosterone. Aldosterone is synthesised in the body from corticosterone - a steroid derived from cholesterol. Production of aldosterone is regulated by the renin-angiotensin system. Renin is an enzyme secreted by the kidneys in response to variations in blood pressure and volume, as well as blood sodium and potassium levels. Renin acts on a protein circulating in blood plasma called angiotensinogen, converting this substance into angiotensin I. Angiotensin I is subsequently converted to angiotensin II, which stimulates the release of aldosterone from the adrenal glands. This hormone helps to maintain the body's salt and water levels, which in turn regulate blood pressure. Without aldosterone, the kidneys would lose excessive amounts of sodium and consequently water, leading to severe dehydration and low blood pressure. Overproduction of aldosterone leads to a condition known as primary hyperaldosteronism, causing salt disturbances and high blood pressure that may be resistant to conventional blood pressure control medication.

The main hormone in the glucocorticoid group is cortisol. This hormone is involved in the response to illness and stress – particularly long-term stress - and also helps to regulate body metabolism. Cortisol stimulates glucose production, helping the body to free up glycogen (stored glucose) from fat and muscle to make glucose for energy. Cortisol also has significant anti-inflammatory effects. The two main glucocorticoid-related disorders are Cushing's syndrome and Addison's disease. Cushing's syndrome can be due to overactive adrenal glands producing excess cortisol, possibly due to a tumour, or by taking corticosteroid medication over a long period of time. If the excess cortisol is due to a problem with the pituitary and ACTH production, it is called Cushing's disease, and signs and symptoms of both Cushing's syndrome and Cushing's disease are the same.

Addison's disease - also referred to as adrenal insufficiency - is due to underactive adrenal glands associated with a lack of cortisol and aldosterone, and it may be acute or chronic. Symptoms of chronic adrenal insufficiency include low blood pressure, fatigue, weight loss, anorexia, nausea, vomiting, abdominal pain, salt craving and low blood sugar. Skin and mucous membranes may show increased pigmentation and there may be a reduced sex drive or loss of interest in sex - especially among women. Certain women with Addison's disease may also get irregular periods or skip their period entirely on some months. Acute adrenal insufficiency is a medical emergency and must be identified and promptly treated. The signs of acute adrenal insufficiency are severe weakness, confusion, delirium, low blood pressure, low blood sugar, severe abdominal pain, and vomiting and diarrhoea leading to dehydration.

The adrenal cortex also secretes androgens (sex hormones), mainly dehydroepiandrosterone (DHEA) and small amounts of testosterone as well as some oestrogen. All have weak effects, but play a role in the early development of male sex organs in childhood and female body hair during puberty. Overproduction of adrenal androgens is fairly rare but may result in excessive facial or body hair growth, or menstrual period disturbances in females if excess testosterone is produced. Male oestrogen levels that are too high, or are out of balance with testosterone levels can cause gynecomastia - an increase in the amount of breast gland tissue in males.

The adrenal medulla produces catecholamines including adrenaline (also known as epinephrine), noradrenaline (also known as norepinephrine) and small amounts of dopamine. These hormones are responsible for all the physiological characteristics of the stress response ('fight or flight'), which is described in more detail in Chapter 14. The medulla also produces protein hormones (peptides) called somastatin and substance P, which are thought to play a role in the regulation of catecholamine secretion from the adrenal medulla.

Tumours of the adrenal gland are mostly benign and do not always result in over - or underproduction of adrenal hormones. Most tumours are discovered when people undergo scans for various other reasons. Adrenal tumours may require surgery if they are large or overproduce hormones, but adrenal cancer is very rare. U.S. Naturopath James Wilson, PhD who has written a book on the subject, coined the term 'adrenal fatigue' in 1998. He describes it as "a group of related signs and symptoms (a syndrome) that results when the adrenal glands function below the necessary level". He says it is usually associated with intense stress and often follows chronic infections like bronchitis, flu or pneumonia. Wilson says that those with adrenal fatigue may not have any physical signs of illness but still may feel tired, 'gray' and have fatigue that doesn't get better with sleep. The theory behind it is that if a person experiences long-term stress (like the death of a family member or a serious illness), the adrenal glands burn out from prolonged production of cortisol, and adrenal fatigue sets in. Another problem that may affect females when the adrenal glands are in overdrive is that progesterone may be diverted to the adrenals to support cortisol production. With reduced progesterone, oestrogen dominance may occur, with signs and symptoms such as PMS, hot flashes, night sweats, migraines, fibroids, heavy bleeding, breast tenderness, weight gain, etc.

As well as addressing the causes of stress, suggested treatments for healthy adrenal function are a diet low in sugar, caffeine and junk food, along with targeted nutritional supplementation if necessary. Unlike chronic fatigue syndrome - also known as myalgic encephalomyelitis (ME) - which is often triggered by a viral infection and can come on quite suddenly, adrenal fatigue usually takes years to develop. Sometimes people with chronic fatigue syndrome go on to develop adrenal fatigue as their illness progresses. This is because stress - which is common to both conditions - can predispose a person to its onset, or exacerbate the symptoms.

The function of the ovaries is controlled by gonadotropin-releasing hormone (GnRH) released from nerve cells in the hypothalamus, which send their messages to the pituitary gland to produce luteinising hormone (LH) and follicle stimulating hormone (FSH). These are carried in the bloodstream to control the menstrual cycle. The major hormones secreted by the ovaries themselves are oestrogens (oestriol, oestrone, oestradiol) and progesterone, both important hormones in the menstrual cycle. Oestrogen production dominates in the first half of the menstrual cycle before ovulation, and progesterone production dominates during the second half of the menstrual cycle, when the corpus luteum – a yellow mass of hormone-secreting tissue that forms immediately after ovulation - has formed from the empty follicle (egg sac). Both hormones are important in preparing the lining of the uterus for pregnancy and the implantation of a fertilised ovum. If conception occurs during any one menstrual cycle, the corpus luteum does not disintegrate and continues to secrete oestrogen and progesterone, allowing the embryo to implant in the lining of the uterus and form a placenta. At this point, development of the foetus begins.

HUMAN REPRODUCTIVE SYSTEM

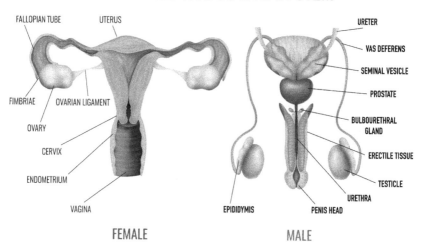

16.10 Ovaries and testes

The testes are the two oval-shaped male reproductive glands that produce sperm and testosterone. Leydig cells in an area of the testes called the seminiferous tubules secrete testosterone, which is important in the first stages of developing the male reproductive organs in a foetus. It also causes the development of male characteristics such as the growth of facial hair, deepening of the voice, and the growth spurt that takes place during puberty. Testosterone is important in maintaining these secondary male characteristics throughout a man's life. From puberty onwards, testosterone provides the main stimulus for sperm production. Less well-known hormones produced by the testes include inhibin B that is released into the blood when sperm count is too high, and anti-Müllerian hormone, a protein hormone that is important in the development of the reproductive tract in a male foetus. Other hormones of the testes include insulin-like factor 3, which is essential for helping the testicles descend from the abdomen during the last couple of months of foetal development, and oestradiol - a reproductive hormone that has a range of actions in both men and women.

The endocrine system is a complex system that we will probably never completely understand, but learning how to keep this system healthy is important to overall wellbeing. There are some basic things we can do to boost the body's ability to create and balance hormones. Following a suitable diet - including healthy fats and protein - is essential for making adequate hormones in the body. Excess caffeine and alcohol can over-stimulate the adrenal glands and carry other health risks, so are best taken in moderation. As well as polluting the body, harmful chemicals found in some pesticides, plastics, household cleaners, cosmetics, cigarettes etc. may contain hormone disruptors that mimic hormones and keep the body from producing real hormones.

Getting adequate sleep is very important, as that is when the body is actively removing toxins, recharging the mind, and creating hormones. Getting adequate and suitable exercise and fresh air - particularly during daylight hours – can help to boost serotonin and melatonin levels, as well as vitamin D3. Making time for leisure is important in providing a sense of balance, alleviating stress and improving overall quality of life.

17. The Urinary System

The urinary system is the body's filtration and waste removal system. It is composed of two kidneys, two ureters leading from the kidneys to the bladder, one bladder, and one urethra leading from the bladder to outside the body. It rids the body of waste substances through the processes of filtration and excretion. The kidneys also remove acid that is produced by body cells and maintain a healthy balance of water, salts and minerals (sodium, calcium, phosphorus and potassium) in the blood. Without this balance, nerves, muscles and other body tissues would not function normally.

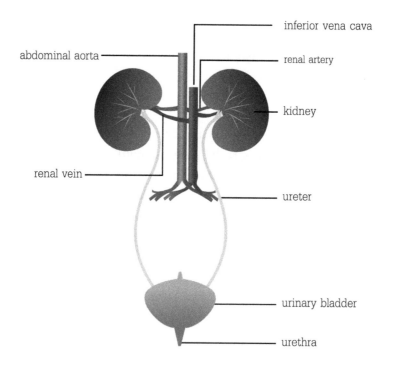

Urinary system

17.1 Urinary system

The kidneys are two bean-shaped organs, about 10-12 centimetres long, 5-7 centimetres wide and 2.5 centimetres thick (around the size of a large fist) situated in the posterior abdomen, above the waistline and on either side of the spine. The left kidney is slightly higher up than the right kidney due to the larger size of the liver on the right side of the body. Unlike other abdominal organs, the kidneys lie behind the peritoneum that lines the abdominal cavity rather than inside it.

Three layers of connective tissue protect each kidney. A fibrous membrane called the renal fascia holds the kidneys in place, binding them to surrounding structures. An adipose capsule of fatty tissue cushions the kidneys, while an inner layer of tissue - the renal capsule - composed of a smooth membrane continuous with the ureters, protects the kidneys and helps maintain their shape.

Kidneys have an outer 'cortex' and an inner 'medulla', just like the adrenal glands that sit on top of them. The inner medulla is composed of cone-shaped renal pyramids whose tips point towards the centre of the kidney. The renal pelvis of the kidney is the funnel-like dilated part of the ureter inside the kidney, where urine collects and is directed down into the ureter. On the medial side of each kidney is an indentation called the renal hilus (hollow), where blood vessels, lymph vessels, nerves and the ureter enter the kidney.

Kidney tissue consists of over a million microscopic structures called nephrons, composed of twisted tubes where filtration, absorption and excretion occur. The nephrons - sometimes described as sorting stations - filter blood and reabsorb materials needed by the body. The blood circulates through the kidneys around twenty times each hour for purification. Some of this flow becomes urine and is sent to the bladder for storage until it can be conveniently expelled, and the remainder is returned to the bloodstream.

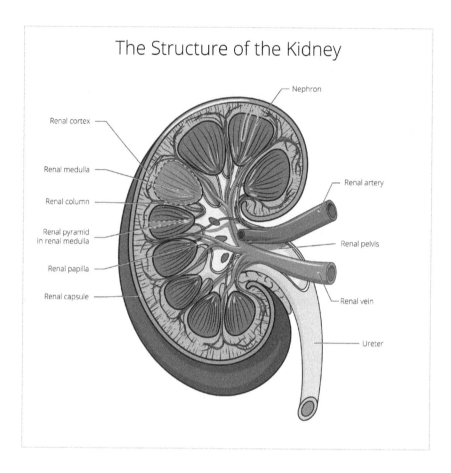

The Structure of the Kidney

Nephron

Renal cortex

Renal medulla

Renal column

Renal pyramid
in renal medulla

Renal papilla

Renal capsule

Renal artery

Renal pelvis

Renal vein

Ureter

17.2 Anatomy of the kidneys

There are several parts to a nephron. The glomerulus is a specially modified blood vessel - like a cluster of capillaries - that filters blood in the kidneys to create urine.

The tubules are millions of tiny structures that collect fluid and waste from the glomeruli. The nephrons work through a two-step process, with the glomerulus filtering the blood while the tubule returns needed substances to the blood and removes waste.

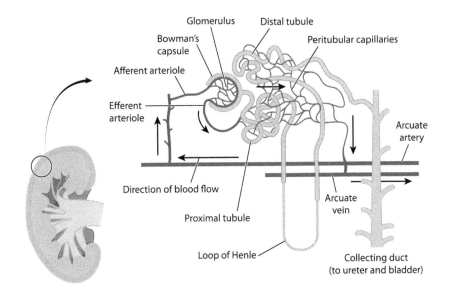

Glomerulus   Distal tubule

Bowman's
capsule   Peritubular capillaries

Afferent arteriole

Efferent
arteriole   Arcuate
                                                       artery

Direction of blood flow   Arcuate
                                           vein
Proximal tubule

Loop of Henle   Collecting duct
                                   (to ureter and bladder)

17.3 Nephron anatomy

As blood flows through the renal arteries into each nephron, it enters the cluster of tiny blood vessels in the glomerulus that sits in an area of the tubule called the Bowman's capsule. The thin walls of the glomerulus allow smaller molecules, wastes and fluid (mainly water) to pass into the tubule. Larger molecules like proteins and blood cells stay in the glomerulus. A blood vessel runs alongside the tubule and as the filtered fluid moves along the tubule, the blood vessel reabsorbs most of the water, along with minerals and nutrients the body needs. The tubule also helps remove excess acid from the blood. The remaining fluid and wastes in the tubule become urine. The amount of water in the blood must be kept more or less the same all the time to keep blood pressure normal. Anti-diuretic hormone (ADH) secreted by the pituitary gland controls the ability of water to pass through cells in the walls of the collecting ducts in the tubules. A diuretic is something that increases urine production in the kidneys, promoting the removal of salt and fluid from the body – and ADH does the opposite. As the level of water in the blood falls, negative feedback to the pituitary gland ensures that the amount of ADH rises, and more water is reabsorbed back into the bloodstream. As the level of water in the blood rises, negative feedback ensures that the amount of ADH falls. Diabetes insipidus (DI) is a rare disease that causes frequent urination and excessive thirst due to the pituitary not making or releasing enough ADH (central DI), or the kidneys not responding properly to ADH (nephrogenic DI). The kidneys filter around 200 litres of blood and produce an average of 1.5 litres of urine daily. After the blood is filtered, it flows out of each kidney through the renal veins.

As well as filtering blood, the kidneys also produce hormones that make red blood cells, keep bones strong and healthy, and regulate blood pressure. Erythropoietin (EPO) is a hormone produced in the kidneys that stimulates stem cells of the bone marrow to increase the production of red blood cells in order to maintain healthy oxygen levels in the tissues. During ascent to moderate or higher altitudes, EPO levels in the body rise rapidly, peaking in the first 48 hours of altitude exposure. By training at high altitudes, athletes aim to allow their bodies to produce extra red blood cells before competing at lower elevations to take advantage of their changed physiology, which should last for 10 to 20 days. Some professional athletes have used synthetic EPO (known as blood doping) to improve their performance - particularly to increase endurance. Artificially increasing EPO levels produces more haemoglobin and red blood cells, and therefore improves the amount of oxygen that can be delivered to tissues - particularly muscles. This can improve performance - although this type of doping practice is banned by most professional sports committees and can be dangerous to the body in the long term e.g. it can encourage blood clot formation and cause dizziness, headaches and seizures. When used for legitimate medical reasons, EPO can help with the treatment of anaemia related to cancer or kidney disease.

The liver and kidneys convert vitamin D (produced in the skin as well as absorbed from food) into an active hormone called calcitriol. Active vitamin D helps to increase the amount of calcium absorbed from digested food into the bloodstream, and also prevents calcium loss from the kidneys via the urine. Vitamin D is important to the body in many other ways e.g. it helps maintain bone and muscle strength, nerve function and the immune system e.g. a deficiency in vitamin D is associated with increased autoimmunity as well as an increased susceptibility to infection. Studies on these less known functions of Vitamin D are listed in the references section. The kidneys also produce hormone-like substances called prostaglandins from fats. Prostaglandins control processes such as inflammation, pain, blood flow, the formation of blood clots and the induction of labour.

The liver creates and releases a protein called angiotensinogen that affects blood pressure. Angiotensin is broken up by renin, an enzyme produced in the kidneys, to form angiotensin I, a precursor for angiotensin II. Angiotensin I is converted to angiotensin II by an angiotensin-converting enzyme (ACE), which is found mainly in the lungs. Angiotensin II increases blood pressure, thirst sensation, body water and sodium content if blood pressure gets too low. An increase in renin production occurs if there is a decrease in sodium levels and a decrease in blood pressure, which is sensed by the kidneys. In addition, low blood pressure can stimulate the sympathetic nervous system to increase renin production, which results in increased conversion of angiotensinogen to angiotensin I and so on, and the cycle continues. Angiotensin II also stimulates the adrenal glands to secrete the hormone aldosterone and this causes the kidneys to hold onto more sodium, leading to more water remaining in the body. The increased blood volume helps stretch the heart muscle and causes it to generate more pressure with each beat, thereby increasing blood pressure. The actions of the kidneys to regulate blood pressure are especially important during traumatic injury, when it is necessary to maintain blood pressure and conserve the loss of body fluids. However, consistently high blood pressure can have a damaging effect on the kidneys due to the excessive force placed on the renal blood vessels and the nephrons. Damaged kidneys cannot filter blood properly, and cannot regulate blood pressure efficiently.

Once the kidneys have filtered blood, the waste (urine) enters the ureters, two tubes, 25-30 centimetres long connecting the kidneys to the bladder. Each ureter drains from the renal pelvis of the kidney and inserts into the back of the bladder. Their walls are composed of three layers of tissue. The presence of urine within the ureters stimulates a contraction of the smooth muscle in their walls, forcing urine onwards to the bladder.

The bladder is a sac-like, hollow, muscular organ in the pelvic cavity, held in place by folds of the peritoneum that lines the abdominal cavity and covers abdominal organs. Like the stomach, the inner lining of the bladder tucks into folds when empty and expands out to accommodate liquid. The bladder can hold about 200 millilitres of urine before its walls contract to allow urination - also called 'micturition'. It has an internal sphincter that can relax and allow urine into the urethra and an external sphincter that is controlled voluntarily.

The urethra is a narrow tube passing from the bladder to outside the body. The female urethra is about 4 centimetres long and in males it is 15-20 centimetres long. It contains mucous glands - called 'urethral glands' - that secrete mucus into the urethra, and has an external sphincter under voluntary control. The function of the urethra is to take urine from the bladder out of the body, and in males it also forms a passage for semen. During sexual arousal, muscles at the base of the male bladder contract to close off the passageway from the bladder into the urethra. Examples of waste products in urine are the remains of drugs and alcohol, ammonia from protein metabolism, uric acid from the breakdown of ingested compounds such as protein, and excess minerals. The amount of urine produced depends on consumption of food and drink, physical activity, and the amount of fluid lost through breathing and perspiration. The average person urinates anywhere between 800 and 2,000 millilitres per day - between 33.3 and 83.3 millilitres per hour - and should be drinking no less than 2 litres of fluid per day. These numbers may change depending on individual circumstances.

BENIGN PROSTATIC HYPERPLASIA

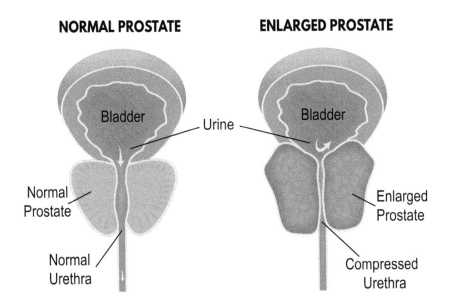

17.4 Prostate gland

Although it is regarded as an organ of the reproductive system as it secretes fluid that nourishes and protects sperm, the male prostate gland needs a mention here too. The prostate is a walnut-sized gland located between the bladder and the penis, just in front of the rectum. The urethra runs through the center of the prostate, from the bladder to the penis, letting urine flow out of the body. The prostate undergoes two main growth spurts. The first is activated by testosterone during puberty and this prompts the prostate to reach an average weight of 20 grams in adulthood. For reasons that are unclear, the second growth spurt of the prostate gland begins when men are in their 30's and it continues to enlarge with age to an average weight of 40 grams by the time men are in their 70's.

Many men experience urinary symptoms as they age, which may be caused by inflammation of the prostate gland (prostatitis). In older men, symptoms may be due to a blockage in the urethra caused by benign prostatic hyperplasia (BPH) - a benign enlargement of the prostate gland. The most common symptoms are difficulty emptying the bladder, and nocturia - the need to urinate regularly during the night. Nocturia is common in the elderly in general, and also during pregnancy due to excess pressure on the bladder. Urinary symptoms due to prostate issues may become bothersome enough that they require treatment e.g. if the flow stops completely, a catheter is required to empty the bladder. Not all urinary symptoms are due to changes to the prostate, and some men have enlarged prostates and yet experience few symptoms. Prostate cancer is one of the most common types of cancer in men. It usually grows slowly and is initially confined to the prostate gland, where it may not cause serious damage and can be successfully treated if detected early. However, some types of prostate cancer are aggressive and can spread quickly, so regular prostate screening is recommended.

Illness or injury can prevent the kidneys from filtering blood completely or block the passage of urine. When the kidneys are not functioning efficiently, waste products and excess fluid can build up and the levels of sodium, potassium, phosphorous and calcium are not regulated correctly. An excess of these minerals can cause symptoms of kidney disease that may include high blood pressure, excessive tiredness, fluid retention and lower back pain. Kidney damage can be due to diabetes, high blood pressure, infections, and a group of diseases that affect the glomerulus. The kidneys need an adequate supply of blood, so if there is something wrong with blood vessels to the kidneys - e.g. a narrowing - this will prevent them from working efficiently.

A urinary tract infection (UTI) is an infection in any part of the urinary system - kidneys, ureters, bladder and urethra. Most infections involve the lower urinary tract i.e. the bladder and the urethra. Cystitis - inflammation of the bladder - is a common UTI caused by infection, and is usually accompanied by frequent painful urination. It is more common in females due to a shorter urethra and its close proximity to the anal canal. Interstitial cystitis is a chronic bladder disorder also known as painful bladder syndrome. In this disorder, the bladder wall can become inflamed and irritated. The inflammation can lead to scarring and stiffening of the bladder, spot bleeding, decreased bladder capacity, and in rare cases, ulcers in the bladder lining. The cause of interstitial cystitis is unknown at this time.

Urethritis is inflammation of the urethra causing dysuria i.e. pain on urination. Urethritis is commonly due to infection by bacteria and typically treated with antibiotics. Nephritis - sometimes named Bright's disease after British physician Richard Bright, who described the symptoms in the late 1820's - is acute or chronic inflammation of the nephrons caused by infection, degeneration or vascular disease. Glomerulonephritis is acute or chronic nephritis that involves inflammation of capillaries in the glomeruli. It can have various causes e.g. streptococcal infection, lupus, or may be of unknown cause. It is characterised by blood or protein in the urine and by oedema, and if untreated can lead to kidney failure. Pyelonephritis refers to a kidney infection that generally begins in the urethra or bladder and travels to one or both kidneys. Kidney infections require prompt medical attention to prevent permanent kidney damage, or the spread of bacteria to the bloodstream leading to a serious infection.

Kidney stones - also called renal calculi - are hard deposits of salts and minerals (e.g. calcium) that form inside the kidneys. Diet, excess body weight, some medical conditions, and certain supplements and medications are among the many causes of kidney stones. Kidney stones can affect any part of the urinary tract from the kidneys to the bladder, causing trouble with the passage of urine and extreme pain - referred to as renal colic. Most small kidney stones do not usually require invasive treatment and can sometimes pass by drinking more water. Large stones may need to be surgically removed.

Healthy kidneys take waste out of the blood but leave in protein. Proteinuria (albuminuria) is the presence of protein in the urine, which does not cause a problem by itself, but may indicate that the kidneys are not functioning properly. Pregnant women are routinely screened for proteinuria because its development is associated with preeclampsia - also known as toxemia of pregnancy. Preeclampsia is a pregnancy-specific disorder where proteinuria and hypertension develop at the same time. Symptoms include oedema, nausea and headaches. In rare cases, it can cause severe symptoms such as seizures. Preeclampsia can be dangerous for both mother and baby due to rising blood pressure leading to complications e.g. it can prevent the placenta from getting enough blood and can lead to premature birth with added complications.

Nephroblastoma – Wilms' tumour - is a rare kidney cancer that primarily affects children aged 3 to 4 and becomes much less common after age 5. It occurs most often in just one kidney, though it can sometimes be found in both kidneys at the same time. Over the years, advancements in the diagnosis and treatment of nephroblastomas have greatly improved the prognosis for children with this disease. Signs and symptoms of Wilms' tumour vary widely, and include an abdominal mass that can be easily felt, abdominal pain, fever, nausea, vomiting, constipation, loss of appetite, shortness of breath, high blood pressure and hematuria - blood in the urine. The presence of blood in urine should always be medically investigated as it can be due to any number of conditions, some of which may be serious e.g. it is the most common symptom of urinary system cancers. Persistent back pain, extreme fatigue, unexplained weight loss and painful or frequent urination are also common symptoms of urinary system cancers.

Uremia - a raised level in the blood of urea and other nitrogenous waste compounds that are normally eliminated by the kidneys - is another condition that warrants prompt medical attention. Uremia is a major symptom of chronic kidney disease and renal failure, and if untreated, can be life-threatening. As waste and fluid build up in the blood, it causes various symptoms including nausea, itching, loss of appetite or taste for certain foods, feeling more tired than usual, weight loss, difficulty concentrating, pain, or numbness and cramps in the legs and feet caused by damage to nerves.

A less serious but nonetheless distressing problem - more common in children - is enuresis, commonly known as bed-wetting. Nocturnal enuresis - bed-wetting at night - is the most common type. Daytime wetting is called diurnal enuresis, and some children experience either or a combination of both. Enuresis can be due to a small bladder, persistent urinary tract infections, severe stress, anxiety, or developmental delays that interfere with toilet training.

Urinary incontinence - the loss of bladder control - is a common and often embarrassing problem, ranging from occasionally leaking urine when coughing or sneezing to having an urge to urinate that's so sudden and strong you don't get to a toilet in time. Women are affected by urinary incontinence more often than men, and contributing factors are pregnancy, childbirth and menopause.

Weak or overactive bladder muscles and nerve damage may also cause urinary incontinence. Though it occurs more often as people get older, urinary incontinence is not an inevitable consequence of ageing, and can be addressed by appropriate strengthening exercises or medical treatment.

Renal failure results when the kidneys are not able to regulate water and chemicals in the body, or remove waste products from the blood. Anuria or anuresis occurs when the kidneys are not producing any urine and this may indicate renal failure. A person may first experience oliguria - low output of urine - and then progress to anuria. Acute renal failure (ARF) is the sudden onset of kidney failure. This can be caused by an accident that injures the kidneys, loss of a lot of blood, or some drugs or poisons. ARF may lead to permanent loss of kidney function. However, if the kidneys are not seriously damaged, they may recover. Chronic renal failure (CRF) is the gradual reduction of kidney function that may lead to permanent kidney failure or end-stage renal disease (ESRD). A person may go several years without knowing they have CRF. Efforts to control blood pressure and diabetes may be the best way to prevent chronic kidney disease and its progression to kidney failure. If the kidneys fail completely, the only treatment options available are dialysis or transplant.

Dialysis, which has been used since the 1940's to treat people with kidney problems, is a treatment that filters and purifies the blood using a machine. This helps keep fluids and electrolytes in balance when the kidneys can't do their job. Hemodialysis is the most common type of dialysis. This process uses a machine called a dialyser to remove waste and extra fluid from the blood. The blood is removed from the body and filtered through the dialyser, and the filtered blood is then returned to the body. To get the blood to flow to the dialyser, surgery is needed to create an entrance point into a blood vessel. The three types of entrance points are: arteriovenous (AV) fistula, which connects an artery and a vein (the most common option), a looped tube called an AV graft, or a vascular access catheter that may be inserted into a large vein in the neck. Hemodialysis treatments usually last three to five hours and are performed about three times a week.

However, treatment can also be completed in shorter, more frequent sessions.

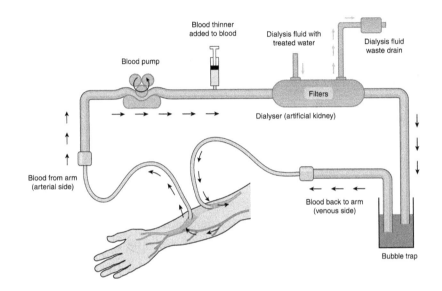

17.5 Hemodialysis

Peritoneal dialysis (PD) involves surgery to implant a catheter into the abdomen, and this helps filter the blood through the peritoneum. During treatment, a special fluid called dialysate flows into the peritoneum and this absorbs waste. Once the dialysate draws waste out of the bloodstream, it is drained from the abdomen. This process takes a few hours and needs to be repeated four to six times a day. However, the exchange of fluids can be performed while sleeping or awake. Both hemodialysis and peritoneal dialysis can be performed at home. Peritoneal dialysis can be performed alone, while hemodialysis requires a partner e.g. a friend, family member or a dialysis nurse. With either type of treatment, the patient receives thorough training from a medical professional beforehand.

Continuous renal replacement therapy (CRRT), also known as hemofiltration, is mainly used in intensive care units for people with acute kidney failure. A machine passes the blood through tubing, and a filter removes waste products and water. The blood is returned to the body, along with replacement fluid. This procedure is performed 12 to 24 hours a day, generally every day.

Some people whose kidneys have failed may qualify for a kidney transplant. In this procedure, one or both kidneys are replaced with donor kidneys from a live or deceased person. Because the body can function perfectly well with just one healthy kidney, a family member with two healthy kidneys may choose to donate one of them to another family member who needs it.

It is possible but fairly uncommon to be born with three kidneys and this is usually only discovered by accident as it rarely causes symptoms. It usually means that one of the kidneys was split into two prior to birth. It can be associated with infections and kidney stones, but usually causes no problems at all.

The best way to prevent urinary tract complications is to keep the urinary system healthy, and this can be done through proper diet and nutrition as well as healthy habits. It is best not to wait too long to use the bathroom if you feel the urge, as withholding urination can put added pressure on the bladder which can lead to infection. Some soaps and showering products can irritate the lower urinary tract so choose carefully, and it is advisable to shower thoroughly after swimming in pools or outdoors. Certain foods and drinks may irritate the bladder e.g. carbonated and caffeinated drinks and alcohol, and are best taken in moderation.

Keeping well hydrated by drinking plenty of water throughout the day will help to flush the urinary system and remove waste products. If you suspect something is wrong, seek prompt medical attention.

18. The Reproductive System

The organs of the reproductive system, unlike most other organs, are completely different in a male and a female. They are located within the pelvic region and their purpose is to enable human reproduction. Reproductive cells - gametes - are produced in the gonads - sex glands. Oogenesis is the process of development of female gametes - also called ova or eggs - that takes place in the female ovaries. Spermatogenesis is the process by which the male produces gametes called spermatozoa (sperm) in the testes.

As already described in Chapter 4, mitosis and meiosis are processes that occur during cell division. Mitosis involves the division of body cells, while meiosis involves the division of sex cells. The division of a cell occurs once in mitosis but twice in meiosis. Instead of creating two new cells with equal numbers of chromosomes as in mitosis, the cell does a second division soon after the first. The second division divides the number of chromosomes in half, creating a 'haploid' cell. Diploid is the opposite (two strands), and other body cells, apart from sperm and ova, are considered diploid cells.

Hormones play a vital role in the functioning of the reproductive system, so you may wish to go back to Chapter 16 and recap on the functions of follicle stimulating hormone (FSH), luteinising hormone (LH), oestrogen and testosterone before you read any further, as these hormones are mentioned regularly in this chapter.

The female anatomy includes the external genitalia and the internal reproductive organs. The external anatomy includes the mons pubis (pubic mound), which is the fleshy area on the pubic bone covered with hair after puberty, along with the vulva consisting of the labia majora (large lips), the labia minora (small lips) and the clitoris.

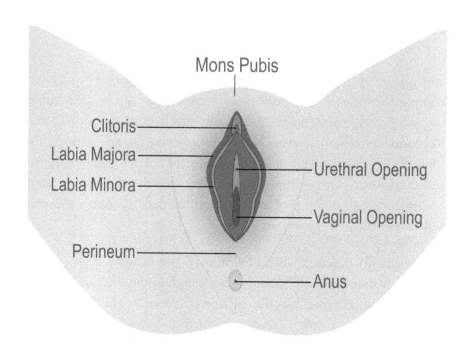

Mons Pubis

Clitoris

Labia Majora

Labia Minora

Urethral Opening

Vaginal Opening

Perineum

Anus

18.1 Female external genitals

The labia majora are the fleshy outer lips on either side of the vaginal opening, usually covered with pubic hair. The labia minora are the inner lips that usually sit inside, but in some females, these inner lips can extend beyond the outer lips. The clitoris sits at the top of the vulva, where the inner lips meet. It is usually around the size of a pea, but varies from person to person. Only the tip of the clitoris is visible, but it has two shafts that extend into the body by as much as 11 centimetres. The clitoris contains many nerve endings that are very sensitive, especially during sexual stimulation. The clitoral hood is the fold of skin that surrounds the head of the clitoris and protects it from friction. The urethral opening is a tiny hole located right below the clitoris.

Aesthetic surgery of the female genitalia – sometimes referred to as 'designer vaginas' - includes a number of surgical procedures designed to improve their appearance. It is thought that occasionally, sexual function may also be enhanced. Procedures include labial reduction ('labiaplasty'); vaginal tightening ('vaginaplasty'); liposuction to the mons pubis; fat injections to the labia majora or mons in order to give a more youthful appearance to these areas; removal or reduction of skin around the clitoris ('hoodectomy') to improve sensitivity; and reconstruction of the hymen for cultural reasons. Laser therapy has been used for the removal of labial wrinkles, and hair transplantation for lack of hair on the mons pubis. The availability of all such surgery in the UK is limited. Some women choose to groom their pubic hair through shaving, waxing or laser treatments and pubic hair styling is a growing trend.

The World Health Organization (WHO) defines female genital mutilation or cutting (FGM/C) as "all procedures involving partial or total removal of the external female genitalia or other injury to the female genital organs for non-medical reasons." These procedures, which are traditional in some cultures, include piercing, cutting, removing, or sewing closed all or part of a female's external genitals. Although FGM/C is often viewed as part of the culture of countries where it is practiced, it has no health benefits, and can lead to immediate and long-term health problems that can affect obstetric, gynaecological, sexual, and psychological health. The practice is regarded internationally as a violation of female human rights and as an extreme form of gender discrimination, reflecting deep-rooted inequality between the sexes. As it is often practiced on young girls without consent, it is also regarded a violation of the rights of children.

The internal female anatomy begins at the vagina, a canal leading from the vulva to the uterus and allowing the flow of menstrual blood, the exit of a baby in childbirth, and penetration in sexual intercourse. The average length of a vagina is 9.6 centimetres but during arousal it expands, and as blood flows to the area the cervix and uterus are pushed up by the upper two-thirds of the vagina to create more space. The vagina contains two pea-sized Bartholin's glands that sit on either side of the vaginal opening and secrete a lubricant to keep vaginal tissues moisturised. Skene's glands are located on the anterior wall of the vagina, around the lower end of the urethra. They secrete a fluid that helps lubricate the urethral opening, and are surrounded by tissue that swells with blood during sexual arousal. Oestrogen helps keep vaginal tissues healthy by maintaining normal vaginal lubrication - hence reduced oestrogen levels after menopause can cause vaginal dryness.

In 1950, German gynaecologist Ernst Gräfenberg described a distinct erotic region on the inner top wall of the vagina – about 2-3 centimetres inside. It was named the G-spot in his honour. Responses to G-spot stimulation vary, with some females saying they cannot find it, or do not believe that they have one, some finding stimulation of the area painful or unpleasant, and others reporting intense pleasure from stimulation.

Vaginitis is inflammation of the vaginal lining characterised by painful urination and increased vaginal discharge. It can be caused by bacterial or fungal infection, poor hygiene, or wearing tight, non-absorbent underwear. Vulvovaginal candidiasis (thrush) is a yeast infection of the lower reproductive tract causing vaginal discharge, irritation and itching. In some cases, male partners can suffer candidal balanitis - inflammation at the end of the penis. Causes include wearing tight clothing that prevents natural ventilation, using products that irritate the vagina such as vaginal douches or bubble baths, diabetes, use of antibiotics or steroid medications, chemotherapy for cancer, or drugs to suppress the immune system. Some people find that avoidance of sugar and yeast in the diet can help alleviate this condition. If symptoms are mild, a short course of antifungal medicine is usually prescribed. If symptoms are more severe, the treatment course will be longer. A variety of treatment options are available including taking tablets orally, inserting them into the vagina (pessaries), using an antifungal cream, or the use of various natural remedies. Professional advice should always be sought as to the best course of action.

The cervix (Latin for 'neck') is the lower portion or neck of the uterus, separating the vagina from the rest of the uterus. During the birthing process, the cervix stretches from a tightly closed hole to a fully dilated 10 centimetres. During a vaginal examination, cervix dilation is measured by how many finger widths fit into the opening of the cervix. If one fingertip fits, the cervix is 1 centimetre dilated, if 2 fingertips fit, that signifies a 2-centimetre dilation and so on. Cervical cancer is a type of cancer that affects the cells of the cervix, mainly due to the human papillomavirus (HPV). When exposed to HPV, the body's immune system usually keeps the virus in check, but in a small percentage of women the virus survives for years and can cause some cells to become cancerous. Regular screening tests are advised to check for any cancerous cells in the cervix.

The hymen is a membrane that covers the external vaginal opening. It is named after Hymenaeus, the Greek god of marriage, and is sometimes referred to as the 'maidenhead' or 'cherry'. The hymen can rupture as a result of pelvic injury, sports activity, pelvic examination, tampon use or sexual intercourse. When the hymen is separated for the first time, there may be some slight bleeding and a little pain.

The perineum is the name given to the diamond shaped area between the external genitals and the anus in males and females. In females, this area relaxes in response to hormones that facilitate childbirth. In some cases, it is torn or cut during childbirth if necessary – this is called an episiotomy.

FEMALE REPRODUCTIVE SYSTEM

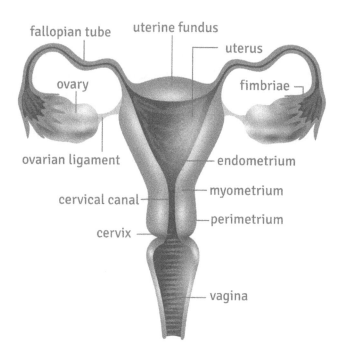

18.2 Female reproductive system

The uterus - commonly called the womb - is located in the middle of the pelvic cavity. This muscular sac houses the foetus during pregnancy. The top (fundus) opens into the fallopian tubes while the lower end - the cervix or neck - opens into the vagina. The walls of the uterus have three layers: the perimetrium is the outer layer, the myometrium is the middle layer – this is a thick layer of smooth muscle that contracts during childbirth - and the inner lining is called the endometrium. During a female's monthly menstrual cycle, the endometrium thickens in preparation for the release of an egg from one of the ovaries. This is to prepare a nourishing environment for a foetus if pregnancy occurs. If pregnancy does not occur, the endometrium is shed, and this is called the menstrual period, which occurs around every 28 days, though cycle length varies between females.

Problems can sometimes affect the uterus. A prolapsed uterus refers to the uterus dropping down from its normal position, sometimes affecting only the cervix, but in some cases the whole uterus can prolapse through the vagina. It can be due to weakness or injury to ligaments, connective tissue or muscles of the pelvis during vaginal delivery, or following pregnancy, chronic coughing, obesity, straining during bowel movements or lifting heavy objects. Symptoms are feelings of heaviness and pressure in the vagina, and treatment can range from pelvic floor exercises to surgery, depending on the severity of the condition.

A hysterectomy refers to surgical removal of the uterus, and sometimes the surgery also removes the ovaries and fallopian tubes. If both ovaries are taken out, menopause will begin. A hysterectomy may be recommended in cases such as fibroids, endometriosis that hasn't been resolved by medication or surgery, uterine prolapse, cancer of the uterus, cervix or ovaries, vaginal bleeding that persists despite treatment, or chronic pelvic pain.

Fibroids - also called 'myomas' or 'fibromyomas' - are abnormal, benign growths of unknown cause that develop in or on the uterus. They are quite common and often cause no problems at all, but sometimes they become quite large and cause severe abdominal pain and heavy periods. If fibroids are situated on the back or top of the uterus they can prevent a blastocyst from implanting in the best sites for successful conception. Myomectomy - surgery to remove fibroids - may be recommended if they are very large and affecting a woman's chances of becoming pregnant. However, the surgery may cause scarring that can lead to infertility, and the fibroids can sometimes grow back. Fibroid embolisation is a medical procedure that blocks the arteries feeding a fibroid, causing it to shrink. One in 5 women commonly between the ages of 30 and 50 may develop fibroids at some stage in their lives.

Endometriosis is a condition of unknown cause where tissue that normally lines the uterus grows in other areas of the body. This can cause pain, irregular menstrual bleeding, and infertility for some women if the tissue blocks the fallopian tubes or damages sperm or ova. One suggested cause is retrograde menstruation, where menstrual blood containing endometrial cells flows back up through the fallopian tubes and into the pelvic cavity instead of out of the body. These endometrial cells stick to the pelvic walls and surfaces of pelvic organs, where they grow and continue to thicken and bleed over the course of each menstrual cycle. Treatment of endometriosis may include hormone therapy or surgery. Hormones come in the form of a pill, an injection, or a nasal spray, and treatment helps the body regulate the monthly hormonal changes that promote the tissue growth that occurs due to endometriosis.

The ovaries are egg-shaped organs located on either side of the uterus and held in place by broad ligaments. Each ovary is roughly the size of an almond. Most females are born with two ovaries that produce eggs called ova. A woman is born with 1-2 million immature ova in sacs called follicles, but at puberty only about 400,000 follicles remain. With each menstrual cycle about 1,000 are lost, and usually only one will mature into an ovum that is released into one of the fallopian tubes at ovulation. As well as producing ova, the ovaries also produce the hormones oestrogen and progesterone.

Polycystic ovarian syndrome (PCOS) - also called Stein-Leventhal Syndrome - is a hormonal disorder characterised by incomplete development of Graafian (dominant) follicles, which fail to ovulate and remain as multiple cysts distending the ovary. First officially documented as a health condition in 1935 by American gynaecologists Irving F. Stein, Sr. and Michael L. Leventhal, this condition is now said to affect 5-10% of women of childbearing age. The exact cause of PCOS is unclear, but in some cases it is due to inadequate secretion of luteinising hormone (LH), although a high level of LH is found in about 4 in 10 women with PCOS. Some women suffer from polycystic ovaries but do not develop the full-blown syndrome. Most women with PCOS have 'insulin resistance' i.e. cells in the body are resistant to the effects of a normal level of insulin, so more insulin is produced to keep blood sugar normal. This raised level of insulin in the bloodstream is thought to be the main underlying reason why PCOS develops, as it can cause the ovaries to make too much testosterone. A high level of insulin and testosterone interferes with the normal development of follicles in the ovaries. As a result, many follicles tend to develop but often do not develop fully. This causes problems with ovulation as well as menstrual period problems and reduced fertility. Increased testosterone levels in the blood cause excess hair growth on the body and thinning of scalp hair, and the increased insulin also contributes towards weight gain.

Ovarian cancer is the fifth most common female cancer and rarely causes any symptoms in the early stages, but advanced-stage ovarian cancer can present with symptoms that are often mistaken for more common benign conditions. These include abdominal bloating or swelling, feeling full quickly when eating, weight loss, discomfort in the pelvic area, changes in bowel habits e.g. constipation and a frequent need to urinate. It can affect females of any age but is more common in post-menopausal women. Any worrying signs or symptoms should be medically investigated.

The fallopian tubes are two muscular tubes that extend from near the top of the uterus on each side, run laterally, and then curve over and around the ovaries. They have an outer serous membrane, a middle layer of smooth muscle, and an inner ciliated mucosa. The open ends of the fallopian tubes lie very near the ovaries but are not directly attached to them. Instead, the fimbriae (Latin for fringe) of the fallopian tubes sweep ovulated eggs into the tubes and towards the uterus for potential fertilisation. Fertilisation is when the sperm with 23 chromosomes and the ovum with 23 chromosomes unite to form a single cell called a zygote with 46 chromosomes. After a few days of cell division, the zygote becomes a blastocyst, reaching the uterus around day 5 and implanting itself into the uterine wall around day 6. The membrane lining the fallopian tubes gives off a glucose rich secretion that helps to transport the zygote and keep it alive. If the zygote begins to grow in the fallopian tube rather than the uterus, this is called an ectopic pregnancy, which requires prompt medical treatment as the fallopian tube can burst, causing internal abdominal bleeding, shock and serious blood loss.

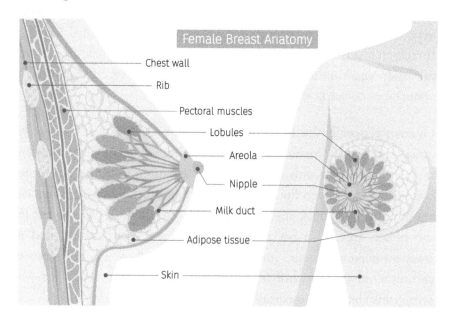

18.3 Anatomy of the female breast

The breasts - or mammary glands - are regarded as accessory organs of the female reproductive system, as they are responsible for supplying milk to an infant after childbirth. The nipple is the rounded area where milk drains to feed the baby. Nipples have many nerve endings, making them an area of sexual stimulation. The areola is the pigmented area surrounding the nipple and containing small 'Montgomery' glands that secrete a lubricant to keep the nipples from drying out, especially when breastfeeding. Breast tissue is composed of areolar tissue, fat, muscle and ligaments, as well as an intricate network of blood vessels and glands. The amount of fat determines breast size, but this has no bearing on the amount of milk someone is able to produce. Alveoli are the milk secreting cells that are grouped into clusters inside the breasts. The clusters form lobules (small lobes), which drain into lactiferous sinuses and then into lactiferous ducts (milk ducts) - the channels that open from the alveoli onto the surface of the nipple, allowing the breast milk to exit when suckling begins.

Mastalgia - more commonly known as breast pain - affects many women at some point in their lives e.g. pre-menstrually. Mastitis is inflammation, swelling and tenderness in the breast of a woman who is breastfeeding, and may be caused by a blocked milk duct or a bacterial infection. A 2017 study at a private maternal and children's hospital in Singapore concluded that cold cabbage leaves reduced the engorgement that can lead to mastitis. Most advocates agree that the leaves need to be chilled, and some recommend cooking them first to release beneficial chemicals from the cells. Galactorrhea is the spontaneous flow of milk from the breasts, unassociated with childbirth or nursing. It can be due to deregulation of prolactin or local causes such as excessive nipple stimulation.

A fibroadenoma is a common type of benign breast tumour, and in most cases it does not increase the risk of breast cancer. Although women of any age can develop fibroadenomas, they are more common in premenopausal women. A fibroadenoma presents as a fairly soft, smooth, moveable lump, whereas a cancerous tumour is generally a hard, fixed lump that is attached to the adjoining tissue.

Breast cancer can also affect males but is much more common in females. There are different types of breast cancer, but most present with a lump that feels distinctly different from surrounding tissue. In advanced stages, symptoms can include swollen bumps and sores on the breast, with skin appearing dimpled or leathery. Risk factors include increasing age, obesity, never having been pregnant, or genetics. 'BRCA' is an abbreviation for 'BReast CAncer gene' and BRCA1 and BRCA2 are two different genes that have been found to impact a person's chances of developing breast cancer. Everyone has both BRCA1 and BRCA2 genes that do not cause breast cancer, and are regarded as tumour suppressor genes because of their role in helping to repair DNA breaks that can lead to uncontrolled tumour growth. However, in some people these tumour suppression genes can become altered or broken and don't function properly. This is called a gene mutation, and carriers are more likely to develop breast cancer, particularly at a younger age. As genes are inherited, knowing your family history is important when determining breast cancer risks e.g. if one of your parents has a BRCA mutation, you have a 50% chance of inheriting the mutated gene. Genetic testing using blood or saliva samples can test for BRCA or other breast cancer gene mutations.

A mastectomy is a method of treating breast cancer by surgically removing a breast and sometimes nearby tissues. In the past, a radical mastectomy with complete removal of the breast, lymph nodes in the underarm and some chest muscles under the breasts, was the standard treatment for breast cancer. Nowadays less invasive treatments are available.

These include a lumpectomy to remove the tumour and a small cancer-free area of tissue surrounding it, or a quadrantectomy to remove the tumour and more breast tissue than a lumpectomy. The surgery is often followed by radiation therapy to kill any remaining cancer cells and prevent them from spreading or reoccurring. If a mastectomy is required, synthetic implants or tissue flaps from another part of the body can be used to reconstruct the breast(s), and sometimes the skin and nipple covering the original breast can be saved and re-used over the newly constructed breast.

Breast awareness by regular self-examination as well as breast cancer screening programmes, can help identify any unusual signs and symptoms before they develop further. Breast cancer survival rates have increased, and the number of deaths associated with this disease is steadily declining due to factors such as earlier detection, a personalised approach to treatment and a better understanding of the disease.

FEMALE SEXUAL CYCLE

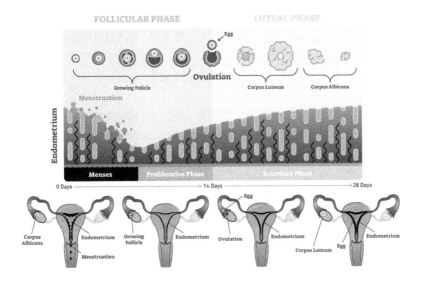

18.4 Female reproductive cycle

The female reproductive cycle is the female body's preparation for reproduction and occurs on average every 28 days, from menarche (first ovulation - normally before the age of 16), lasting for about 35 years to the last ovulation (menopause – usually after the age of 50).

The first phase of the cycle is the menstrual period and the first day of the menstrual period is regarded as day one of the cycle. The menstrual period lasts an average of five days, and if no ovum is fertilised hormone levels fall, resulting in a breakdown of the endometrium and the menstrual bleed or flow. The flow consists of mucus secretions, cells lining the uterus, blood from broken capillaries in the endometrium and the unfertilised ovum. During this phase, FSH levels rise, stimulating several follicles on the surface of one of the ovaries to enlarge.

Next comes the preovulatory or proliferative phase, which can last anywhere from 6-13 days. During this phase, rising FSH levels causes one of the follicles to become larger than the rest. This 'dominant follicle' is called the 'Graafian follicle' – so named after Dutch physician and anatomist R. de Graaf (1641-73). The dominant follicle begins to produce oestrogen that inhibits FSH but stimulates LH, and also causes growth of the endometrium. At the end of this phase - around day 14 - ovulation occurs, triggered by a surge of LH.

The postovulatory or secretory phase lasts for approximately 14 days. In this phase, LH stimulates the ruptured follicle to grow into the corpus luteum, which secretes oestrogen and progesterone that suppress FSH and LH. Progesterone causes changes in the uterus that make it more suitable for implantation of the fertilised ovum and the nourishment of the embryo e.g. it stimulates the endometrium to retain fluid and secrete mucus. Following ovulation, an egg can only be fertilised between 12 and 24 hours from when it was released. Under ideal conditions, sperm can live for several days once inside the reproductive tract, so any unprotected sex within about 5 days of ovulation may leave enough sperm waiting and ready to fertilise an ovum. After fertilisation, the tail of the sperm breaks down and the nucleus (head) grows. Together, the sperm and ovum create a single cell called a 'zygote' with 46 chromosomes. If the ovum is not fertilised, the corpus luteum becomes inactive after 10-14 days and menstruation occurs. As the corpus luteum breaks down it becomes white and is referred to as the 'corpus albicans'. Oestrogen and progesterone decrease and the cycle begins again.

In the case of fertilisation of the ovum by the sperm (conception), the corpus luteum or empty follicle continues secreting progesterone until the placenta takes over this job. The new zygote travels down the fallopian tube and develops into a mass of 16 cells called a morula (Latin for 'mulberry') after 3–4 days, and then into a blastocyst after 4-5 days. The blastocyst has a diameter of about 0.1–0.2 mm and comprises up to 150 cells following rapid cell division. Once it reaches the blastocyst stage, it's ready to implant in the uterine lining and continue growing into an embryo. Implantation usually happens between 6-10 days after fertilisation. Without implantation, the blastocyst will break down and be expelled with the rest of the uterine lining during the menstrual period. If it successfully implants in the uterine wall, a double-layered membrane begins to form around the blastocyst. The amnion is the innermost layer, and fills with a liquid known as amniotic fluid. The outer layer - the chorion - develops villi (vascular finger-like projections) and later becomes part of the placenta. The chorion secretes a hormone called human chorionic gonadotropin (hCG) that can be detected by pregnancy tests in blood or urine samples - it can usually be detected in the blood around 11 days after conception and 12-14 days in a urine sample. As hCG levels start to increase, the uterine lining will not receive the signal to shed, and the menstrual periods cease.

By day 24 after fertilisation, the blastocyst has formed a fluid filled amniotic cavity containing the embryo. Part of the endometrium and the chorion unite to form the placenta, allowing the passage of nutrients, oxygen and waste to and from mother and baby. The placenta also takes over the role of the ovaries and starts producing progesterone and oestrogen. In the early stages of embryonic development, three 'germ layers' called the ectoderm, endoderm and mesoderm form when the blastocyst begins to differentiate into different types of cells. Each layer produces specific types of organs, tissues and groups of cells. Endoderm, the most internal germ layer, forms the lining of the gut and other internal organs. Ectoderm, the most exterior germ layer, forms the brain, nervous system, skin, hair and nails, as well as other structures including the eyes and ears. Mesoderm, the middle germ layer, forms a number of critical structures and organs including the skeletal system, the muscular system, the excretory system, the circulatory system, the lymphatic system and the reproductive system. From week 8, the embryo is known as the foetus and develops in the amniotic cavity. Amniotic fluid is generated from maternal plasma that passes through the foetal membranes, and from about week 16, foetal urine also contributes to this fluid. Just before birth, the membrane of the amniotic cavity breaks and amniotic fluid is released via the vagina – this is called the 'waters breaking'.

The most common way to calculate the due date of childbirth (parturition) is by counting 40 weeks from the first day of the last menstrual period, and if the woman happens to know the day she conceived, she can calculate the due date by counting 38 weeks from that date. This method is based on the idea that women typically ovulate about 2 weeks after their menstrual period starts, and pregnancy typically lasts about 38 weeks.

The first trimester lasts from the first to the thirteenth week of pregnancy. In the first trimester all organs, muscles and limbs are formed. Most birth defects and miscarriages occur during this period. Miscarriages can be caused by structural, hormonal, immunological, environmental or genetic factors. Women who have had three or more miscarriages are candidates for genetic testing to determine if chromosomal reasons e.g. translocations, are the source of the problem. The first trimester is the time when the mother's body undergoes major changes. These changes often cause a variety of symptoms including nausea, fatigue, breast tenderness and frequent urination. Although these are common pregnancy symptoms, every woman has a different experience. Many pregnant women have morning sickness, thought to be due to the increased circulation of pregnancy-related hormones, specifically circulating oestrogen, progesterone and hCG. A small percentage of women experience an extreme version of nausea called hyperemesis gravidarum that generally strikes between the 4th and 6th week of pregnancy, and may be at its worst around weeks 9 to 13. The nausea and vomiting is so severe that most affected women are unable to go about their typical daily activities, and some may require hospitalisation. In most cases, symptoms improve by the 20th week.

The first ultrasound scan is carried out between week 8 and week 13 - depending on how the pregnancy is going. The sonographer estimates when the baby is due (the estimated date of delivery, or EDD) based on the baby's measurements. This scan can also include a nuchal translucency (NT) scan, which is part of the combined screening test for Down syndrome and other genetic abnormalities. The NT scan measures the baby's nasal bone as well as the fluid under the skin at the back of the baby's neck. A high volume of fluid can be a sign of problems. If the scan results are normal, the baby has a low risk of chromosomal abnormalities. If they're abnormal, further tests may be suggested to rule out problems. These could include ultrasounds, or invasive procedures like chorionic villus sampling (CVS) or amniocentesis. In CVS, cells are taken from tiny finger-like projections on the placenta called the chorionic villi and sent to a laboratory for genetic analysis.

Amniocentesis is a prenatal test in which a small amount of amniotic fluid is removed from the sac surrounding the foetus for testing. Different tests can be performed on a sample of amniotic fluid, depending on the genetic risk and indication for the test. Because it presents a small risk for both mother and baby, amniocentesis is generally only offered to women who have a significant risk for genetic diseases.

In the second trimester (weeks 13-27), fingerprints, nails, eyebrows, eyelashes and handgrip have formed, and the foetus can grimace and frown. The second trimester is when most women can feel their baby move for the first time, usually by 20 weeks. The baby can even hear and recognise the mother's voice during the second trimester. Some screening tests may be performed at this time, and the sex of the baby can be revealed. The second trimester is typically the most comfortable period of time for the majority of pregnant women, as most of the early pregnancy symptoms gradually disappear. Common complaints in this trimester are leg cramps and heartburn. Pregnancy hormones can cause the cardiac sphincter between the stomach and oesophagus to relax, allowing stomach acids to flow back up into the oesophagus and cause heartburn. The downward pressure of the uterus from this period onwards compresses the bladder, leading to frequent urination. The maternal urinary system processes both maternal and foetal wastes, and this increases the total volume of urine.

The second scan offered to pregnant women usually takes place between 18 and 21 weeks of pregnancy. This checks for physical conditions in the foetus, and looks in detail at the bones, heart, brain, spinal cord, face, kidneys and abdomen. It allows the sonographer to look for a number of rare conditions but cannot guarantee to find everything that might be wrong. Some women may be offered more than 2 scans, depending on their health and their pregnancy.

The third trimester lasts from the 28th week until the birth of the baby. In the third trimester, the sense of hearing starts to develop and the foetus can focus and blink. Somewhere between weeks 35 and 37, the mother will usually be screened for a bacterium called group B streptococcus. Group B strep - also called GBS - can pose a serious threat to newborns if passed to them during delivery. If the mother is GBS positive, she will receive antibiotics in labour to prevent it affecting her baby.

As mentioned in Chapter 5, the dermis stretches extensively during pregnancy to accommodate the growing uterus, breast tissue, and fat deposits on the thighs and hips. Torn connective tissue beneath the dermis can cause stretch marks on the abdomen that appear as red or purple marks during pregnancy, fading to a silvery white colour after childbirth. An increase in melanocyte-stimulating hormone, in conjunction with oestrogens, darkens the areolae and creates a line of pigment from the umbilicus to the pubis called the linea nigra (dark line). Melanin production during pregnancy may also darken the skin of the face to create chloasma (melasma) - sometimes referred to as the 'mask of pregnancy'.

DIASTASIS RECTI

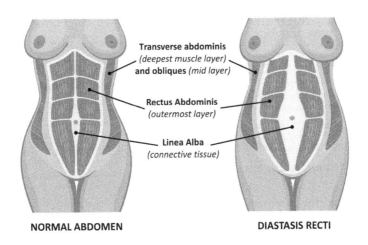

18.5 Diastasis recti

Pregnancy puts so much pressure on the abdominal muscles that sometimes they can't keep their shape, leading to a condition called 'diastasis recti'. 'Diastasis' means separation and 'recti' refers to the rectus abdominis muscles in the abdomen. When the muscles separate like this, the uterus and digestive organs have only a thin band of connective tissue in front to hold them in place, and without muscle support, a vaginal delivery can be more difficult. The condition also can cause lower back pain, constipation and urine leakage, as well as difficulty in breathing and moving normally. In extreme cases, the tissue may tear and organs may herniate out of the opening. The muscle opening often shrinks after giving birth, but in some studies of women with diastasis recti, the muscle wasn't back to normal even a year later. Diastasis recti is conventionally treated through targeted abdominal exercise therapy, supervised by a professional.

The mucous membranes in the respiratory system swell in response to increased blood flow during pregnancy, often leading to nasal congestion and nosebleeds, particularly when the weather is cold and dry. This can be alleviated by the use of a humidifier and increased fluid intake. During the second half of pregnancy, the volume of gases inhaled or exhaled by the lungs per minute increases by 50% to compensate for the oxygen demands of the foetus and the increased maternal metabolic rate. The growing uterus puts upward pressure on the diaphragm, sometimes causing shortness of breath (dyspnoea). During the last few weeks of pregnancy the pelvis becomes more elastic, and the foetus descends lower in a process called 'lightening' that helps alleviate dyspnoea.

Blood volume increases by up to 50% during pregnancy to manage the demands of foetal nourishment and foetal waste removal. With increased blood volume, the pulse and blood pressure rise moderately. As the foetus grows, the uterus compresses underlying pelvic blood vessels, hampering venous return from the legs and pelvic region. As a result, many pregnant women develop varicose veins or hemorrhoids. Water retention during pregnancy – particularly in the third trimester - is common due to the extra blood and body fluids during that time period. This can lead to swelling in the legs, feet and hands, sometimes causing carpal tunnel pain if the median nerve is compressed. Gentle exercise like swimming or yoga, wearing comfortable shoes, putting the feet up as much as possible, avoiding excess salt, and drinking plenty of water can all help alleviate fluid retention.

Preeclampsia is when there is high blood pressure, protein in the urine and swelling in the legs, feet and hands during pregnancy. It can range from mild to severe and usually happens late in pregnancy, though it can come earlier or just after delivery. Symptoms include severe headache and problems with vision, such as blurring or flashing before the eyes. Preeclampsia can lead to eclampsia, a very serious condition including seizures that can have health risks for mother and baby, and in rare cases it can be fatal. The only cure for preeclampsia is to give birth. Even after delivery, symptoms of preeclampsia can last for 1 to 6 weeks or more.

The foetal life-support system comprises the placenta, the umbilical cord and the amniotic fluid. Amniotic fluid helps the developing baby to move, allowing for proper bone growth. It also keeps a relatively constant temperature around the baby, protecting from heat loss and outside injury by cushioning sudden blows or movements. Tiny blood vessels carrying the foetal blood run through the placenta, which is full of maternal blood. Nutrients and oxygen from the mother's blood supply are transferred to the foetal blood, while waste products are transferred from the foetal blood to the maternal blood via the umbilical cord, without the two blood supplies mixing. One possible problem in pregnancy is placenta previa, where the placenta is attached near or over the cervix. As the foetus grows, pressure on the placenta can cause bleeding. This condition requires medical intervention to ensure a safe labour and delivery.

A common sign that labour will soon occur is the so-called 'bloody show'. During pregnancy, a plug of mucus accumulates in the cervical canal, blocking the entrance to the uterus. This prevents any bacteria or other sources of infection from getting into the uterus and harming the developing foetus. Approximately 1–2 days before the onset of true labour, this plug loosens as the cervix dilates, and is expelled - along with a small amount of blood from ruptured cervical blood vessels. Meanwhile, the posterior pituitary boosts its secretion of oxytocin, stimulating the contractions of labour by the myometrium. As contractions become stronger and more painful, this stimulates the secretion of prostaglandins from foetal membranes, enhancing uterine contractions. The foetal pituitary also secretes oxytocin, which increases prostaglandins even further. When a pregnancy is not progressing to labour and needs to be induced, a pharmaceutical version of these compounds called Pitocin is often administered by intravenous drip.

The three stages of childbirth are cervical dilation, expulsion of the newborn, and the afterbirth. For vaginal birth to occur, the cervix must dilate fully to 10 centimetres in diameter, which is wide enough to deliver the baby's head. The dilation stage is the longest stage of labour and typically takes 6 - 12 hours, but it varies widely and may take minutes, hours or even days. If a mother has given birth before, labour tends to be shorter. The amniotic membranes typically rupture at the end of the dilation stage in response to excessive pressure from the foetal head entering the birth canal, but in some women, they rupture before the onset of labour.

The expulsion stage begins when the foetal head enters the birth canal and ends with birth of the baby. It typically takes up to 2 hours, but can last longer or take just minutes, depending on the orientation of the foetus i.e. foetus head down and facing the maternal spinal cord is associated with the greatest ease of vaginal birth. A breech presentation is when the foetus presents buttocks or feet first. In a complete breech, the knees are flexed and the feet are close to the baby's bottom. In a frank breech presentation, the legs point upwards towards the baby's head. A footling breech is when one or both legs present first, but this is quite rare. Before the 1960's it was common for breech presentations to be delivered vaginally, but nowadays, most breech births are by Caesarean section, unless the baby 'turns' before delivery. A Caesarean or C-section is a surgical procedure where the baby is removed from the uterus through a cut in the lower abdomen. This operation is so named after Roman dictator Julius Caesar who some say was born in this way. The World Health Organisation recommends that caesarean sections be performed only when medically necessary, although nowadays many C-sections are performed upon request, without a medical reason.

Vaginal birth stretches the vaginal canal, the cervix and the perineum, and in the past it was routine procedure for an obstetrician to numb the perineum and perform an episiotomy, which is an incision in the posterior vaginal wall and perineum. The perineum is now more commonly allowed to tear during birth, and both an episiotomy and perineal tear need to be stitched shortly after birth to ensure optimal healing. Upon birth of the baby's head, an obstetrician will aspirate mucus from the mouth and nose before their first breath. Once the head is birthed, the rest of the body usually follows quickly. The umbilical cord is then double-clamped and a cut is made between the clamps. This completes the second stage of childbirth.

Historically, the umbilical cord was discarded with the placenta as medical waste, but over the past few decades, cord blood has been shown to contain stem cells that can be used for life-saving stem cell transplantation for children and adults in need of a transplant. Cord blood is more tolerant of a new host than normal tissue and can be used without full matching, providing increased access to transplantation for patients who cannot find a suitable donor. To collect the cord blood, the umbilical cord is clamped on one side and a needle is used to draw out the blood. This is sealed in a bag and sent to a laboratory or cord blood bank for testing and storage. The process only takes a few minutes, and is painless for mother and baby. Many women donate cord blood to public blood banks, where it is used to help those with life-threatening diseases that may be treated with a stem cell transplant.

The delivery of the placenta and associated membranes - commonly referred to as the afterbirth - is the final stage of childbirth. After expulsion of the baby, the myometrium continues to contract, shearing the placenta from the back of the uterine wall for delivery through the vagina. If the placenta does not birth spontaneously within approximately 30 minutes, it is considered retained, and the obstetrician may attempt manual removal, or in some cases surgery may be required to remove it. Uterine contractions continue for several hours after birth, and this helps return the uterus to its pre-pregnancy size and allows the mother's abdominal organs to return to their pre-pregnancy locations.

Although postpartum uterine contractions limit blood loss from the detachment of the placenta, the mother does experience a postpartum vaginal discharge called 'lochia', made up of endometrial cells, erythrocytes, leucocytes, and other debris. Placentophagy - eating the placenta - is something that is increasing in popularity. Fans of the practice say that eating the placenta can ward off anaemia, help increase milk supply, balance hormones, and lower the chances of post partum depression. The most popular way to do this is by placenta encapsulation, a process whereby the placenta is dehydrated and transformed into capsules that can be taken postpartum.

Many women experience a mild form of postnatal depression in first few weeks after childbirth. 'Baby blues' is quite normal, but some women experience a more extreme form of depression or sadness that can last for weeks or months. The exact causes are unknown, but it is linked to sudden hormone changes, lack of sleep, and the stress of caring for a newborn. Prolactin, which produces breast milk, is also known to affect dopamine, which gives feelings of euphoria and happiness, so this can sometimes be the reason behind moodiness, low energy levels, and slowed metabolism after childbirth. Many women experience noticeable hair loss around three months after having a baby. This is normal, and is caused by falling oestrogen and progesterone levels. Most women see their hair return to its normal fullness by their child's first birthday and many women regain normal fullness even earlier.

As everyone is different, it is hard to be exact about when menstrual periods resume after pregnancy. If the mother bottle-feeds the baby, or combines bottle-feeding with breastfeeding, the first period could start as soon as 5 to 6 weeks after giving birth. If she fully breastfeeds without any bottle feeding, periods may not start again until she stops breastfeeding. This is because prolactin, the hormone that causes the body to make breast milk, can inhibit ovulation. As the baby starts breastfeeding less often, 'spotting', which is light and irregular bleeding, may occur. A woman may find that her first period after pregnancy may be different from how it was before e.g. she may have irregular periods, cramping, heavier periods, or small blood clots in her menstrual flow. Medical advice should be sought if there is severe blood clotting or a much heavier blood loss than before.

Some women get through their monthly periods easily with few or no concerns, but others experience a host of physical and/or emotional symptoms just before and during menstruation. From heavy bleeding and missed periods to unmanageable mood swings, these symptoms can disrupt a woman's life in major ways. Abnormal uterine bleeding includes excessive, diminished, too frequent or infrequent menstrual flow, as well as post-menopausal bleeding. It can have various causes, including hormonal or emotional factors or fibroids.

Amenorrhea is the absence of menstrual periods and can be due to obesity, extreme weight loss, stress, excessive exercise, or abnormal levels of oestrogen due to a deficiency of pituitary or ovarian hormones. Problems with the sexual organs themselves also can cause amenorrhea. Examples include uterine scarring, lack or abnormal development of reproductive organs, or a structural abnormality of the vagina e.g. a membrane or wall may be present in the vagina that blocks the outflow of blood from the uterus and cervix. Dysmenorrhea is severe menstrual pain sometimes accompanied by headaches, nausea, diarrhoea or constipation, and the urge to urinate frequently. It can be due to another disorder such as pelvic inflammatory disease, fibroids or endometriosis. Menorrhagia is the term given to an abnormally heavy menstrual flow, usually associated with a condition such as fibroids, endometriosis or pelvic inflammatory disease.

Pelvic inflammatory disease (PID) is a generic term for inflammation of the uterus, fallopian tubes and/or ovaries that can in some cases progress to scar formation with adhesions to nearby tissues and organs. It may lead to tissue death (necrosis) and abscess formation. Symptoms tend to occur around the end of menstruation, and include fever, abdominal pain, irregular vaginal bleeding and foul smelling vaginal discharge.

Premenstrual syndrome (PMS) also known as premenstrual tension (PMT) affects many women and refers to the physical and emotional distress that occurs after ovulation, sometimes extending into the menstrual phase. Symptoms vary from person to person and may include oedema, bloating, weight gain, breast swelling and tenderness, backache, joint pain, headaches, constipation, skin eruptions, fatigue, lethargy, depression, anxiety, mood swings, irritability, food cravings, poor coordination and clumsiness. A more severe form of PMS, known as premenstrual dysphoric disorder (PMDD) occurs in a small number of women and leads to significant loss of function because of unusually severe symptoms. There is no exact cause of PMS and several theories have been put forward to explain why it occurs, but none of these have been proven. Some experts suggest that PMS results from the alterations in or interactions between the levels of sex hormones and brain chemicals i.e. neurotransmitters.

Toxic shock syndrome is a rare, life-threatening complication of certain types of bacterial infections e.g. staphylococcus aureus (staph) bacteria or group A streptococcus (strep) bacteria. Risk factors include the use of tampons and other devices such as menstrual cups, contraceptive sponges or diaphragms. It can also result from skin wounds or surgery, and can affect anyone including men, children and postmenopausal women. Signs and symptoms of toxic shock syndrome include a sudden high fever, low blood pressure, vomiting or diarrhoea, a sunburn-like rash on the palms and soles, muscle aches, redness in the eyes, mouth and throat, headaches, confusion and seizures. This condition requires immediate medical attention.

Infertility is generally defined as the inability to conceive after trying for at least one year. Males or females can be infertile, and causes can include problems with ovulation, sperm or fallopian tubes. Fertility drugs or IVF may be prescribed in some cases. IVF stands for 'in vitro fertilisation', which means facilitating the process of the sperm fertilising the egg outside the human body.

During IVF, mature eggs are retrieved from the ovaries and fertilised by sperm in a laboratory. Then the fertilised egg (embryo) or eggs (embryos) are transferred to the uterus. One full cycle of IVF takes about three weeks, but sometimes the steps are split into different parts over a longer period of time. Before beginning an IVF cycle, various screening tests are done to check the health of ova and sperm as well as infectious disease screening and a uterine examination.

IN VITRO FERTILIZATION

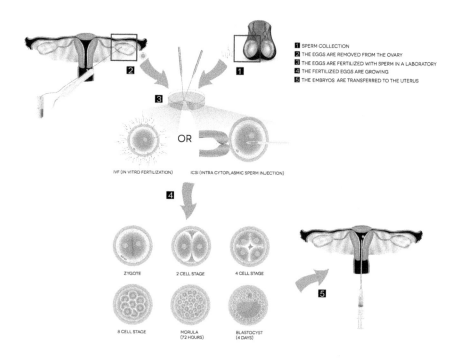

1 SPERM COLLECTION
2 THE EGGS ARE REMOVED FROM THE OVARY
3 THE EGGS ARE FERTILIZED WITH SPERM IN A LABORATORY
4 THE FERTILIZED EGGS ARE GROWING
5 THE EMBRYOS ARE TRANSFERRED TO THE UTERUS

IVF (IN VITRO FERTILIZATION)   ICSI (INTRA CYTOPLASMIC SPERM INJECTION)

ZYGOTE   2 CELL STAGE   4 CELL STAGE

8 CELL STAGE   MORULA (72 HOURS)   BLASTOCYST (4 DAYS)

18.6 IVF

The IVF cycle begins with synthetic hormone treatment that stimulates the ovaries to produce multiple eggs, rather than the single egg that normally develops each month. Multiple eggs are needed because some will not fertilise or develop normally after fertilisation. Follicle-stimulating hormone (FSH), luteinizing hormone (LH) or a combination of both are injected for this purpose. Human chorionic gonadotropin (hCG) or other medication is used to help the eggs mature, as well as medication to prevent the body from releasing the developing eggs too soon. On the day of egg retrieval or at the time of embryo transfer, progesterone supplements may be recommended to make the lining of the uterus more receptive to implantation. Vaginal ultrasound and blood tests are used to determine when the eggs are ready for collection. Sometimes IVF cycles need to be cancelled before egg retrieval due to issues such as too few follicles developing, premature ovulation, too many follicles developing, or other medical issues. In this case, the medical practitioner may recommend changing medications or their doses to promote a better response during future IVF cycles, or the use of an egg donor may be advised. If all is going to plan, egg retrieval is done 34 to 36 hours after the final injection and before ovulation. The ova are removed from the follicles through a needle connected to a suction device. Multiple eggs can be removed in about 20 minutes. Eggs that appear healthy and mature will be mixed with sperm in an attempt to create embryos. However, not all eggs may be successfully fertilised.

The male provides a semen sample on the morning of egg retrieval. Testicular aspiration, using a needle or surgical procedure to extract sperm directly from the testicle, is sometimes required or donor sperm can be used. Sperm are separated from the seminal fluid in the laboratory. Fertilisation can be attempted using two common methods. In conventional insemination, healthy sperm and mature eggs are mixed and incubated overnight. In intra-cytoplasmic sperm injection (ICSI), a single healthy sperm is injected directly into each mature egg. ICSI is often used when semen quality or number is a problem, or if fertilisation attempts during prior IVF cycles failed. If successful, an embryo will implant in the lining of the uterus about six to ten days after egg retrieval. Embryo freezing is a procedure that allows people to store embryos for later use. A person can also freeze eggs that are not fertilised.

Menopause (meno/month; pause/stop) is the time that marks the end of a female's reproductive cycles and is diagnosed after a woman has gone for twelve months without a menstrual period because her ovaries have stopped functioning, or have been removed or damaged. It usually occurs when women are in their 40's or 50's but can happen earlier, either naturally or for a medical reason, such as when both ovaries are removed in a hysterectomy. Menopause is a natural biological process, but the physical and emotional symptoms of menopause can make life uncomfortable for many women. In the months or years leading up to menopause – commonly referred to as the 'perimenopause' - women may experience some or all of these signs and symptoms:

Vasodilation (hot flushes/flashes/sweating): it is thought that the hormonal changes responsible for hot flashes are the increased levels of FSH and LH.

Palpitations: generally considered a result of fluctuating hormones.

Sleep disturbances: oestrogen decline causes a variety of physical side effects, including a reduction in the neurotransmitter serotonin that is used to create the hormone melatonin.

Bone loss: oestrogen helps bones absorb calcium and decreased levels post-menopause play a major role in the onset of osteoporosis.

Thinning of skin and hair: collagen production slows down, leading to thinner skin. Oestrogen helps hair grow faster leading to thicker, healthier hair, so drops in this hormone can lead to thinner drier hair. Male hormones increase as oestrogen levels decrease and this can cause androgenic alopecia, another form of hair loss.

Vaginal dryness: the decrease in oestrogen is the primary cause of vaginal dryness during menopause. Reduced oestrogen levels often cause the vulva and vaginal tissues to become thinner, drier and less elastic. Skin in general becomes drier too.

Mood swings: hormones such as oestrogen influence the production of serotonin - a mood regulating neurotransmitter, and other causes of mood changes include some of the symptoms already mentioned.

Many women can successfully manage the symptoms of menopause by following a healthy lifestyle, but in some cases hormone replacement therapy (HRT) - sometimes referred to as menopausal hormone therapy (MHT) - may be advised. HRT is given under medical advice in the form of tablets, patches, creams or gels. Medical practitioners generally suggest a low dose of oestrogen only, for women who have had a hysterectomy or for women who've had surgical removal of both the uterus and ovaries. Combination therapy, combining low doses of oestrogen and progestin (the synthetic form of progesterone) is recommended for women who still have a uterus. The current recommendations are for the lowest dose for the shortest possible time to control symptoms.

All types of HRT are linked with an increase in the risk of breast cancer, and some therapies increase the risk of uterine (endometrial) cancer. A 2019 study in over 100,000 women found that compared with women who never used MHT, women who did had a significantly higher risk of developing invasive breast cancer. They estimated that 6.3% of women who never used MHT developed breast cancer, compared to 8.3% of women who used the combination drug continually for five years. That's roughly one extra cancer diagnosis for every 50 users. The longer women used MHT, the greater their risk of breast cancer. Women who were no longer using MHT had a lower relative risk than women who were currently using it, but they remained at an elevated risk for more than a decade after they stopped taking the drug. The study also found that women who took the combination drug were more likely to develop cancer than women who took the oestrogen-only drug.

There are some benefits of HRT including strengthening the bones, which reduces the risk of osteoporosis and broken bones, but this is only during the time of taking HRT. HRT also reduces the risk of getting bowel cancer, but does not prevent heart disease, strokes or dementia. Natural alternatives to hormone replacement therapy include lifestyle changes, complementary and alternative therapies, and hormone regulating herbal supplements – all of which should be used under the guidance of a professional.

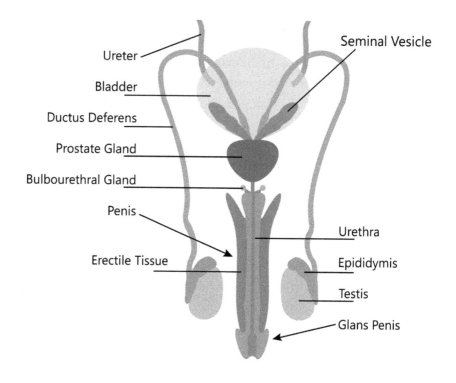

18.7 Male reproductive system

Unlike a female, most of the male's reproductive system is located outside the body. These external structures include the penis, the scrotum and the testicles. The functions of the male reproductive system are to produce, maintain and transport sperm and semen, and to produce and secrete male sex hormones.

The penis is the main external sex organ of the male, and has three main parts. The root of the penis is attached to the wall of the abdomen, the body (shaft) is the central part, and the glans is the cone-shaped head of the penis. The glans is covered with a loose layer of skin called the foreskin that is sometimes removed in a procedure called circumcision. The opening of the urethra is at the tip of the glans. The penis contains many sensitive nerve endings, and its body consists of three internal chambers made up of sponge-like erectile tissue. This tissue contains thousands of large spaces that fill with blood when a male is sexually aroused. When the penis fills with blood, it becomes rigid and erect, which allows for penetration during sexual intercourse. The skin of the penis is loose and elastic to allow for changes in penis size during an erection. Semen - which contains sperm - is expelled (ejaculated) through the end of the penis when a male reaches sexual climax or orgasm. When the penis is erect, the flow of urine is blocked from the urethra, allowing only semen to be ejaculated at orgasm. Erectile dysfunction or impotence is a condition where the penis does not become or stay hard enough for sex. Some men who have had long-term diabetes become impotent if their nerves or blood vessels become damaged. It can also be due to other nerve damage, illness, fatigue or stress. The term frigidity is usually used in reference to females to indicate sexual indifference, inability to attain orgasm, or low sexual desire.

The scrotum is the loose pouch-like sac of skin that hangs behind the penis. It contains the testicles - sometimes referred to as the testes - and many nerves and blood vessels. For healthy sperm development, the testes must be at a temperature slightly cooler than normal body temperature. Specialised muscles in the wall of the scrotum allow it to contract and relax, moving the testicles closer to the body for warmth and protection, or farther away from the body to cool the temperature.

The testes are two oval organs about the size of very large olives and lie in the scrotum, secured at either end by the spermatic cord. The testes are responsible for making testosterone - the primary male sex hormone - and for producing sperm. Within the testes are coiled masses of tubes called seminiferous tubules. These tubules are responsible for producing the sperm cells through a process called spermatogenesis. Testicular cancer is characterised by an irregularly shaped testis with a solid growing lump in the testis or scrotum. The cause is unknown but it is more common in those with undescended testes in early childhood.

The epididymis is a long, coiled tube at the top and to the back of each testicle. It feels like a soft swelling and can be quite tender if pressed firmly. It stores the sperm cells that are produced in the testes and brings them to maturity, since the sperm that emerge from the testes are immature and incapable of fertilisation. During sexual arousal, contractions force sperm into the vas deferens - also called the ductus deferens - a coiled duct about 30-45 centimetres long and 5 millimetres in diameter that arises from the epididymis and carries sperm to the ejaculatory duct and the urethra. A vasectomy is a surgical procedure in which the vas deferens are cut, tied or cauterised (burned or seared). The semen no longer contains sperm after the tubes are cut, so conception cannot occur. The testes continue to produce sperm, but they die off and are absorbed by the body.

As well as the vas deferens, the other internal organs of the male reproductive system include the ejaculatory ducts, the urethra, the seminal vesicles, the prostate and the bulbourethral glands.

The ejaculatory ducts are formed by the fusion of the vas deferens and the seminal vesicles and they empty into the urethra. The seminal vesicles are small pouches that open into the vas deferens, near the base of the bladder. They secrete an alkaline fluid containing energy rich sugars that provide sperm with a source of energy and help with their ability to move. This fluid makes up 60% of semen, and helps to neutralise the acidity of the vagina during sexual intercourse. The prostate gland contributes additional fluid that helps to nourish sperm in the seminal fluid. The paired bulbourethral glands are pea-sized structures located on the sides of the urethra, just below the prostate gland. They are also referred to as 'Cowper's glands' since they were first documented by anatomist William Cowper in the late 1600's. They contribute a lubricating mucous and an alkaline substance to the seminal fluid. These substances lubricate the urethra, and help to neutralise any acidity that may be present due to residual drops of urine in the urethra, thus aiding sperm survival.

The primary hormones involved in the functioning of the male reproductive system are FSH, LH/ICSH and testosterone. FSH is necessary for stimulating sperm production (spermatogenesis) and LH/ICSH stimulates the production of testosterone that is needed to continue the process of spermatogenesis. Testosterone is also important in the development of male characteristics including muscle mass and strength, fat distribution, bone mass and sex drive.

SPERM CELL

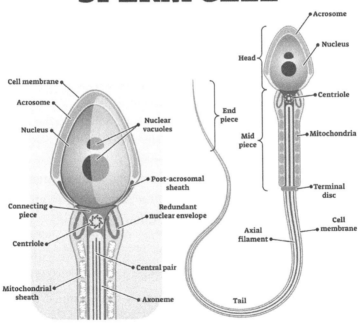

18.8 Sperm cell

Sperm cells are microscopic structures consisting of a head, a mid-piece and a tail called the 'flagellum'. The genetic material is located in the head and motility or movement occurs by means of the flagellum. Covering the head of the sperm is a cap called the acrosome containing enzymes that help sperm enter an ovum. Only one sperm fertilises each ovum, even though 300,000,000 to 400,000,000 sperm are contained in an average ejaculation. Each ovum and sperm produced has slightly different genetic information carried in the chromosomes, accounting for the differences and similarities between children of the same parents. Humans have two sex chromosomes - X and Y. Females have two X chromosomes in their cells, while males have both an X and a Y chromosome in their cells. Female ova all contain one X chromosome, while male sperm cells may contain either an X or a Y chromosome. This arrangement means that it is the male who determines the sex of the offspring when fertilisation occurs. Identical twins result from one ovum splitting after being fertilised by a single sperm, while fraternal twins are the result of two sperm fertilising two ova.

While both males and females are diagnosed with sexually transmitted diseases (STDs) in about equal numbers, they are not affected equally. Females are more likely than males to experience long-term health complications from untreated STDs, and a pregnant woman can also pass an infection along to her baby during pregnancy or childbirth. STDs are generally acquired by sexual contact, and the organisms like bacteria, viruses or parasites that cause them may pass from person to person in blood, semen or vaginal and other bodily fluids - sometimes without any symptoms.

A female's anatomy makes her more vulnerable to sexually transmitted infections than a male. Unlike the relatively thick skin of the penis, a woman's vagina is covered by a thin, delicate mucous membrane that more easily allows viruses and bacteria to pass through and cause infection. The vagina is also a warm and moist environment that can encourage bacterial growth. Women are less likely to have symptoms of common STDs such as chlamydia and gonorrhoea compared to men, and if symptoms do occur, they can go away even though the infection may remain. Women are more likely to confuse symptoms of an STD for something else. For example, women regularly have normal discharge or may think that burning or itching is related to a yeast infection, while men usually notice symptoms like discharge because it is unusual. Genital ulcers - e.g. from herpes or syphilis - can occur in the vagina and may not be easily visible, while men are more likely to notice sores on the penis.

Chlamydia is one of the most common STDs spread by having unprotected sex with someone infected with the bacteria 'chlamydia trachomatis'. These bacteria are found in the urine and genital secretions of infected people. In women, untreated chlamydia can lead to infertility, chronic pelvic pain or ectopic pregnancy. Chlamydia can affect several areas of the reproductive system, causing urethritis, vaginitis, cervicitis or pelvic inflammatory disease (PID). Chlamydia also can cause eye infections and pneumonia in newborns delivered by mothers who have the disease. Gonorrhoea is caused by infection with the pus producing 'neisseria gonorrhoeae' bacterium. Women are at greater risk of long-term complications from untreated gonorrhoea, as it may travel up the female reproductive tract and affect the uterus, fallopian tubes or ovaries, leading to PID with severe and chronic pain and damage to the female reproductive organs.

Syphilis is a highly contagious STD that is mostly spread through sexual activity, including oral and anal sex. The infected person often doesn't know that they have the disease and can pass it on to their sexual partner. It is caused by the bacterium 'treponema pallidum' and can lead to serious long-term problems such as arthritis, brain damage and blindness. Syphilis was once a major public health threat until the late 1940's, when penicillin was developed. Another common STD is trichomoniasis ('trich'), caused by infection with a parasite called 'trichomonas vaginalis'. Symptoms of the disease vary, and most people who have the parasite cannot tell they are infected. Trichomoniasis can cause vaginal infections with a foul-smelling discharge in women, and inflammation of the urethra in both sexes. In pregnant women, it can increase the risk of premature rupture of the membranes and preterm delivery.

Engaging in safe sex is paramount to preventing STDs that can have a devastating effect on the body. Regular screening such as having pap smears for cervical cancer, breast screening, prostate checks, and testing for STDs and infections can save lives, as early detection has a marked difference in the survival rate. Eating a healthy balanced diet, making time for exercise, maintaining a healthy body weight, and getting enough sleep are the best ways to keep the reproductive system healthy. Keeping stress levels in check is also important, as being under constant stress can lower the body's immune system and encourage an imbalance of hormones.

19. Ageing and the body

"The oldest trees often bear the sweetest fruit." (Proverb)

19.1 From birth to old age

Gerontology is the study of ageing and older adults, and is concerned with the physical, mental and social aspects and implications of ageing. Geriatrics is a medical specialty that focuses on the care and treatment of older people. Both gerontology and geriatrics have the goal of understanding the ageing process, so that people can maximise their functioning and achieve a good quality of life. Ageing is a natural process, which in many cultures is seen as a mark of wisdom and power, and something to be celebrated. Sadly this is not always a popular concept in western society as our obsession with anti-ageing products and procedures clearly shows. It is not that appearances don't matter, as looking good can help us feel good, and as the years advance, our interest in skin and hair care, make-up, dress-sense, healthy diet and exercise does not have to diminish. Looking after

415

ourselves properly can bring self-confidence, vitality, energy, good health and radiance, no matter what age we may be.

Ageing is a complex process and varies as to how it affects different people, and even different organs. Many gerontologists feel that these variations are due to the interaction of various lifelong influences - including heredity, environment, culture, diet, exercise, leisure and past illnesses, and each person ages at a unique rate. However there are some common factors that can affect everyone.

Cells & Tissues

With age, cells become larger and are less able to divide and multiply. There is an increase in pigments and fatty substances inside cells, and many lose their ability to function, or begin to function abnormally. Cell membranes change, so many tissues have more trouble getting oxygen and nutrients and removing carbon dioxide and other wastes.

Cellular replication is sometimes compared to photocopying, as the more a cell copies itself, the blurrier the image becomes. Over time, the cell's DNA begins to fracture and the cell becomes a poor copy of its original self, until eventually programmed cell death – apoptosis - occurs. The Hayflick limit is the number of times a cell will divide before cell division stops. It is named after American anatomist Leonard Hayflick from the Wistar Institute in Philadelphia, USA, who in 1961 demonstrated that a normal human foetal cell could divide between 40 and 60 times in a cell culture before apoptosis occurred. Each division progressively degraded the genetic material - specifically the part of DNA called a telomere. As already discussed in Chapter 4, telomeres are small structures - often compared to the plastic tips at the ends of shoelaces – that protect the ends of chromosomes and prevent them from unravelling, sticking to each other, or fusing into a ring. Each time a cell divides, the telomeres get shorter, and eventually they can no longer maintain the integrity of the chromosome, leading to apoptosis. It is though that some external factors can accentuate telomere shortening e.g. smoking, stress, obesity, inflammation, cardiovascular disease and poor health.

As ageing continues, waste products build up in body tissues. A fatty brown pigment called lipofuscin - sometimes referred to as 'age pigment' - collects in many tissues, as do other fatty substances. Connective tissue becomes stiffer and less flexible, and this makes organs, blood vessels and airways more rigid. Many tissues lose mass, and ageing organs function less efficiently. Organs normally have a reserve ability to function beyond the usual needs of the body e.g. when we are young, our organs have more capacity than is needed to simply function, but as we age, this 'reserve' diminishes and organs have to work harder. When an organ is worked harder than usual, it may not be able to increase function, and heart failure or other problems can develop. The biggest changes in organ reserve occur in the heart, lungs and kidneys. The amount of reserve lost varies between people, and between different organs in a single person.

Skin

Regardless of claims made by the beauty industry, the ageing process cannot be reversed or stopped. Even if we lived in a perfect world and applied the best skin care products money could buy, we would still go through the process of ageing as this is what we are genetically programmed to do. The effects of ageing are most evident in parts of the body that are continuously exposed to the elements - namely the face, neck and hands.

The most obvious sign of ageing skin is the appearance of wrinkles, which are of two different types. Expression wrinkles are mostly transverse lines on the forehead, temples and around the eyes and mouth, whereas lowering wrinkles are mostly vertical and due to changes in the subcutaneous layer of the skin as well as changes in facial bone structure i.e. the shrinking of facial bones due to ageing, leading to looser slacker skin. Although it varies from one individual to the next, a general pattern emerges - from small, fine expression lines, to deeper lines, slacker, thinner and drier skin, and altered facial contours. Cell regeneration in the epidermis slows down, there are fewer and less resilient collagen and elastin fibres in the dermis, sebum production decreases due to hormonal influences, and there is a loss of subcutaneous tissue. Blood vessels in the dermis become more fragile and this can lead to bruising, bleeding under the skin (often called senile purpura), small bright red 'blood spots' called cherry angiomas, and other conditions.

How quickly skin ageing occurs depends largely on genetics as well as external factors - we can do little about the former but can definitely do something about the latter through making wise choices with regards to sun exposure, nutrition and fluid intake, exercise, getting adequate sleep, managing stress, and adopting beneficial skincare routines.

Hair

A change in hair colour is one of the clearest signs of ageing as hair follicles make less melanin, causing the hair to become gray or white. Most people have some hair loss with ageing, and the rate of hair growth also slows down as follicles stop producing new hairs. Men may start showing signs of baldness by the time they are 30 years old, and many men are nearly bald by the age of 60. Male-pattern baldness - related to the sensitivity of hair follicles to testosterone - can also affect some post-menopausal women, with the hair becoming less dense and the scalp becoming more visible.

With age, the body and face may also lose hair, but women's remaining facial hair may get coarser - most often on the chin and around the lips. Men may grow longer and coarser eyebrow, ear and nose hair.

Nails

With age, nails grow more slowly and may become dull, brittle and sometimes yellow and opaque. Toenails may become harder and thicker, and ingrown toenails may be more common. Lengthwise ridges may develop in the fingernails and toenails. Pits, ridges, lines, changes in shape or any other changes can be related to nutritional deficiencies or may signal an underlying medical condition, and should be investigated if the changes cause any concern.

Skeletal System

Bone density decreases with age as bones lose calcium and other minerals. This particularly affects women after menopause, as oestrogen - which helps bones absorb calcium - diminishes.

In the spine, the gel-like discs gradually lose fluid and become thinner, and this leads to the middle of the body (trunk) becoming shorter. The long bones of the arms and legs become more brittle due to mineral loss, but they do not change length and this can make them appear longer when compared with a shortened trunk. The vertebrae lose some of their mineral content making them thinner, and the spinal column can become curved and compressed. Bone spurs caused by ageing and overall use of the spine may also form on the vertebrae.

The foot arches become less pronounced, contributing to a slight loss of height. Joints of the body generally become stiffer and less flexible, and fluid in the joints may decrease. Minerals may deposit in and around some joints leading to calcification e.g. in the shoulder. The cartilage that covers the ends of bones may begin to rub together and wear away, leading to osteoarthritis. This particularly affects the hip and knee joints. The finger joints also lose cartilage and the bones thicken slightly, particularly in women - these changes may be inherited.

It is never too late to start eating foods and partaking in weight-bearing exercise that can help to keep bones strong and joints flexible as life progresses.

Muscular System

Sarcopenia is the term given to the loss of muscle mass due to ageing and is thought to be influenced by various factors, including physical activity, nutrition, genetics and a reduction in endocrine function. Muscle mass decreases approximately 3–8% per decade after the age of 30, and this rate of decline is even higher after the age of 60. Muscle changes often begin in the 20's in men and in the 40's in women. The age-related changes seen in muscles are mainly due to loss of muscle cells, decreased size of muscle fibres and increased muscle stiffness. The age-related pigment lipofuscin as well as fat are deposited in muscle tissue. Muscle fibres shrink and muscle tissue is replaced more slowly. This is most noticeable in the hands, which may look thin and bony. Muscles are less toned and less able to contract because of changes in the muscle tissue and normal age-related changes in the nervous system. The best treatment for sarcopenia is exercise - particularly resistance training that can help to improve muscle strength and stamina. Resistance training can also help balance hormone levels and can improve the ability to turn protein into energy in older people. Good nutrition, including adequate protein, can help in preventing or treating sarcopenia.

As well as changes in skeletal muscle, cardiac muscle becomes less able to propel large quantities of blood quickly through the body. As a result, a person may tire more quickly and take longer to recover. Contractions of smooth muscle in the internal organs becomes less efficient as the body ages due to hardening and stiffening of the muscle fibres, and this can lead to decreased peristalsis in the digestive system and less efficient movement of fluids around the body e.g. blood and lymph.

Cardiovascular System

The sinoatrial node - the natural pacemaker that controls the heartbeat - loses some of its cells and this may result in a slightly slower heart rate. In some people, there is a slight increase in the size of the heart but the heart wall thickens so the amount of blood that the chambers can hold may actually decrease, and the heart may fill with blood more slowly. Abnormal heart rhythms (arrhythmias) such as atrial fibrillation are more common in older people, and are sometimes caused by heart disease. It is normal to find deposits of the ageing pigment lipofuscin in the heart as a person gets older, and the cardiac muscle cells degenerate slightly so the pumping capacity of the heart declines. The heart valves that control the direction of blood flow may thicken and become stiffer, and a heart murmur caused by valve stiffness is fairly common in older people.

The nerve receptors that monitor blood pressure and make changes to help maintain a fairly constant blood pressure when a person changes positions become less sensitive with ageing. This can lead to blood pressure falling when a person goes from lying or sitting to standing, and may cause dizziness due to reduced blood flow to the brain. The capillary walls thicken slightly and this may hinder the exchange of nutrients and wastes. The aorta becomes thicker, stiffer and less flexible, increasing blood pressure and making the heart work harder, which may lead to thickening of the heart muscle. The other arteries also thicken and stiffen, and in general older people have a moderate increase in blood pressure.

Normal ageing causes a reduction in total body fluids so there is less fluid in the bloodstream, and blood volume decreases. The speed with which red blood cells are produced in response to stress or illness is reduced, creating a slower response to blood loss and anaemia. Most of the white blood cells stay at the same levels, although some white blood cells important to immunity (e.g. neutrophils) decrease in number and in their ability to fight off infection.

Exercise, avoidance of smoking, eating a healthy balanced diet, keeping well hydrated and having regular health checks, can help to keep the cardiovascular system as healthy as possible as the body ages.

Lymphatic System and Immunity

With age, the immune system becomes slower to respond to infection and this increases the risk of getting ill. Flu shots or other vaccines may not work as well or protect the body as long as expected. The thymus gland shrinks with age and the number and effectiveness of T lymphocytes decreases. Autoimmune disorders may develop, and the body may heal more slowly as there are fewer immune cells to bring about healing. Lymph vessels may become more permeable, and bacteria may be able to escape more easily from aged lymph vessels than from younger vessels. The immune system's ability to detect and correct cell defects also declines. This can result in an increased risk of cancer.

Regular exercise, adequate sleep, a healthy diet, stress management, health checks and regular hand washing can go a long way to keeping the lymphatic and immune system healthy.

Respiratory System

With age, bones - including those of the ribcage - may become thinner and change shape, and as a result, the ribcage may not expand and contract as well during breathing. The diaphragm and intercostal muscles weaken and may prevent enough air getting in and out of the lungs. This may lower oxygen levels in the body and less carbon dioxide may be removed, leading to symptoms such as tiredness and shortness of breath. Muscles and other tissues near the airways may lose their ability to keep the airways completely open, and the alveoli generally become less flexible. These changes in lung tissue can allow air to get trapped in the lungs, leading to less oxygen entering the blood vessels and less carbon dioxide being removed.

The part of the brain that controls breathing may lose some of its function, so the lungs may not get enough oxygen or get rid of enough carbon dioxide, and breathing may become difficult.

Nerves in the airways that trigger coughing become less sensitive, leading to difficulty in getting rid of inhaled particles like smoke or germs. A weaker immune system means the body is less able to fight respiratory infections.

We can help keep the respiratory system healthy by avoidance of smoking and doing physical exercise to improve lung function and prevent mucus accumulating in the system. Avoidance of mucous forming foods can help if excess mucus is an issue.

Digestive System

With age, the surface enamel on teeth becomes thinner and may expose the underlying dentin, often leading to sensitivity and pain. The expression 'long in the tooth' alludes to the gums receding with age and making the teeth appear longer! Many elderly people also lose teeth, which can affect eating habits, unless dentures are provided. The muscles of mastication become weaker, and as a result older people tend to chew their food less before swallowing. Regular brushing and daily flossing as well as regular dental check-ups can help to keep teeth and gums healthy.

The connective tissue layers of the digestive tract (submucosa and serosa) tend to get thinner and the blood supply decreases. Goblet cells produce less mucus and there is a decrease in the number of smooth muscle cells, resulting in decreased peristalsis in the digestive tract. Digestive enzymes secreted by the stomach and accessory organs of digestion are reduced, so food is broken down less efficiently. Because the connective tissue of the digestive tract becomes thin with age, and because the protective mucous covering is reduced, the digestive tract of elderly people is less protected from materials from the outside environment, some of which may cause mechanical damage or be toxic to the digestive tract.

The liver's ability to detoxify certain chemicals tends to decline and its ability to store glycogen decreases. Elderly people are more likely to develop ulcerations and cancers of the digestive tract.

Gastroesophageal reflux disorder (GERD) increases with advancing age, and is the main reason that elderly people take antacids and inhibitors of hydrochloric acid secretion.

By making healthy lifestyle choices such as keeping weight in check, exercising, keeping hydrated, eating a healthy balanced diet and reducing stress, the digestive system will serve us better through the years. Persistent digestive problems should be medically investigated and treated to aid a return to healthy digestion.

Nervous System

The brain and nervous system go through natural ageing changes as the brain and spinal cord lose nerve cells and weight. The cerebral cortex of the brain shrinks, and reflexes slow down. This can lead to problems with movement and safety. Nerve cells may begin to pass messages more slowly than in the past, and waste products can collect in brain tissue as nerve cells break down. This can cause abnormal changes in the brain such as the formation of plaques and tangles - these are two major findings in the brains of those with Alzheimer's disease.

The age-related fatty pigment, lipofuscin can also build up in nerve tissue. Slowing of thought, memory and thinking is a normal part of ageing, and these changes are not the same in everyone. Some people have many changes in their nerves and brain tissue, while others have few changes.

A healthy diet as well as mental and physical exercise can help the brain stay sharp e.g. doing crosswords and other puzzles, learning new skills, reading, and participating in stimulating conversations. Physical exercise promotes blood flow to the brain and can help reduce the loss of brain cells.

Senses

The ability to see and hear clearly and to taste and smell usually declines with age and can adversely affect overall health and wellbeing.

Vision

The muscles that control movement of the eyes can malfunction with age, and the muscles that control the eyelids may become weak, causing the supporting connective tissue and skin around the eyes to droop and sag. The lacrimal and meibomian glands that produce tears to keep the eyes clean and lubricated may start to malfunction, decreasing tear production. This can lead to dry, burning, itchy eyes and other eye irritations.

Vision problems may result when various structures in the eyes deteriorate or become diseased. The pupils get smaller, altering how much light passes through, and this affects accuracy of vision. Age-related macular degeneration is the leading cause of blindness in people over 50. This condition affects an area on the retina called the macula that makes clearly defined, central vision possible. Age is a risk factor for glaucoma, which is caused by an abnormal rise in pressure in the fluid-filled chambers of the eyes, damaging the optic nerve and leading to blindness in some cases.

Cataracts can develop, clouding the normally clear lens of the eye and blocking light from reaching the retina, or scattering light and creating glare. Glare from excessive light scattering may lead to difficulty driving at night or difficulty navigating in the dark. People with cataracts may also suffer from night blindness (nyctalopia) and it may be hard to distinguish certain colours - especially blue from green. Presbyopia affects the normally flexible lens of the eye, causing it to become rigid and making it difficult to focus on objects close-up. This condition that can begin around the age of 40 affects most people. Regular eye examinations at a younger age can reduce the chances of developing any of these problems.

Hearing

With age, some degree of hearing loss is inevitable as the structures and nerve network in the middle and inner ears slowly begin to break down. Presbycusis is the gradual loss of hearing in both ears and is a common problem linked to ageing, with one in three adults over the age of 65 having some form of hearing loss. Most often, it affects the ability to hear high-pitched noises such as a phone ringing or the beeping of a machine. The ability to hear low-pitched noises is usually not affected.

Tinnitus, in which a person periodically or persistently hears abnormal noise and sounds such as ringing, is also prevalent among the older population. It can occur on its own, or as a symptom of another condition such as Meniere's disease, which is associated with a build up of fluid in the inner ear and sense of spinning.

Certain risk factors may play a role in the onset of hearing problems including chronic exposure to loud sounds, smoking and numerous middle ear infections. If hearing loss is significant enough, a person may need some type of hearing aid to communicate with others.

Taste and Smell

As the body ages, the keenness of taste and smell naturally diminishes. Although they are two distinct senses, taste and smell often work together to detect pleasurable sensations or warn a person of danger. They also play an important role in the enjoyment of food.

Although it's not exactly clear how the sense of taste diminishes, one theory is that the production of saliva decreases and this can cause a condition called 'dry mouth', which can reduce taste perception. Other factors that can affect the sense of taste include mouth sores, tooth decay or poor daily mouth care as well as certain drugs and medical treatments, including chemotherapy and radiotherapy to treat cancer. Diseases affecting the mouth e.g. gum disease, can alter the sense of taste in later years, as can diseases affecting other parts of the body e.g. diabetes, cancer, thyroid disease, stroke. A diminished sense of taste can lead to poor appetite and nutrition and may put a person at risk of eating contaminated or spoiled food that could cause food poisoning or other illnesses.

The keenness of smell diminishes faster with age than taste does, and in the average octogenarian the sense of smell is half as sharp as it was during their youth. Factors that can affect the sense of smell include nasal congestion e.g. sinusitis or heavy cold, certain drugs or medical treatments, diseases affecting the nose or sinuses or some neurological diseases e.g. Alzheimer's.

Touch

In later life, the sense of touch may become less sensitive as changes in the structure of the skin can cause it to become dryer, thinner, less elastic and less supple, sometimes reducing an older person's sensitivity to certain pressures and vibrations. There can also be a change in temperature sensitivity. Other factors that can cause a diminished sense of touch include poor blood circulation, skin and nerve damage caused by diabetes or other diseases, neurological or brain disorders, and certain drugs and medical treatments. A diminished sense of touch may put older people at an increased risk of sustaining serious injuries such as pressure sores, skin ulcers, heat stroke, burns and hypothermia.

Endocrine System

With age, levels of some hormones decrease, some do not change and some increase. Hormones that decrease with age include aldosterone, calcitonin, growth hormone and renin from the kidneys that is involved with regulating blood pressure. In women, oestrogen, progesterone and prolactin levels usually decrease significantly.

Some hormones remain unchanged or only slightly decrease with age. These include cortisol, adrenaline, insulin and thyroid hormones. Testosterone levels usually decrease gradually as men age. Hormones that may increase include noradrenaline that works alongside adrenaline in 'fight or flight' reactions, parathyroid hormone, follicle-stimulating hormone (FSH), luteinizing hormone (LH) and interstitial-cell-stimulating hormone (ICSH).

Being sensitive to the body's functions, monitoring medical conditions, eating well, getting adequate sleep, exercising and managing stress, can all help to keep the endocrine system functioning at its best.

Urinary System

Age-related changes in the kidneys and bladder can affect their function. The amount of kidney tissue and the number of filtering units (nephrons) decreases and blood vessels supplying the kidneys can become hardened, so the kidneys filter blood more slowly. The elastic tissue in the bladder wall becomes tough and less flexible, and the bladder cannot hold as much urine as before. The bladder muscles weaken and the urethra can become blocked. In women, this can be due to weakened muscles that cause the bladder or vagina to prolapse. In men, the urethra can become blocked by an enlarged prostate gland. In a healthy ageing person, kidney function usually remains fairly normal, but illness, medication and other conditions can affect kidney function. Some age-related urinary system problems include bladder control issues, such as leakage or urinary incontinence, urinary retention (not being able to completely empty the bladder) and chronic kidney disease. Urinary tract infections (UTIs) occur more frequently because the bladder muscles cannot tighten enough to empty the bladder completely.

Eating a healthy, balanced diet, keeping well hydrated, regular exercise (including exercises for the pelvic floor and the muscles that prevent urine leakage) and promptly attending to UTIs, can all contribute to a healthy urinary system as the body ages.

Reproductive System

Ageing changes in the female reproductive system result mainly from changing hormone levels. Menopause - when menstrual periods stop completely - is one clear sign of ageing that is discussed in more detail in Chapter 18. The ovaries stop making the hormones oestrogen and progesterone, and also stop releasing ova. As hormone levels fall, other changes occur in the reproductive system, including thinner and drier vaginal walls that are less flexible and easily irritated. Sometimes sex becomes painful due to these vaginal changes, and the risk of vaginal yeast infections increases.

There is an increased risk of bone loss (osteoporosis) due to reduced oestrogen levels. Loss of tone in the pubic muscles can result in prolapse of the vagina, uterus or bladder. Hormone replacement therapy (HRT) may help menopause symptoms such as hot flashes, vaginal dryness or pain with intercourse. Hormone therapy has risks, so it is not for every woman and should only be used under the supervision of a medical practitioner.

With age, a woman's breasts lose fat, tissue and mammary glands. Many of these changes are due to the decrease in oestrogen that occurs at menopause. The connective tissue that supports the breasts becomes less elastic, so the breasts sag. The areola surrounding the nipple becomes smaller, and the nipple may also turn in slightly. Lumps are common around the time of menopause and are often noncancerous cysts - however, all lumps should be investigated.

Ageing changes in the male reproductive system usually occur gradually, and may include changes in testicular tissue, sperm production and erectile function. Unlike females, males do not experience a major, rapid change in fertility as they age. Changes in the male reproductive system occur primarily in the testes, as testicular tissue mass decreases and the level of testosterone gradually decreases. The testes continue to produce sperm, but the rate of sperm cell production slows and the tubes that carry sperm may become less flexible. The epididymis, seminal vesicles and prostate gland lose some of their surface cells, but they continue to produce the fluid that helps carry sperm. There may be difficulty in achieving erection during sexual intercourse, but this is usually a general slowing rather than a complete lack of function. The volume of fluid ejaculated usually remains the same, but there are fewer living sperm in the fluid. Some men may have a lower sex drive (libido) and this may be related to decreased testosterone levels. It may also result from changes due to ageing, illness, chronic medical condition or medication.

Erectile dysfunction (ED) is a concern for some ageing men, and is most often the result of a medical problem rather than ageing or psychological issues. Medicines, such as those used to treat hypertension and certain other conditions, can prevent a male from getting or keeping enough of an erection for intercourse, and disorders such as diabetes can also cause ED. ED that is caused by medication or illness is often treated successfully.

The prostate gland enlarges with age as some of the prostate tissue is replaced with scar-like tissue. Benign prostatic hyperplasia (BPH) affects about 50% of men, and may cause problems with slowed urination and ejaculation as the enlarged prostate partially blocks the urethra. Changes in the prostate gland can also cause urinary tract infections, as urine may back up into the kidneys if the bladder is not fully drained and this can lead to kidney problems. Prostate gland infections or inflammation (prostatitis) may also occur. Prostate cancer and bladder cancer becomes more likely as men age. Testicular cancers are possible, but these occur more often in younger men.

Getting adequate sleep, having regular health checks, eating a diet rich in nutrients and low in unhealthy fats and engaging in regular physical activity will help to ensure that the reproductive system is functioning as efficiently as possible in spite of inevitable age-related changes.

The 'winter' of life can bring some of the most rewarding years, as a person will (hopefully!) have gained wisdom and patience and may be more confident than their younger self. Ageing does not have to mean becoming decrepit and not enjoying life, and we should aim to grow old with body and mind as healthy as they can possibly be. In this period when we finally have time, we can take an interest in our own functioning, claim our personal power and take control of our health and our future. Adopting healthy habits and behaviours, staying involved in activities with friends and loved ones, using preventive services and managing health conditions can all contribute to a productive and meaningful life.

Hippocrates - regarded as the father of western medicine - was the most important figure in Greek medicine, and some of his basic principles of healthy living still resonate today – some 2,500 years later. Here are my favourites from a selection of his best-known quotes:

"Let your food be your medicine, and your medicine be your food."

"Walking is man's best medicine."

"If you are in a bad mood, go for a walk. If you are still in a bad mood, go for another walk."

"Natural forces within us are the true healers of disease."

"Before you heal someone, ask him if he's willing to give up the things that make him sick."

"If we could give every individual the right amount of nourishment and exercise, not too little and not too much, we would have found the safest way to health."

"It is more important to know what sort of person has a disease than to know what sort of disease a person has."

General References (Books)

Anne Waugh & Allison Grant (2018) *Ross and Wilson: Anatomy and Physiology in Health and Illness* (Elsevier): Excellent book for students of anatomy & physiology. Great diagrams and text is easy to read! Comes with access to the Elsevier Evolve material online, which is helpful with revision.

Chris Jarmey (2008) *The Concise Book of Muscles* (Lotus Publishing, Chichester, UK) This is a great book for anyone studying human anatomy - particularly muscles and how they interact to move the body – also covers major facial muscles- newer editions are available.

Daniel E. Lieberman (2013) *The Story of the Human Body: Evolution, Health, and Disease 1st Edition* Pantheon Books – a division of Random House: Expores how many modern day diseases are caused by the discrepancy between our contemporary lifestyles and the original hunter-gatherer purposes for which the human body evolved.

David Lesondak (2017) *Fascia: What it is and Why it Matters* (Handspring Publishing Ltd.): This book presents a clear and easy to understand explanation of what fascia is, and the role it plays in the body.

Donna Rae Siegfried (2002) *Anatomy & Physiology for Dummies* (Wiley Publishing Inc.): As with all the Dummies series, subjects are covered in straightforward language. Newer editions are available.

Elizabeth A. Martin (Editor), Tanya A. McFerran (Editor) (2017) *Minidictionary for Nurses* (Oxford University Press): An invaluable little reference book with over 10,000 clear and concise medical definitions and around 100 helpful illustrations and tables

Elizabeth Blackburn and Elissa Epel (2017) *The Telomere Effect: A Revolutionary Approach to Living Younger, Healthier, Longer* (Grand Central Publishing): Telomerase and role of telomeres in the ageing process and how specific lifestyle and psychological habits can protect telomeres, slowing disease and improving life.

Francesca Gould (2005) *Anatomy & Physiology for Holistic Therapists* (Nelson Thornes): Good if you want simple explanations and contains crosswords for revision.

Gerard J. Tortora & Nicholas P. Anagnostakos (1990) *Principles of Anatomy & Physiology 6th Edition* John Wiley and Sons Ltd: This was my first Anatomy & Physiology textbook and a great reference book - very well illustrated and very thorough. It is quite large and heavy so not good for carrying around! Newer editions are available.

James Wilson (2001) *Adrenal Fatigue: The 21st Century Stress Syndrome* (Smart Publications): An informative and reader-friendly book about the effects of stress on the body and the importance of good mental and physical health choices.

Louise Tucker (2011) *An Introductory Guide to Anatomy and Physiology* Holistic Therapy Books: The basic International Therapies Examination Council (ITEC) course book. Newer editions are available.

Mel Cash (1999) *Pocket Atlas of the Human Body* (Ebury Press, London): A handy little reference/reminder of musculoskeletal anatomy and function.

Nelson R. Cabej (2018) *Epigenetic Principles of Evolution – Second Edition* (Academic Press): Examines evolution from an epigenetic point-of-view. Epigenetics is the study of the way in which the expression of heritable traits is modified by environmental influences or other mechanisms without a change to the DNA sequence – it helps to explain the how genetic makeup interacts with the environment to produce certain characteristics. For example external events such as neglect, trauma or stress may trigger chemical changes to DNA, which

434

affect how a person's genes are expressed and these changes can pass to the next generation.

Ruth Hull (2019) *Anatomy and Physiology for Therapists & Healthcare Professionals* Lotus Publishing: A comprehensive text with great detail and illustrations – there is also an accompanying workbook with revision tests. Several earlier editions are also available.

Tom Myers (2014) *Anatomy Trains: Myofascial Meridians for Manual and Movement Therapists 3rd Edition* (Churchill Livingstone – Elsevier): Presents the role of fascia in healthy movement and postural distortion - ideal for all professionals who have an interest in human movement and the body and now with an accompanying website www.myersmyofascialmeridians.com

Nancy L. Etcoff (2000) *Survival of the Prettiest: The Science of Beauty* (Anchor): A provocative and thoroughly researched inquiry into what we find beautiful and why. Nancy Etcoff, a faculty member at Harvard Medical School and a practicing psychologist at Massachusetts General Hospital, argues that beauty is neither a cultural construction, an invention of the fashion industry, nor a backlash against feminism - it's in our biology.

National Health Service UK: https://www.nhs.uk

Health and medical news and information:

https://www.mayoclinic.org
https://www.healthline.com
https://www.who.int
https://www.webmd.com
https://medlineplus.gov
https://www.nih.gov/health-information
https://patient.info

Web References by Chapter

NOTE: All website links referenced here were checked and live in October 2020. However, due to the dynamic nature of the Internet, some web addresses or links may have changed since publication and may no longer be valid.

1. Introduction

https://collegeofmedicine.org.uk/complementary-medicine-roundup-december-2017/

"House of Lords Select Committee on Science & Technology – sixth report": This published report was ordered by the House of Lords to be printed on 21 November 2000:
http://www.rebhp.org/articles/House.pdf

Professional Standards Authority:
https://www.professionalstandards.org.uk

Federation of Holistic Therapists: https://www.fht.org.uk

Social Prescribing:

https://www.socialprescribingnetwork.com

https://www.bmj.com/content/364/bmj.l1285

https://www.england.nhs.uk/personalisedcare/social-prescribing/

https://westminsterresearch.westminster.ac.uk/download/e18716e6c96cc93153baa8e757f8feb602fe99539fa281433535f89af85fb550/297582/review-of-evidence-assessing-impact-of-social-prescribing.pdf

https://assets.publishing.service.gov.uk/government/uploads/syste
m/uploads/attachment_data/file/753688/Prevention_is_better_tha
n_cure_5-11.pdf

Integrated Healthcare:

https://icamhub.com/wp-content/uploads/2019/01/PGIH-
Report-Download.pdf

https://collegeofmedicine.org.uk

https://www.kingsfund.org.uk

https://www.theihc.org.uk/

https://integrativehealthconvention.co.uk

All Party Group for Beauty, Aesthetics and Wellbeing:
https://baw-appg.com

2. A Message from the Body

Disease Categories:

https://www.nimh.nih.gov/health/statistics/global/global-leading-
categories-of-diseases-disorders-ylds.shtml

https://en.wikipedia.org/wiki/Disease

https://www.healthwriterhub.com/disease-disorder-condition-
syndrome-whats-the-difference/

Obesity and Chronic Metabolic Disease is Killing COVID-19
Patients: https://www.europeanscientist.com/en/article-of-the-
week/COVID-19-and-the-elephant-in-the-room/

3. Body Compounds

Discovery of Vitamins:
https://pubmed.ncbi.nlm.nih.gov/23798048/

Water: https://www.usgs.gov/special-topic/water-science-school/science/water-you-water-and-human-body

Vitamin D:
https://www.irishexaminer.com/breakingnews/ireland/irish-studies-find-vitamin-d-can-build-COVID-19-resistance-991995.html

Vitamin K and COVID-19: https://uk.yahoo.com/news/vitamin-k-could-help-fight-135056644.html

https://www.researchgate.net/publication/341725935_Reduced_Vitamin_K_Status_as_A_Potentially_Modifiable_Prognostic_Risk_Factor_in_COVID-19

4. Histology

Cell Division: http://leavingbio.net/CELL%20DIVISION.htm

Recurrent Miscarriages and Balanced Translocations:
https://www.ncbi.nlm.nih.gov/pmc/articles/PMC558686/

Telomeres: https://www.tasciences.com/telomeres-and-cellular-aging/

Genetics: https://ghr.nlm.nih.gov

Chromosome Translocations:
https://www.undiagnosed.org.uk/support_information/what-are-chromosome-translocations/

Cancer is a Preventable Disease that Requires Major Lifestyle Changes:
https://www.ncbi.nlm.nih.gov/pmc/articles/PMC2515569/

Fascia: https://myofascialrelease.com/about/fascia-definition.aspx

http://www.fasciaresearch.com

https://www.anatomytrains.com/fascia/

Fascia and Biotensegrity:

https://www.researchgate.net/publication/236146722_Biotensegrity-_The_Mechanics_of_Fascia

https://fasciaguide.com/research/what-is-biotensegrity/

www.myersmyofascialmeridians.com

5. Skin

Skin: https://anabolicminds.com/community/threads/the-real-reason-our-faces-age.45735/

Facial Bone Density: Effects of Aging and Impact on Facial Rejuvenation https://pubmed.ncbi.nlm.nih.gov/23012659/

Filaggrin: https://www.ncbi.nlm.nih.gov/pubmed/18774165

https://www.healthawareness.co.uk/dermatology/eczema-prone-skin-you-probably-need-to-feed-your-filaggrin/#

Lyme Disease and Long Term Symptoms:
https://www.nejm.org/doi/10.1056/NEJMe1502350

Skin Signs and Systemic Disease:
https://www.dermnetnz.org/topics/skin-signs-and-systemic-disease/

Scar Tissue: https://www.doctorschierling.com/blog/what-is-scar-tissue1

Protein Glycation: https://www.elle.com/beauty/makeup-skin-care/tips/a2471/sugar-aging-how-to-fight-glycation-614621/

Genome Scans Provide Evidence for Keloid Susceptibility Loci on Chromosomes: https://www.jidonline.org/article/S0022-202X(15)30798-3/fulltext

Skin Diseases: https://www.skin-diseases.org/diseases/

Images of Skin Diseases: https://www.dermnetnz.org/image-library/

6. Hair

Hair Structure: https://www.hairgrowthsos.com/hair-structure.html

7. Nails

Dermatophyte Infections:
https://www.aafp.org/afp/2003/0101/p101.html

8. The Skeletal System

Heads, Shoulders, Elbows, Knees, and Toes: Modular Gdf5 Enhancers Control Different Joints in the Vertebrate Skeleton: https://dash.harvard.edu/bitstream/handle/1/29739168/5130176.pdf

Correlation of Smartphone Use Addiction with Text Neck Syndrome and SMS Thumb in Physiotherapy Students:

https://www.researchgate.net/publication/325308744_Correlation_of_smartphone_use_addiction_with_text_neck_syndrome_and_SMS_thumb_in_physiotherapy_students

Paget's Disease of Bone Overview:

https://www.bones.nih.gov/health-info/bone/pagets/patient-info

9. The Muscular System

A Review of the Theoretical Fascial Models: Biotensegrity, Fascintegrity, and Myofascial Chains:
https://www.ncbi.nlm.nih.gov/pmc/articles/PMC7096016/

Myofascial chains: https://www.ptonthenet.com/articles/the-functional-role-of-fascia-in-posture-and-movement-part-1-3871

Fascia: https://www.upmc.com/-/media/upmc/services/integrative-medicine/documents/upmc-cim-newsletter-winter-2016.pdf

Insufficient Lumbopelvic Stability: A Clinical, Anatomical and Biomechanical Approach to 'A-Specific' Low Back Pain:
https://pubmed.ncbi.nlm.nih.gov/11487296/

History of Botox: http://www.bbc.co.uk/news/magazine-24551945

The Role of Cortisol in Concurrent Training:
https://www.unm.edu/~lkravitz/Article%20folder/cortisol.html

Vitamin D and Muscle Strength:
https://www.medicalnewstoday.com/articles/315863

10. The Cardiovascular System

Clinical Characteristics and Outcomes of 112 Cardiovascular Disease Patients Infected by 2019-nCoV:
https://pubmed.ncbi.nlm.nih.gov/32120458/

Complications from COVID-19 may depend on Von Willebrand factor in the blood: https://medicalxpress.com/news/2020-07-complications-covid-von-willebrand-factor.html

https://www.hemophilia.org/Newsroom/COVID-19-Information/COVID-19-and-VWF

11. The Lymphatic System & Immunity

Structure and Distribution of an Unrecognized Interstitium in Human Tissues: https://www.nature.com/articles/s41598-018-23062-6 https://www.scientificamerican.com/article/meet-your-interstitium-a-newfound-organ/

Breast Cancer Metastasis and the Lymphatic System:
https://www.ncbi.nlm.nih.gov/pmc/articles/PMC4533217/

Reflexology Lymph Drainage:
https://www.reflexologylymphdrainage.co.uk

Deep Breathing and Lymphatic Health:
https://lymphaticyoga.net/deep-breathing-and-the-lymphatic-system/

Interferons as a Potential Treatment Against COVID-19:
https://www.sciencedirect.com/science/article/pii/S0166354220302059

https://www.medicalnewstoday.com/articles/who-launch-trial-testing-4-potential-COVID-19-treatments#Antiretrovirals-and-interferon-beta

Do C-section babies have a weaker immune system?
https://www.nature.com/articles/s41467-018-07631-x

Dynamics and Stabilization of the Human Gut Microbiome during the First Year of Life:
https://www.ncbi.nlm.nih.gov/pubmed/25974306

Human Breast Milk and the Gastrointestinal Innate Immune System:
https://www.ncbi.nlm.nih.gov/pmc/articles/PMC4414019/

How Breastfeeding Transfers Immunity To Babies:
https://www.sciencedaily.com/releases/2008/10/081026101713.htm

Innate & adaptive immune systems:
https://www.informedhealth.org/the-innate-and-adaptive-immune-systems.2255.en.html

Vitamin D and the Immune System:
https://www.ncbi.nlm.nih.gov/pmc/articles/PMC3166406/

Interferon: Potential COVID-19 Treatment:
https://www.medicinenet.com/interferon/article.htm#can_interferons_treat_COVID-19_coronavirus_disease

Immunity and COVID-19: https://www.npr.org/sections/health-shots/2020/04/07/828091467/why-some-COVID-19-patients-crash-the-bodys-immune-system-might-be-to-blame

Regulation of Human NK-cell Cytokine and Chemokine Production by Target Cell Recognition:
https://www.ncbi.nlm.nih.gov/pmc/articles/PMC2844017/

Into the Eye of the Cytokine Storm:
https://www.ncbi.nlm.nih.gov/pmc/articles/PMC3294426/

Cytokines in Psoriasis:
https://www.ncbi.nlm.nih.gov/pmc/articles/PMC4437803/

Inflammation and Its Discontents: The Role of Cytokines in the Pathophysiology of Major Depression:
https://www.ncbi.nlm.nih.gov/pmc/articles/PMC2680424/

The Interferons: 50 Years after Their Discovery, There Is Much More to Learn: https://www.jbc.org/content/282/28/20047.full

Link between Kawasaki Disease and Coronavirus:
https://www.cnbc.com/2020/05/15/coronavirus-who-raises-alert-on-mysterious-inflammatory-disease-in-children.html

Immunotherapy and Cancer:
https://www.cancerresearchuk.org/about-cancer/cancer-in-general/treatment/immunotherapy/types

Psychoneuroimmunology:

https://www.ncbi.nlm.nih.gov/pmc/articles/PMC3801168/

https://www.healthline.com/health/psychoneuroimmunology

https://www.sciencedirect.com/topics/neuroscience/psychoneuroimmunology

Germ Theory Versus Terrain Theory:
https://www.differencebetween.com/difference-between-germ-theory-and-vs-terrain-theory/

12. The Respiratory System

World Health Organisation (WHO) - Coronavirus:
https://www.who.int/health-topics/coronavirus#tab=tab_1

Blood clotting and COVID-19:
https://www.webmd.com/lung/news/20200424/blood-clots-are-another-dangerous-COVID-19-mystery

Effects of Smoking on Chest Expansion, Lung Function, and Respiratory Muscle Strength of Youths:
https://www.ncbi.nlm.nih.gov/pmc/articles/PMC3944281/

13. The Digestive System

Web Resource for Students:
https://teachmeanatomy.info/abdomen/gi-tract/small-intestine/

Clinical Characteristics and Outcomes of 112 Cardiovascular Disease Patients Infected by 2019-nCoVA:
https://pubmed.ncbi.nlm.nih.gov/32120458/

High Prevalence of Obesity in Severe Acute Respiratory Syndrome Coronavirus-2 (SARS-CoV-2) Requiring Invasive Mechanical Ventilation: https://pubmed.ncbi.nlm.nih.gov/32271993/

High liver fat associated with a higher risk for severe COVID-19:
https://perspectum.com/news/high-liver-fat-associated-with-a-higher-risk-for-severe-COVID-19

Gut Microbiota's Effect on Mental Health: The Gut-Brain Axis:
https://www.ncbi.nlm.nih.gov/pmc/articles/PMC5641835/

Gut-Brain Axis: https://www.nature.com/collections/dyhbndhpzv

https://www.dietvsdisease.org/gut-brain-axis/

The Effects of Probiotics on Depressive Symptoms in Humans: A Systematic Review: https://www.ncbi.nlm.nih.gov/pmc/articles/PMC5319175/

The Efficacy of Probiotics in the Treatment of Irritable Bowel Syndrome: A Systematic Review:

https://gut.bmj.com/content/59/3/325.short

Role of Serotonin in Gastrointestinal Motility and Irritable Bowel Syndrome: https://www.ncbi.nlm.nih.gov/pubmed/19361459

The Role of Microbiota and Intestinal Permeability in the Pathophysiology of Autoimmune and Neuroimmune Processes with an Emphasis on Inflammatory Bowel Disease Type 1 Diabetes and Chronic Fatigue Syndrome: http://www.eurekaselect.com/145540/article

Autoimmune Diabetes Mellitus and the Leaky Gut: https://www.pnas.org/content/116/30/14788.long

Body Fat our own Janus: https://westminsterresearch.westminster.ac.uk/item/8yvx0/body-fat-our-own-janus

14. The Nervous System

Hans Seyle – Stress: http://stressmechanism.com/default.asp.pg-WHOWASHANSSELYE

Eye Movement Desensitization and Reprocessing (EMDR) Therapy: https://www.ncbi.nlm.nih.gov/pmc/articles/PMC3951033/

http://www.emdr.com/research-overview/

CranioSacral therapy:
https://www.upledger.com/therapies/index.php

Vagus Nerve Stimulation: https://selfhacked.com/blog/32-ways-to-stimulate-your-vagus-nerve-and-all-you-need-to-know-about-it/

Treadmill Exercise Elevates Striatal Dopamine D2 Receptor Binding Potential in Patients with early Parkinson's Disease:
https://insights.ovid.com/pubmed?pmid=23636255

Consensus Paper: The Cerebellum's Role in Movement and Cognition:
https://www.ncbi.nlm.nih.gov/pmc/articles/PMC4089997/

Brain Basics: Understanding Sleep:
https://www.ninds.nih.gov/Disorders/Patient-Caregiver-Education/Understanding-Sleep

Regular Exercise Changes the Brain to Improve Memory and Thinking Skills: https://www.health.harvard.edu/blog/regular-exercise-changes-brain-improve-memory-thinking-skills-201404097110

Stress and Neuro-Inflammation: A Systematic Review of the Effects of Stress on Microglia and the Implications for Mental Illness
https://www.ncbi.nlm.nih.gov/pmc/articles/PMC4828495/

Pain: https://www.iasp-pain.org

https://painconcern.org.uk/new-classification-for-chronic-pain/

https://journals.lww.com/pain/Fulltext/2019/01000/Chronic_pain_as_a_symptom_or_a_disease__the_IASP.3.aspx

15. The Senses

Affects of Ageing on Touch: https://amac.us/how-the-five-senses-change-with-age/

https://www.ncbi.nlm.nih.gov/pmc/articles/PMC2563781/

Humans Can Discriminate More than 1 Trillion Olfactory Stimuli:

https://science.sciencemag.org/content/343/6177/1370

COVID-19 and anosmia:
https://advances.sciencemag.org/content/6/31/eabc5801

Smell training: https://abscent.org/smell-training

https://pubmed.ncbi.nlm.nih.gov/26624966/

UV Rays and Cataracts: https://www.nei.nih.gov/about/news-and-events/news/new-research-sheds-light-how-uv-rays-may-contribute-cataract

Misophonia: https://misophonia-research.com/current-research/

Taste - Umami:
https://academic.oup.com/chemse/article/27/9/847/305861

16. The Endocrine System

An Overview of the Metabolic Functions of Osteocalcin:
https://www.ncbi.nlm.nih.gov/pmc/articles/PMC4499327/
Osteocalcin:
https://www.sciencemag.org/news/2019/09/hormone-secreted-bones-may-help-us-escape-danger

Quality of Sexual Experience in Women Correlates with Post-Orgasmic Prolactin Surges: Results from an Experimental Prototype Study https://onlinelibrary.wiley.com/doi/abs/10.1111/jsm.12097

Evidence of an Interaction between Leptin and the Melanocortin Signalling System: https://www.ncbi.nlm.nih.gov/pubmed/14765998

Overview of Human Oxytocin Research: https://pubmed.ncbi.nlm.nih.gov/28864976/

Sunshine, Serotonin, and Skin: A Partial Explanation for Seasonal Patterns in Psychopathology: https://www.ncbi.nlm.nih.gov/pmc/articles/PMC3779905/

Why Is Blue Light before Bedtime Bad for Sleep? https://www.scientificamerican.com/article/q-a-why-is-blue-light-before-bedtime-bad-for-sleep/

Foods with Natural Melatonin: https://nutritionfacts.org/2014/04/03/foods-with-natural-melatonin/

Food and Sleep: https://www.prevention.com/food-nutrition/a20495914/eating-habits-impact-sleep/

Cortisol: https://www.wellnessresources.com/news/is-cortisol-good-or-bad

17. The Urinary System

Vitamin D Metabolism and Action in Human Bone Marrow Stromal Cells: https://www.ncbi.nlm.nih.gov/pmc/articles/PMC2803155/

Vitamin D and the Central Nervous System: https://www.ncbi.nlm.nih.gov/pubmed/23744412/

Vitamin D and Pain:
https://www.hindawi.com/journals/prt/2015/904967/

18. The Reproductive System

G Spot: https://onlinelibrary.wiley.com/doi/10.1111/j.1743-6109.2012.02668.x

Female Genital Mutilation: https://www.who.int/health-topics/female-genital-mutilation#tab=tab_1

Mastitis – Cabbage Leaves:
https://www.ncbi.nlm.nih.gov/pubmed/28941842

Pathophysiology of Premenstrual Syndrome and Premenstrual Dysphoric Disorder:
https://www.ncbi.nlm.nih.gov/pubmed/22611222

The Quality of Sexual Experience in Women Correlates with Post - Orgasmic Prolactin Surges: Results from an Experimental Prototype Study: https://onlinelibrary.wiley.com/doi/abs/10.1111/jsm.12097

https://pubmed.ncbi.nlm.nih.gov/23421490/

Diastasis Recti and Pregnancy:
https://torontophysiotherapy.ca/diastasis-recti-and-pregnancy-closing-the-gap-between-current-treatment-practices-and-clinical-evidence/

The Role of Prostaglandins in Labour and Delivery:
https://pubmed.ncbi.nlm.nih.gov/8665768/

Type and Timing of Menopausal Hormone Therapy and Breast Cancer Risk: Individual Participant Meta-analysis of the Worldwide Epidemiological Evidence:

https://www.thelancet.com/journals/lancet/article/PIIS0140-6736(19)31709-X/fulltext

19. Ageing and the body

General Ageing: https://nurseslabs.com/aging-body-systems-explaining-physiological-aging/

Human Ageing: https://www.britannica.com/science/human-aging

'Ageotypes': https://www.scientificamerican.com/article/peoples-body-systems-age-at-different-rates/

Personal Ageing Markers and 'Ageotypes' Revealed by Deep Longitudinal Profiling: https://www.nature.com/articles/s41591-019-0719-5.epdf

Ageing Changes in Organs, Tissues, and Cells: https://medlineplus.gov/ency/article/004012.htm

Lipofuscin: Mechanisms of Formation and Increase with Age: https://www.ncbi.nlm.nih.gov/pubmed/9531959

Skin: https://anabolicminds.com/community/threads/the-real-reason-our-faces-age.45735/

Muscle Tissue Changes with Ageing: https://www.ncbi.nlm.nih.gov/pmc/articles/PMC2804956/

Lymphatic System: http://www.einstein.yu.edu/departments/pathology/News/Aging-related-Changes-Detected-in-Lymph-Vessels.aspx

Endocrine System and Ageing: https://www.ncbi.nlm.nih.gov/pubmed/17200939

Where to find research articles

The Cochrane Database of Systematic Reviews has a wealth of evidence that can be searched for specific topics: https://www.cochranelibrary.com/cdsr/reviews

Research Gate provides access to over 135 million pages of scientific research - you can also share your research and collaborate with your peers: https://www.researchgate.net

NICE Evidence Services provide access to high quality authoritative evidence and best practice. Search using filters: https://www.nice.org.uk/about/what-we-do/evidence-services

PubMed is a free search engine that provides access to a huge database of references and research abstracts, including those relevant to specific conditions and complementary therapies: https://www.ncbi.nlm.nih.gov/pubmed

BMJ Open is an online, open access journal, dedicated to publishing medical research from all disciplines and therapeutic areas: https://bmjopen.bmj.com

The latest Open Access articles published in European Journal of Integrative Medicine: https://www.journals.elsevier.com/european-journal-of-integrative-medicine/open-access-articles

Picture credits

2.1 © [normaals]/123RF.COM
2.2 © [Iryna Timonina]/123RF.COM
3.1 © [normaals]/123RF.COM
3.2 © [seamartini]/123RF.COM
4.1 © [Alila Medical Media]/FOTOLIA.COM
4.2 © [designua]/123RF.COM
4.3 © [designua]/123RF.COM
4.4 © [onnere]/123RF.COM
4.5 © [Aldona]/ADOBE.COM
4.6 © [normaals]/123RF.COM
4.7 © [Arindam Ghosh]/123RF.COM
5.1 © [Alila Medical Media]/FOTOLIA.COM
5.2 © [Alila Medical Media]/FOTOLIA.COM
5.3 © [Tetyana Hripliva]/123RF.COM
5.4 © [designua]/123RF.COM
5.5 © [designua]/123RF.COM
5.6 © [designua]/123RF.COM
6.1 © [designua]/123RF.COM
6.2 © [Alila Medical Media]/FOTOLIA.COM
6.3 © [Alex Papp]/ADOBE.COM
7.1 © [bilderzwerg]/FOTOLIA.COM
8.1 © [adimas]/FOTOLIA.COM
8.2 © [Balint Roxana]/123RF.COM
8.3 © [normaals]/123RF.COM
8.4 © [normaals]/123RF.COM
8.5 © [Iryna Timonina]/123RF.COM
8.6 © [Peter Lamb]/123RF.COM
8.7 © [guniita]/123RF.COM
8.8 © [designua]/123RF.COM
8.9 © [Belinda Pretorius]/FOTOLIA.COM
8.10 © [Belinda Pretorius]/FOTOLIA.COM
8.11 © [Alila Medical Media]/FOTOLIA.COM
8.12 © [elina33]/123RF.COM
8.13 © [Iryna Timonina]/123RF.COM
8.14 © [normaals]/123RF.COM
8.15 © [Peter Lamb]/123RF.COM
8.16 © [Peter Lamb]/123RF.COM
8.17 © [Peter Lamb]/123RF.COM
8.18 © [Viktoriia Kasyanyuk]/123RF.COM
9.1 © [corbacserdar]/123RF.COM
9.2 © [Teguh Mujiono]/123RF.COM

11.4 © [Peter Lamb]/123RF.COM
11.5 © [elenabsl]/123RF.COM
12.1 © [Alila Medical Media]/FOTOLIA.COM
12.2 © [Alila Medical Media]/FOTOLIA.COM
12.3 © [designua]/123RF.COM
12.4 © [normaals]/123RF.COM
12.5 © [sahua]/123RF.COM
13.1 © [Christos Georghiou]/123RF.COM
13.2 © [snapgalleria]/123RF.COM
13.3 © [Ewelina Kowalska]/123RF.COM
13.4 © [guniita]/123RF.COM
13.5 © [guniita]/123RF.COM
13.6 © [designua]/123RF.COM
13.7 © [normaals]/123RF.COM
14.1 © [Alila Medical Media]/FOTOLIA.COM
14.2 © [Alila Medical Media]/FOTOLIA.COM
14.3 © [designua]/123RF.COM
14.4 © [designua]/123RF.COM
14.5 © [normaals]/123RF.COM
14.6 © [Alila Medical Media]/FOTOLIA.COM
14.7 © [Alexander Pokusay]/123RF.COM
14.8 © [normaals]/123RF.COM
15.1 © [designua]/123RF.COM
15.2 © [Peter Lamb]/123RF.COM
15.3 © [Axel Kock]/123RF.COM
15.4 © [Alila Medical Media]/FOTOLIA.COM
15.5 © [Peter Hermes Furian]/123RF.COM
16.1 + 18.5 © [normaals]/123RF.COM
16.2 © [Alila Medical Media]/FOTOLIA.COM
16.3 © [Peter Lamb]/123RF.COM
16.4 © [normaals]/123RF.COM
16.5 © [designua]/123RF.COM
16.6 © [designua]/123RF.COM
16.7 © [Science Pics]/123RF.COM
16.8 © [designua]/123RF.COM
16.9 © [designua]/123RF.COM
16.10 © [macrovector]/123RF.COM
17.1 © [Poemsuk Kinchokawat]/123RF.COM

Acknowledgements

I am forever grateful to the many students I have taught in my role as complementary therapy lecturer over the past 20 years. Your eagerness, curiosity, interest and though provoking questions kept me learning too, and helped me become a better teacher.

During my years of private practice, the trust of my clients gave me the confidence and encouragement to seek a better understanding of the human body and health issues in general – thank you for trusting me to be your therapist.

To my friends and colleagues who read the text and made helpful suggestions and comments: Lesley Hart, Emma Holly, and Emma Charlton - thank you for your invaluable feedback, advice and support.

To Dr. Michael Fenster, MD FACC, FSCA&I, PEMBA and Dr. Kaur T. Birinder, MB BS MRCOG – thank you for reading my text and for your helpful comments – it was a privilege to have your viewpoints as medical professionals.

To Gabriel Mojay - thank you for giving me the opportunity to teach anatomy and physiology to your students and for taking time to read this text and write the wonderful foreword.

To my talented niece, Grainne Aldred - thank you for designing and creating the eye-catching book covers.

To Jo Harrison – thank you for turning my writing into this book.

To Angela Pruden – thank you for proofreading and polishing my final manuscript.

To my patient husband Patrick, thank you for your help and support – especially with the index.

Formatting: https://www.ebook-formatting.co.uk
Proofreading: https://www.facebook.com/Angela-Pruden-Proofreading-103981077759046
Cover design: http://www.grainnealdred.co.uk

About the Author

Following a career in education, Mary Dalgleish qualified as an aromatherapist at the Tisserand Institute of Holistic Aromatherapy in London in 1999 and later worked there as an anatomy and physiology lecturer and student mentor. Her aromatherapy studies sparked an interest in natural health, and since then she has completed a variety of complementary therapy training courses including reflexology and various forms of massage.

Mary has worked as a lecturer in the complementary therapy departments of several London adult education colleges including Kingston, Merton, Sutton and Morley Colleges. She has also lectured at several private colleges, including Maureen Burgess AOR Accredited School of Reflexology, Westminster School of Yoga, the School of Natural Therapies, and more recently at the Institute of Traditional Herbal Medicine & Aromatherapy (ITHMA) based at Regent's University in London. Over the years, Mary has also taught a range of continuing professional development massage courses for qualified therapists.

Mary was awarded a 'Certificate of Excellence' for teaching anatomy & physiology at Merton Adult College in May 2005 and again in May 2008 (nominated by her students). Mary was also awarded a 'Commended Tutor of the Year' Certificate at the Federation of Holistic Therapists Excellence in Education Awards in 2012.

Mary has co-authored two books to date "Indian Head Massage – the Essential Guide" and "Ear Candling – the Essential Guide" (both originally published by Hodder Arnold as part of the "In Essence" series). Mary is a Fellow and Vice-President of the Federation of Holistic Therapists (FHT), and holds a Master's Degree in Education. Mary regularly contributes articles to various health and wellbeing magazines and has recently retired from running her clinical practice.

Personal note from the author:

Thank you for reaching the end of this book. I hope you have enjoyed it and found it helpful. You may also enjoy the accompanying WORKBOOK. Please spread the word about 'KNOW YOUR BODY The Essential Guide to Human Anatomy and Physiology" and feel free to get in touch with any queries or comments relating to the book or workbook.

Mary Dalgleish

https://anatomyandphysiology.co.uk

Index

7

7-dehydro cholesterol 64

A

abdominal muscles 130, 167, 396
acetabulum... 136
acetylcholine............................... 149, 288
Achilles tendon 172, 173
acne.............................. 64, 69, 78, 97
acromioclavicular joint..................... 133
action potential........................... 287, 295
adductors 144, 170
adenine............................... 42, 50
adenosine tri-phosphate 37
adhesive capsulitis 176
adrenal gland.. 62, 233, 290, 338, 340,
    355, 356, 357, 358, 361, 363, 367
adrenaline..... 154, 202, 232, 233, 253,
    290, 358, 428
AIDS... 230
alanine aminotransferase................. 267
albinism 72
aldosterone ... 340, 356, 357, 367, 428
alleles..43
allergens 231, 250
alopecia................................. 95, 96, 406
alveoli ... 242, 243, 244, 245, 248, 251,
    252, 387, 422
amenorrhea... 402
amino acids 25, 26, 38, 39, 42, 151,
    155, 180, 263, 265, 291
ammonia 25, 267, 368
amniocentesis................................. 393

amniotic fluid..........391, 392, 393, 397
amygdala....................................... 296, 318
amylase.................................... 257, 269
amyloid plaques................................. 289
anabolism...37
anaemia 102, 104, 181, 227, 264, 366,
    400, 421
anagen 93, 94, 95
anaphase.............................. 46, 48
anaphylactic shock............................. 231
anatomical planes............................... 19
androgens..................................... 355, 357
angioedema 77
angiotensin.................................. 356, 367
anhidrosis..63
ankylosing spondylitis....................... 135
anorexia......................... 274, 342, 357
anosmia 318, 448
anti-diuretic hormone 337, 340, 341
antihistamines................................ 319
anuria 374
aorta 164, 192, 193, 195, 196, 197,
    199, 201, 236, 421
apocrine sweat glands...................... 331
apoptosis........................... 185, 219, 416
appendicular skeleton 19, 107
appendix..................................... 214, 265
aqueous humor......................... 321, 322
arachidonic acid.................................. 342
arachnoid mater 301
arrector pili..65
arrhythmias 421
ascorbic acid 33
asthma 76, 232, 249, 251, 275
astrocytomas 284
ataxia... 298

atherosclerosis 205, 252
ATP 26, 37, 149, 236
axial skeleton 19, 107, 135
axon 285, 286, 287, 293

B

B cells.... 183, 185, 212, 215, 223, 224, 352
basal cell carcinoma 53, 86
basal ganglia 297
basophils 182, 219
bed sore 79
bed-wetting 373
belching 270
biceps 144, 147, 161, 170
bicuspid 192, 193
bifidobacterium 278
bile..14, 180, 261, 263, 265, 266, 267, 269, 331
bilharzia 271
bilirubin 180, 265
biotensegrity 439
bladder....15, 135, 167, 196, 315, 331, 362, 363, 368, 369, 370, 371, 372, 373, 376, 394, 410, 428, 429, 431
blastocyst 383, 386, 391
blood groups 188, 190
body mass index 209, 274
body odour 63, 338
boils 78, 79
bone marrow 14, 32, 53, 108, 180, 181, 183, 185, 186, 215, 217, 223, 224, 226, 227, 242, 246, 351, 366
botox 149
bowel 24, 94, 167, 265, 269, 272, 273, 383, 385, 407
brainstem 196, 236, 297, 298, 304, 310
Braxton Hicks 333

breast cancer 387, 388, 389, 407
bromhidrosis 63
bronchus 242
buccinator muscle 160
bulbourethral glands 410
bulimia 274
bunion 139
burns... 33, 70, 85, 151, 190, 205, 311, 428

C

caecum 265
Caesarean section 399
calcaneus 138, 172
calcitonin 348, 349, 428
calcium 26, 64, 138, 140, 205, 259, 263, 331, 348, 349, 350, 367, 370, 406, 419
calf muscles 157, 171
callus 114
candida 270
canker sores 258
carbohydrates 11, 25, 26, 28, 203, 257, 258, 262, 263, 265, 269, 331
carbon ...25, 29, 36, 37, 180, 195, 236, 242, 243, 245, 251, 252, 341, 416, 422, 423
carbon dioxide......29, 36, 37, 180, 195, 236, 242, 243, 245, 252, 341, 416, 422, 423
carbuncle 78
carcinogens 53
carcinoma 86, 88
cardiac ischaemia 199
cardiac muscle........142, 154, 175, 176, 192, 420, 421
cardiomyopathy 193
carotene 30, 70
carotid 197, 205, 236

carpals 108, 119, 135, 161
cataracts 50, 322, 354, 426
catecholamines 358
cauda equina 299
celiac 19, 307
cellulitis 229
centrioles 41, 46, 285
centromere 44, 46
centrosome 41, 46
cephalic 19
cerebellum 196, 297, 299, 327
cerebral cortex 293, 294, 297, 424
cerebrospinal fluid 34, 294, 343
cerebrum 196, 293, 294, 296, 299, 327
cervical spondylosis 126
cervix 125, 379, 381, 382, 383, 397, 398, 399, 402
Charcot-Marie-Tooth disease 308
chemoreceptors 236
chemotherapy 53, 86, 95, 97, 182, 186, 191, 226, 245, 284, 310, 311, 380, 427
cherry angiomas 418
chicken pox 81, 223
chlamydia 413
chloasma 71, 395
cholecalciferol 30, 64
cholesterol 23, 32, 39, 64, 74, 202, 203, 205, 209, 266, 267, 275, 338, 355, 356
chondrocytes 56
chromatids 46, 48
chromatin 44, 46, 47
chromosome 22, 43, 44, 45, 46, 49, 50, 51, 52, 412, 416, 438
chyle 211, 264
chyme 254, 262, 265, 268
cingulate gyrus 296, 297, 318
circadian rhythm 291, 344, 345
circumcision 409

cirrhosis 267, 273
clavicle 133, 161
clitoris 377, 378, 379
coccygeal nerve 299, 305, 306
coccygeus muscle 167
coccyx 125, 265
cochlea 326
collagen .33, 39, 62, 65, 67, 68, 70, 73, 110, 114, 115, 116, 165, 185, 243, 406, 418
colon 208, 265, 269, 271, 272, 273, 304
colostrum 216
colour blindness 321
comedones 64
conception 51, 300, 359, 383, 391, 410
conjunctivitis 323
connective tissue 12, 54, 55, 56, 62, 67, 92, 103, 110, 116, 120, 138, 143, 145, 165, 173, 179, 195, 212, 215, 219, 230, 241, 242, 244, 256, 259, 283, 284, 301, 318, 354, 363, 383, 395, 396, 423, 425, 430
constipation 26, 167, 168, 209, 250, 273, 276, 348, 372, 385, 396, 402
contractions 26, 27, 55, 145, 148, 150, 151, 164, 175, 176, 200, 213, 244, 272, 288, 333, 342, 398, 400, 410
COPD 249
core muscles 166
cornea 320, 321, 322
corneal ulcers 322
corns 140
coronal plane 19
coronary angioplasty 199
coronavirus 31, 222, 228, 247, 248, 443, 444, 445
corpus albicans 391
corpus luteum 332, 334, 359, 390, 391
corticosteroid 357

corticosterone 356

cortisol.. 153, 155, 233, 338, 340, 357, 358, 428, 441, 449

cortisone.............................. 62, 164, 175

COVID 24, 31, 186, 190, 222, 247, 248, 249, 274, 318, 437, 438, 442, 443, 445, 448

CPR 198

cranial nerves......... 280, 282, 299, 302

craniosacral rhythm............................ 301

cranium..............................122, 123, 301

cretinism.. 348

Creutzfeldt-Jakob disease.................. 289

cribriform plate 318

cuticle 90, 91, 101

cystic fibrosis.. 242

cystitis... 371

cytokine storm....................................... 222

cytokines 219, 220, 221, 222, 225, 232, 233

cytokinesis 47, 48

cytoplasm.......35, 39, 41, 46, 145, 182, 285

cytosine.. 42, 50

dermatophytosis 82

dermis 59, 62, 63, 64, 65, 70, 85, 91, 315, 395, 418

DHEA.. 357

diabetes mellitus 83, 206, 354

dialysis...374, 375

diaphragm..... 160, 164, 167, 212, 236, 244, 266, 298, 396, 422

diaphysis... 110

diastasis recti 396

diencephalon 294, 296

diploid 49, 377

DNA. 25, 26, 28, 41, 42, 43, 44, 45, 47, 49, 50, 79, 221, 388, 416, 434

dopamine 290, 358, 401

Down syndrome............................22, 393

duodenal ulcer 263

duodenum 263, 266, 268, 269

Dupuytren's contracture....... 162, 163

DVT... 206

dwarfism.. 338

dyspnoea 249, 396

dystonia 149, 150

D

dandruff...98

dehydration 12, 69, 148, 239, 341, 356, 357

deltoid bursitis...................................... 161

deltoid muscle 161

dementia 63, 289, 290, 407

dendrites 55, 286, 288, 293

dendritic cell... 220

depression .. 21, 32, 64, 118, 147, 177, 233, 270, 279, 291, 292, 329, 339, 350, 400, 402

dermatitis.....................76, 98, 229, 251

dermatomes... 307

E

eardrum.............................325, 326, 328

earwax...325, 327

ectoderm 391

ectomorph 151

ectopic pregnancy.....................386, 413

eczema 76, 229, 251, 439

Edward Jenner....................................... 224

elastin 62, 65, 70, 243, 418

embryo....56, 110, 300, 360, 390, 391, 403, 404, 405

EMDR...292, 446

emphysema 249, 252

endocarditis... 193

endocardium................................. 192, 193

endoderm 391
endolymph.. 326
endometriosis.................383, 384, 402
endometrium.................382, 390, 391
endomorph 151
endomysium 145
endoplasmic reticulum................. 38, 40
endorphins................................151, 290
endosteum.. 108
endothelial cells........................ 185, 195
enteric nervous system 277
enteritis.. 271
enuresis 373
enzymes..... 25, 27, 39, 40, 42, 43, 182,
    185, 216, 219, 238, 259, 263, 268,
    288, 345, 353, 355, 412, 423
eosinophils.. 182
ependymomas................................... 284
ephilides 72
epidermis 59, 60, 62, 63, 65, 69, 85,
    86, 91, 92, 315, 340, 418
epididymis.................................410, 430
epigastric... 20
epigenetics.. 43
epiglottis......................................56, 240
epimysium 145
epiphyseal disc 110
episiotomy 381, 399
epithalamus....................................... 294
epithelium............56, 67, 241, 242, 318
eponychium....................................... 101
erector pili 65, 92
erector spinae muscles...................... 144
erythema.. 67
erythropoietin 180
estriol.. 333
ethmoid 123, 124, 125, 237, 318
Eustachian tube 240, 325, 328
eustress... 282
extensor muscles............................... 162

F

facial nerve 304, 330
faeces 168, 180, 254, 265, 273
fallopian tubes........382, 383, 384, 385,
    402, 403, 413
fascia...... 4, 56, 57, 138, 143, 144, 163,
    165, 167, 168, 173, 175, 284, 433,
    435, 439, 441
femur.........................108, 136, 168, 170
fertilisation 49, 386, 390, 391, 403,
    404, 405, 410, 412
fibroadenoma.................................... 387
fibrocartilage 116, 135, 136
fibroids.....................359, 383, 401, 402
fibromyalgia 310
fibula...................................... 137, 138
filaggrin 76, 439
flat feet 139
flatulence 270
flexor muscles.............................. 162, 169
foetus 94, 176, 189, 207, 333, 360,
    382, 392, 393, 394, 396, 397, 398
folliculitis.................................... 78, 98
foramen magnum 122, 196
foreskin 409
fornix 296, 297, 318
fovea... 322
fractures 111, 112, 114, 115, 133
Francis Crick 42
frozen shoulder................................. 176
FSH 332, 334, 335, 336, 339, 359,
    377, 390, 404, 406, 411, 428
funny bone 133
furuncles... 78

G

GABA.. 290, 295
galea aponeurotica............................ 158

gallbladder 263, 266, 267, 268, 269, 307

gallstones 266

gametes 377

ganglion cyst 121

gastric juice 260, 261, 262

gastrin 260

gastrocnemius 171

genetics 4, 23, 63, 73, 75, 209, 291, 388, 418, 420

GERD 424

geriatrics 415

germ theory 233

gerontology 415

glandular fever 227

glaucoma 425

glenohumeral joint 133

glioma 284

glomerulus 364, 365, 371

glucagon 268, 354, 355

glucocorticoids 114, 355

gluconeogenesis 155

glucose 36, 37, 39, 142, 151, 155, 197, 263, 281, 313, 331, 353, 354, 357, 386

gluteal muscles 168

glycogen 142, 145, 151, 354, 357, 424

goblet cell 241, 256, 265, 323

Golgi 40, 47

Golgi apparatus 40, 47

gonorrhoea 413

goose bumps 65

gout 120

Graafian follicle 334, 390

gracilis 170, 171

granulocytes 182, 183, 219

granzymes 185

ground substance 55

growth plates 110

G-spot 380

guanine 42, 50

gynecomastia 358

H

haematoma 103, 113

haemoglobin 27, 39, 41, 70, 95, 180, 181, 244, 252, 366

haemostasis 66, 185

halitosis 270

hammertoe 140

hamstrings 144, 170

Haversian canals 108

hay fever 76, 232, 250

hCG 332, 391, 393, 404

heart attack 22, 186, 199, 202, 205, 275, 354

heartburn 260, 394

helicobacter pylori 262

hemangiomas 72

hematopoiesis 179

hematopoietic stem cell 179, 217

hemodialysis 375

hemophilia 442

hemorrhoids 208, 397

heparin 183, 219

hepatitis 190, 221, 273

hepatocytes 266

hernia 165, 167

herpes 81, 105, 221, 311, 413

herpes simplex 81, 105

HGH 336, 337

hippocampus 294, 296, 297, 313, 318

hirsutism 97

histamine 62, 77, 183, 219, 239, 250

histiocytes 62

HIV 190, 225, 230

hives 77, 232

hormone replacement therapy 59, 335, 407

human papillomavirus 80, 381

humectants 69
humerus 133, 161, 162, 164
humoral immunity 223, 225
hyaline cartilage....... 56, 110, 116, 120, 135, 240, 241, 242
hydrochloric acid 25, 261, 424
hydrogen 29, 33, 40
hydrogen peroxide...............................40
hydroxyhempyrolin 32
hymen 379, 381
hyoid bone..130
hyperparathyroidism 350
hyperpigmentation.............................340
hypertension...........201, 339, 372, 430
hyperthyroidism 338, 346, 347
hyperventilation 252
hypocalcemia.......................................350
hypochondriac.......................................20
hypodermis..59
hypogammaglobulinemia..................352
hyponychium 101
hyposmia..319
hypotension 201
hypothalamus. 63, 233, 294, 295, 296, 297, 318, 336, 340, 341, 342, 345, 359
hypothyroidism......231, 338, 346, 347, 348
hysterectomy....................383, 405, 407

impetigo 78
infertility.........250, 339, 383, 384, 413
influenza................................153, 246
infraspinatus 161
inguinal 19, 167, 212
insulin... 268, 269, 295, 331, 354, 355, 360, 385, 428
insulinoma 355
integumentary system 12, 59, 154
intercostal.......164, 236, 298, 306, 422
interferons...................................221, 443
interleukins...221
Interphase.. 46, 47
interstitial fluid.........................210, 223
intrinsic factor 32, 181, 261
inversion.......................................50, 147
iodine...345, 348
iris 320
iron...... 27, 33, 95, 102, 104, 180, 181, 258, 263, 267, 274
ischial tuberosity 135, 170
islets of Langerhans.........353, 354, 355
isometric 148, 308
isotonic 148
IVF 403, 404, 405

J

James Watson 42
jejunum.. 263

I

idiopathic 21
ileocaecal valve 265
ileum.........................215, 263, 265, 271
iliopsoas...169
iliotibial band 144, 168
ilium 135, 164, 168, 170, 196
immunoglobulins......................223, 352
immunotherapy...........................86, 225

K

Karl Landsteiner...................................188
karyotype 49, 52
Kawasaki disease................................227
keloid scar.......................................67, 71
keratin....39, 60, 90, 92, 100, 101, 103
keratinocytes 100

keratohyalin 60
kidney stones 350, 372, 376
kinesthesia 316

L

labyrinth 326
lactic acid 151
lactobacillus 278
L-arginine 39
larynx 56, 240, 241, 251, 252, 304, 329
latissimus dorsi 143
lentigo 72
leptin 340
leucocytes 182, 183, 221, 227, 400
leukemia 191, 227
levator anguli oris 160
levator ani 167
levator labii superioris 160
levator palpebrae 159
levothyroxine 347
libido 340, 430
lice 98
lichen planus 74
limbic system 296, 297, 318
linea alba 165
linea nigra 71, 165, 395
lingual lipase 257
lipofuscin 417, 420, 421, 424
lipoprotein 39, 203
lobectomy 347
lochia 400
lordosis 167
Louis Pasteur 233
lumbar plexus 305
lumbosacral plexus 306, 312
lunula 101
lupus 73, 121, 153, 230, 371
Lyme disease 84

lymph 55, 64, 78, 79, 84, 210, 211, 212, 213, 214, 215, 224, 226, 227, 229, 246, 254, 256, 259, 264, 269, 352, 363, 388, 420, 422
lymphatic trunk 212
lymphocytes 53, 183, 184, 212, 214, 215, 220, 221, 223, 351, 422
lymphoedema 229
lymphoid lineage cells 179, 217, 218
lymphokines 221
lymphoma 226, 227
lysosomes 36, 40
lysozyme 258

M

macrocytes 181
macrophages 62, 66, 214, 220, 221, 238, 242
macula 322, 425
macular degeneration 322, 425
magnesium 27, 114, 148, 155
malassezia 98
mammary glands ... 216, 333, 342, 386, 430
mandible 124, 137, 147, 160, 212, 259
manubrium 130, 133
Marie Strumpell disease 130
masseter muscle 160
mast cell 62, 183, 221, 239
mastectomy 176, 388
mastoidectomy 326
maxilla 160, 259
mediastinum 192, 244
meibomian gland 322, 425
meibum 323
meiosis 48, 51, 377
melanin 53, 70, 71, 72, 80, 88, 90, 101, 418
melanocyte 165, 336, 395

melanoma................................ 23, 88, 105

melasma 71

melatonin...... 294, 295, 343, 344, 361, 406, 449

menarche 389

meninges................................ 56, 301, 302

meningioma 302

meningitis 302

menisci...56, 136

menopause.........64, 96, 332, 333, 335, 339, 373, 380, 383, 389, 406, 407, 419, 429, 430

menstrual cycle......332, 334, 359, 382, 384

mesencephalon................................... 299

mesoderm... 392

mesomorph.. 151

metabolic syndrome 4, 275

metabolism. 12, 32, 37, 110, 142, 151, 213, 295, 331, 346, 357, 368, 401

metacarpals...................................161, 162

metaphase....................................... 46, 48

metastasis......................................53, 225

metatarsals.. 139

midbrain...298, 299

milia 64

mineralocorticoids.....................355, 356

miscarriage 52, 333

misophonia.................................329, 448

mitochondria 37, 47, 145, 156

mitosis... 46, 47, 48, 60, 182, 284, 285, 377

mitral valve.. 192

mole 87, 88

molluscum contagiosum......................81

monocytes 227, 242

monosaccharides 257

mons pubis 377, 379

Morton's neuroma.............................. 140

morula.. 391

motor neurone disease..................... 309

mouth ulcers.. 258

MRSA...79

multifidus.. 144

multiple sclerosis.............286, 298, 309

muscle protein synthesis................... 151

muscular dystrophy............................ 153

myasthenia gravis 177, 308, 352

mycobacterium tuberculosis............. 246

myelin........................231, 284, 286, 308

myeloid lineage cells................ 179, 217

myocardial infarction......................... 199

myocardium.....................192, 199, 200

myofibril 145

myometrium.....................382, 398, 400

myositis.. 153

myotomes.. 307

myxoedema 347

N

navicular... 138

nephrons.........363, 364, 368, 371, 428

neuralgia 82, 303, 311, 312

neurilemma.. 286

neuritis... 310

neuroglia 293

neuromuscular disorder 177

neuropathy... 311

neurotransmitters.149, 276, 285, 288, 290, 295, 403

neutrophils 66, 182, 239, 422

nitrogen 11

NK cells... 185, 218

nocturia 370

nondisjunction 50

nucleic acids 26, 42

nucleolus.....................................41, 46, 47

nucleoplasm..41

nucleus 38, 41, 43, 44, 46, 47, 61, 175, 182, 185, 285, 390

nyctalopia.....................................321, 426

O

obesity 24, 53, 83, 136, 139, 167, 168, 204, 209, 274, 276, 340, 383, 388, 402, 417
occipital... 19, 122, 158, 161, 164, 196, 197, 212, 294, 321
occipitofrontalis....................................158
oesophagus .. 164, 167, 240, 254, 256, 259, 260, 278, 394
oestradiol.............................333, 359, 361
oestrogen.......64, 70, 77, 96, 114, 323, 332, 333, 334, 335, 339, 358, 359, 377, 380, 384, 390, 391, 393, 401, 402, 406, 407, 419, 428, 429, 430
olfactory cortex...............294, 296, 318
olfactory epithelium...............318, 330
olfactory nerve....... 294, 303, 317, 318
oligodendrogliomas...........................284
oliguria 374
onychomycosis...................................103
ophthalmic..19
organelle............................38, 40, 41
Osgood-Schlatter syndrome............170
ossicles.....................................326, 327
ossification...............................110, 114
osteoarthritis.....................120, 126, 136
osteoblasts...110
osteocalcin..331
osteoclasts.........................110, 113, 348
osteocytes.................................108, 110
osteogenesis.......................................110
osteomalacia......................................115
osteopenia...115
osteoporosis. 112, 114, 115, 252, 339, 350, 406, 407, 429
otitis media...328
otosclerosis................................327, 328

ovarian cancer....................................385
overactive thyroid.... 63, 102, 104, 219
oxytocin 331, 333, 337, 340, 342, 398

P

Pacinian corpuscles 315
palate...................................124, 257, 329
pancreas....12, 38, 230, 234, 250, 263, 268, 269, 275, 307, 331, 353, 354, 355
pancreatic cancer.....................269, 355
pancreatitis.................................269, 355
papillary dermis 62
parasympathetic nervous system.. 280, 282, 304
parathyroid gland.....................349, 350
parietal lobe 294
paronychium.......................................101
Patau Syndrome 50
patella.................................108, 137, 170
patellar ligament 170
patellofemoral joint...........................137
pathogen 183, 212, 222, 352
pectineus......................................169, 170
pediculosis capitis 83
pelvic floor.............157, 167, 383, 429
pelvis........ 20, 109, 130, 136, 144, 164, 165, 167, 168, 170, 196, 301, 363, 368, 383, 396
penis 369, 380, 408, 409, 412
peptic ulcer......................... 262, 263
pericardium 192
perichondrium.....................................56
perilymph...326
perimetrium...382
perimysium..145
perineum.............................305, 381, 399
periodontitis..259
periosteum........................108, 110, 145

peripheral neuropathy 311

peristalsis 256, 260, 282, 304, 420, 423

peritoneum.............256, 363, 368, 375

peritonitis.. 257

pernicious anaemia 181, 261

peroneus tertius 171

peroxisomes...40

pertussis 250

pH 26, 28, 63, 179, 252, 257

phagocytes 180, 215, 220

phagocytosis 36, 183, 219, 223

phalanges........ 118, 134, 139, 161, 162

pharynx 240, 241, 251, 254, 256, 260, 329, 330

pheromones...63

phlebitis 206

phlegm 242, 246

phospholipids 25

phosphorus....................................64, 362

phrenic nerve..............................160, 236

pia mater.. 301

piles..41, 208

pineal gland... 294, 295, 343, 344, 345

pinna.. 324

pinocytosis...36

piriformis...................................169, 312

pituitary gland 233, 294, 295, 332, 333, 334, 336, 337, 338, 340, 341, 359, 365

placenta 165, 215, 332, 342, 360, 372, 391, 393, 397, 399, 400

plantar fasciitis 174

plantarflexion 138, 171, 172, 173

platelets 108, 179, 185, 186, 190, 214

platysma 160

pleura 18, 244, 245

pleurisy 245

PMS...359, 402

pneumonia ... 187, 230, 245, 246, 247, 358, 413

pneumothorax 245

polio.. 224, 300

polycystic ovarian syndrome........... 339

polydipsia.. 341

polysaccharides 257

pons...................................236, 298, 299

popliteal 20, 196, 212

posterior oblique sling...................... 143

posterior pituitary..336, 341, 342, 398

postnatal depression 292, 400

potassium .26, 35, 148, 287, 341, 356, 362, 370

preeclampsia 372, 397

presbycusis.. 327

pressure sore...................................... 428

prickle-cell layer.................................. 60

probiotic 278

progesterone 202, 332, 334, 335, 339, 359, 384, 390, 391, 393, 401, 404, 407, 428, 429

prolactin 333, 336, 339, 387, 401, 428

proliferative phase......................67, 390

prophase 46, 48

proprioception 294

prostaglandins...................342, 367, 398

prostate gland 196, 369, 370, 410, 429, 430, 431

prosthesis................................... 113, 136

protein ...26, 27, 35, 38, 39, 41, 42, 46, 47, 60, 62, 76, 95, 115, 142, 145, 150, 153, 155, 181, 216, 220, 221, 232, 262, 263, 287, 289, 291, 321, 331, 356, 358, 360, 361, 367, 368, 371, 372, 397, 420

protein glycation 62

proteinuria... 372

psoas... 169

psoriasis... 75, 102, 104, 105, 121, 233

psoriatic arthritis 75, 121, 135

psychoneuroimmunology 4, 444

pterygoids... 160

PTSD 292

puberty 63, 64, 96, 332, 351, 358, 360, 370, 377, 384

pulmonary semi-lunar valve .. 192, 193, 195

pulmonary trunk 192, 193, 195

pulse 197, 200, 301, 396

purines 121

pyloric sphincter 256, 262

Q

quadratus lumborum 167

quadriceps 169, 170, 307

R

radius 118, 133, 161

Raynaud's disease 65

RDA 33

reciprocal translocation 51

rectum .. 208, 254, 265, 270, 273, 278, 305, 369

rectus abdominis 165, 396

rectus femoris 169, 170

red blood cells ... 27, 32, 38, 39, 44, 70, 108, 179, 180, 181, 182, 188, 190, 195, 244, 252, 366, 421

Reed-Sternberg cell 226

relaxin 333

renal colic 372

renal fascia 363

renin-angiotensin system 356

repetitive strain injury 152

respiration 25, 160, 198, 236, 253, 298, 299

reticular dermis 62

retro-calcaneal bursa 172

rheumatoid arthritis 119, 120, 121, 137, 153, 222, 231

rhinencephalon 296

rhodopsin 321

rhomboids 161

ribosomes 38, 39, 41

ribs 19, 56, 107, 109, 116, 127, 130, 160, 164, 213, 245, 298, 306, 337

rickets 30, 115

ringworm 82, 103

risorius muscle 160

RNA 25, 26, 41, 43, 79, 221

Robertsonian translocation 51

S

sacral plexus 306

sacroiliac joint 130, 144

sacrum .. 125, 130, 135, 144, 164, 168, 265, 301

sagittal plane 19

saliva 227, 257, 258, 260, 329, 331, 388, 427

sarcopenia 420

sarcoplasm 145

SARS 228, 247, 445

sartorius 169, 171

scapula 107, 133, 161

scars 67, 69, 71, 80, 88, 231

Schwann cell 284, 286

sciatic nerve .. 168, 169, 284, 285, 312

scleroderma 73

sebaceous gland 64, 69, 70, 77, 92, 99, 323, 333

seborrheic keratosis 80

sebum 63, 69, 70, 92, 99, 331, 418

seminiferous tubules 360, 409

sepsis 187, 257

septicemia 187

septum 124, 192, 237

serosa 256, 423

serotonin 276, 291, 294, 343, 361, 406

serous membrane 56, 385

sexually transmitted disease 81, 412

shingles 81, 311, 312

shock 95, 116, 127, 138, 187, 232, 259, 292, 312, 386, 403

shoulder girdle 107, 133

sinoatrial node 421

sinuses.. 125, 237, 238, 241, 251, 328, 387, 427

skeletal muscle........143, 145, 146, 148, 150, 157, 158, 175, 176, 213, 256, 280, 297, 420

smell brain 296

smoking 33, 53, 59, 201, 209, 231, 251, 252, 417, 422, 423, 426

smooth muscle........154, 176, 185, 195, 213, 219, 241, 256, 260, 342, 368, 382, 385, 420, 423

sodium 27, 35, 64, 149, 287, 341, 356, 362, 367, 370

sodium-potassium pump.................... 288

solar plexus....................................... 307

soleus... 171

somatosensory system....................... 314

somatostatin...................................... 354

spasticity.. 150

sperm.. 48, 51, 52, 339, 342, 360, 377, 384, 386, 390, 391, 403, 405, 408, 409, 410, 411, 412, 430

spermatogenesis 410, 411

sphenoid............................. 123, 125, 237

spina bifida 300

spinal nerves. 280, 302, 305, 306, 307

spinal stenosis 129, 312

spleen... 180, 214, 215, 224, 226, 230, 269, 307, 353

splenius capitis..................................... 164

splenius cervicus................................. 164

squamous cell carcinoma 53, 88

staphylococcus............ 77, 79, 278, 403

Stein-Leventhal Syndrome................. 384

sternocleidomastoid muscle 160

sternum 107, 109, 116, 130, 133, 165, 214, 244

steroid........ 59, 77, 114, 331, 338, 355, 356, 380

stratum corneum 61

stratum germinativum 59

stratum granulosum............................. 60

stratum lucidum 61

stratum spinosum 60

streptococcus 77, 240, 394, 403

stretch marks........................ 62, 339, 395

styes... 323

subcutaneous layer 59, 62, 63, 85, 417

submucosa........................ 215, 256, 423

sulphur.. 27

suprachiasmatic nucleus.................... 295

supraspinatus 161

sweat glands 63, 191, 250, 281

synaptic vesicles 285

synovial membrane...................... 56, 116

syphilis 413

systemic lupus erythematosus 230

T

T cell...... 183, 184, 212, 214, 215, 218, 224, 225, 230, 351, 352

tarsals......................... 108, 119, 138, 139

taste buds 257, 259, 278, 329, 330

teeth 26, 30, 33, 64, 113, 115, 160, 257, 259, 423

telogen.. 94, 95

telomeres................ 4, 44, 416, 433, 438

telophase 47, 48

temporal lobe 294, 296, 297, 327

temporalis muscle............................. 160

temporomandibular joint 124

tendonitis 152, 172

tennis elbow 152, 162

tensegrity 57

tensor fascia latae 144

teres minor 161

terrain theory 233

testicles 361, 408, 409

testosterone .. 64, 77, 96, 97, 332, 335, 339, 342, 357, 360, 370, 377, 385, 409, 411, 418, 430

thalamus 294, 296, 318

thoracic nerves 305

thorax 116, 130, 164, 165, 351

thrombocytes 108, 185

thrombosis 187, 206, 229

thrush 270, 380

thymine 42, 50

thymus gland 183, 214, 224, 351, 352, 422

thyroidectomy 347

thyroiditis 231, 348

thyroxine 345

tibia 136, 137, 138, 152, 169, 170, 171

tibial tuberosity 170

tibialis anterior 171

tibialis posterior 172

tinea 82

Tom Myers 57, 144, 435

tonsils 214, 240, 304

toxic shock 403

trachea 56, 197, 240, 241, 242, 243, 260

transient ischemic attack (TIA) 205

translocation 51, 52

transverse plane 19

trapezius muscle 161

trematodes 271

trichomoniasis 414

tricuspid valve 192, 193, 195

trigeminal nerve 303, 312

trigger finger 163

triglycerides 74, 202, 203, 205, 262

triiodothyronine 345

tryptophan 291, 343

tuberculosis 230, 233, 242, 246

U

ulcerative colitis 273

ulna 133, 161

umbilical cord 397, 399

ureter 363, 368

urethra . 362, 368, 369, 370, 371, 380, 409, 410, 414, 429, 431

urethritis 413

uric acid 120, 368

urinary incontinence 373, 429

urticaria 77, 248

uterus 58, 110, 176, 196, 208, 333, 334, 342, 359, 379, 381, 382, 383, 384, 385, 390, 394, 395, 396, 398, 399, 400, 402, 403, 404, 405, 407, 413, 429

utricle 327

UV rays 50, 64, 340

uvula 257

V

vaccination 217, 224, 246, 273, 300

vaginitis 413

vagus nerve .. 276, 282, 283, 304, 307, 330

varicella zoster virus 81

varicose veins 207, 208, 396

vas deferens 410

vasectomy 410

vasoconstriction 185

vasopressin 337, 340

vena cava 164, 193, 195, 198

ventricle 192, 193, 195, 201, 206, 244, 294

vertebrae 56, 108, 109, 116, 118, 125, 126, 127, 128, 130, 161, 419

villi 256, 264, 391, 393

Vitamin A 30, 321

Vitamin B 32

Vitamin B1 32

Vitamin B12 32

Vitamin C 33

Vitamin D ... 30, 64, 344, 367, 438, 441, 443, 449, 450

Vitamin D3 .... 64, 344

Vitamin E 31

Vitamin K 31, 438

Vitamin K1 31

Vitamin K2 31

Vitamin P 33

Vitamin U 33

vitiligo 71

vitreous humor 321

vocal cords 150, 241, 309

vomer 124, 237

vulva 377, 378, 379, 406

W

wart 80

Whipple procedure 269

whiteheads 64, 77

whitlow 105

whooping cough 250

windpipe 241

wisdom teeth 259

womb 94, 278, 324, 382

worm 271

wrinkles ... 62, 65, 70, 71, 72, 149, 158, 379, 417

X

xanthomas 74

Z

zoonotic 22

zygomatic bone 108, 124, 160

zygomaticus muscle 160

zygote 386, 390, 391